The No1 Staffordshire Royal Infirmary

1802-1948

A medal commemorating the laying of the Foundation Stone
of the new Infirmary at Hartshill by the Prince of Wales on June 25th 1866.

Alun Davies

Acknowledgements

I thank all those who have helped me with this book, most especially my wife for all her encouragement and assistance with proof reading and for her forbearance. Many people have helped me, given advice and access to papers. I am especially grateful to the North Staffordshire Hospitals Trust, the Trustees of the Wedgwood Museum, Mrs Irene Fenton and the Staff of the North Staffordshire Medical Institute Library, Ms Helen Burton of the Special Collections at Keele University Library, Mrs Thea Randall and the Staff of the Staffordshire County Record Office and the Hanley Archives, and Dr Alannah Tomkins of the Department of History, Keele University for reading the manuscript and making many valuable suggestions. Many others have helped in so many ways, and I thank you all. In the end however the opinions and errors are all my own.

I also acknowledge the use of photographs from the collections of the Trustees of the Wedgwood Museum, the Warrilow Collection Keele, the Annual Reports of the North Staffordshire Infirmary, as well as deposits of illustrative material at the North Staffs Medical Institute. Also to the Department of Medical Illustration at the Royal Infirmary my grateful thanks for the Garner notebooks photos.,

I have drawn on articles of my own in *Midlands Medicine*, (Journal of the North Staffs Medical Institute) and the book began as an expansion of a dissertation submitted for MA in Local History at Keele University

In 1849 concern over the level of the rates caused opposition to the adoption of the Public Health Act locally. The Rev. Macbeth said (paraphrased):
'If you exclude the deaths of the (excessive) children of the poor and the accidents, Stoke would have no need of the act.'

In such a world the Infirmary, despite its shortcomings, was a beacon of hope, self-help and cooperation in an often grim world.

To those who feel I have been unduly harsh here in my depiction of life in the Potteries at this time I can only say that denial is no cure of disease.
Undoubtedly many people lived satisfactory lives, but very many did not. No town can have the unenviable distinction of the worst rate of survival for children under one year in the country without having serious problems. Even in Edwardian times 40% of burials in Stoke on Trent were of children under five.

**ALL AUTHOR PROFITS FROM THIS BOOK ARE
TO BE DONATED TO THE MEDICAL INSTITUTE BICENTENARY FUND**

CHURNET VALLEY BOOKS
6 Stanley Street, Leek, Staffordshire. ST13 5HG 01538 399033
www.leekbooks.co.uk
© Alun Davies and Churnet Valley Books 2006
ISBN 978 1897949 93 1

CONTENTS

Introduction   5

Ch 1   The formation of opinion: newspapers and word of mouth   13

Ch 2   The Dispensary and House of Recovery   21

Ch 3   Raising Money   39

Ch 4   The first Voluntary Institutions in North Staffordshire   57
       The Wedgwood family's involvement with the Infirmary

Ch 5   Treatment   61

Ch 6   The Etruria Infirmary 1819-1869   77

Ch 7   The Lost Physician: Dr Wilson Fox, M.D.,F.R.S.   91

Ch 8   Location: A Move from Etruria   101

Ch 9   Location: The Move to Hartshill   111

Ch 10 Trials and Tribulations: The Chaplain and the Dancing Nurses 127

Ch 11 The Nurses 1802-69   133

Ch 12 The Nurses 1870-1948   143

Ch 13 Advances in Abdominal Surgery   159

Ch 14 A successful Caesarean Section in North Staffordshire, 1876 167

Ch 15 Illness in the Potteries   171

Ch 16 Illness in the Community   181

Ch 17 ICEBERGS, or a Close Run Thing   193

Ch 18 War and the Infirmary   203

Ch 19 The Electrical Department   211

Ch 20 The Infirmary and the Workhouse   217

Ch 21 Between the Wars, World War II and the end of an era   227

Appendices Medical Staff 1902, 1911-12, 1918, 1929, 1941, 1947   242

INDEX   255

The Infirmary becomes the Royal Infirmary in 1925.
Matron, Miss MacMaster curtsies to Queen Mary while a smiling George V looks on. On this day the
Borough of Stoke on Trent became a city and the Infirmary became the Royal Infirmary

INTRODUCTION

This is a book about the North Staffordshire Infirmary and about the people from all walks of life, who conceived, built, served and maintained the Infirmary from small beginnings in very unpromising circumstances to become the principal hospital of North Staffordshire.

During its lifetime as a voluntary hospital, from 1802 until the coming of the National Health Service in 1948, the Infirmary was the largest non-commercial, non-religious organisation in the district. It always strove to provide the best hospital services that could be provided in the area at any particular time. It was largely financed by a highly innovative scheme of Establishment Contributions from working people, a scheme that eventually was supported by and provided hospital care for the majority of industrial workers in North Staffordshire.

Voluntary hospitals began in London in 1719 and spread through the county towns of England and on to the great industrial cities, reaching North Staffordshire in 1802. Beginning as a very modest venture in Shelton, between the Caldon and Trent and Mersey Canals, initially it could only offer a Dispensary supplying advice and medicines to outpatients and a House of Recovery which offered a few fever beds. After ten years a larger building was needed, which had more beds and could offer treatment to the victims of industrial accidents, so the first proper Infirmary was built in Etruria. Fifty years later it was again too outdated and small for the needs of the district as well as being surrounded by industrial pollution and was subsiding due the mines beneath it. In 1869 it moved to Hartshill where it has remained, entering the National Health Service in 1948.

The foundation of a hospital in North Staffordshire ultimately depended on the support of Master Potters and other businessmen who gave time and managerial skills to the Infirmary. The most influential family during the first hundred years of the Infirmary's life were the Wedgwoods. In succession Josiah the second, Francis (Frank) and Godfrey Wedgwood were a constantly positive influence in the management of the Infirmary; in difficult times they were often those who kept their heads when all about were losing theirs. They were of course fortunate in their family. There seem to have been few people of importance in England that they did not know. When the Infirmary was founded, and throughout the 19th century, the Governors had access to a network of well-informed contacts on whom to draw.

We will follow the story using the surviving material, minute books, annual reports and newspaper accounts. Countless thousands of North Staffordshire's people have been treated in the Infirmary by the thousands who have staffed it. It is obviously impossible to name more than a few. Names of individuals are included, but only where they advance the narrative.

Up to the present time the principal source of information for a publication about the Infirmary is always the book written by Ralph Hordley in 1902 and published by the Governors on the occasion of the centenary of the Infirmary's foundation. It is a short book, largely derived from the minutes, accurate in its facts. However it has, in common with all books, its own agenda. Ralph Hordley had devoted his life to the Infirmary as Secretary, i.e. the administrator; additionally his wife and his son had worked there. When he retired, he was granted a pension of £160 per annum, half his salary. He wrote to the Governors thanking them for the pension and their kindness to him during the forty three and a half years (sic) that he had worked there. The mention of the half year is surely significant. Problems, if they are mentioned at all, are not dwelt on.

The Establishment Scheme is barely mentioned, despite it being both innovative and crucial to the survival of the Infirmary. The immense contributions of the local industrialists, particularly the Wedgwood dynasty are not given their proper value. Typically of local histories written a hundred years ago, it is an aristocratic account of events concentrating on the great and the good. Obviously the greatest day in Mr Hordley's life at the Infirmary was the occasion in 1866 when the Prince of Wales laid the foundation stone of the new building in Hartshill. The account of this one day occupies more pages than are concerned with decades filled with crucial events in the Infirmary's history.

To balance this rather golden vision, I have included the problems that the Governors faced because I believe that it is in the overcoming of their problems that we can see the working of the whole social structure of North Staffordshire most clearly. The lives of the working people of the Potteries are still shrouded in smoke, much of it from the potteries themselves. While recognising the centrality of the pottery industry in the history of North Staffordshire, we should not forget that many patients and supporters of the Infirmary were engaged in mining, iron working and agriculture. Many of those who contributed time and money to the Infirmary were engaged in the non-industrial occupations, ministers of religion, lawyers, teachers, doctors, shopkeepers. It is important that we appreciate all their contributions to the life of the district, and I believe that the records of the Infirmary give us a unique opportunity to do this.

Just as Mr Hordley's book has lasted as a source for more than a hundred years, it is possible that this book may be used as a reference point, for want of a better, in the future. I have therefore tried to check the authenticity of some legends about the Infirmary that are often repeated to me, because I believe it would be wrong of me to knowingly include them as history.

The most persistent is the story that Florence Nightingale designed the Hartshill Infirmary on a table cloth while dining with the then Duchess of Sutherland, and that the Duke paid for the site on which the Infirmary was built. The Sutherland family did give some money to the Infirmary and performed some ceremonial functions, but I have found no evidence for the tablecloth. The story as revealed in the archives is much more interesting. Of the Sutherland family Millicent, Duchess of Sutherland was most closely involved with health matters and worked hard on behalf of the crippled children of the district, and those who suffered from lead poisoning.

I hope this book will reveal aspects of the life of the Infirmary and through that the life of the Potteries that have escaped attention having been buried in the archives. I hope it will encourage further study and stimulate debate. I believe that the Infirmary was a remarkable achievement by a remarkably broad spectrum of the population during 146 years of independent life. After 1948, even allowing for local representation on the Management Committee, we must recognise that the National Health Service was, and is, essentially a centrally-funded and centrally -directed organisation. From 1802 to 1948 the Infirmary had to sink or swim on its own without Government support, raising its own funds and making decisions based on local needs and the availability of local financial support. On at least one occasion it was threatened with bankruptcy and having to close its doors. The story of its recovery is one of the highlights of this history. Merging seamlessly into the Health Service the Infirmary has left us a valuable tradition of service from which its successors can take pride and inspiration.

Centenary of the North Staffordshire Infirmary.

A CONCISE HISTORY

OF

THE RISE AND PROGRESS

OF THE

NORTH STAFFORDSHIRE

INFIRMARY & EYE HOSPITAL,

From the Year 1802 to 1902.

At Etruria Vale, as "The Dispensary and House of Recovery,"
1802—1815.

At Etruria, as "The North Staffordshire Infirmary,"
1815— 1869.

At Hartshill, as "The North Staffordshire Infirmary and Eye Hospital,"
1869—1902.

Compiled from the Annual Reports, Minutes of Proceedings,
and other sources.

By RALPH HORDLEY,

Late Secretary and House Steward.

1902.

The title page from Ralph Hordley's 1902 book.

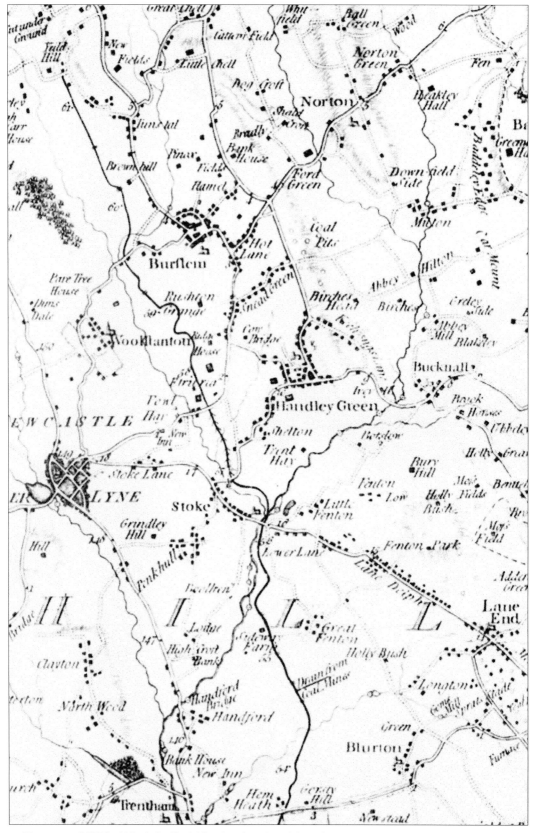

Yates map of 1775 of North Staffordshire showing the origins of the conurbation around small townships which led to six towns each retaining their own administration until 1910.

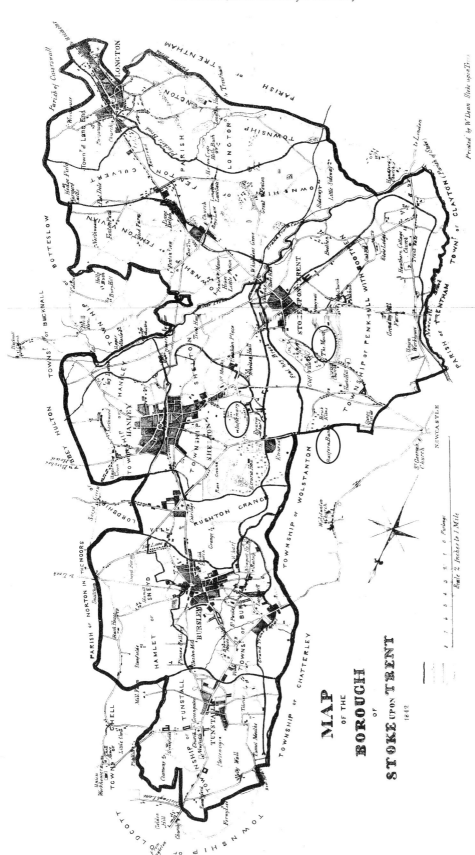

A map produced in 1834 when proposals for a combined borough were afoot. It shows the juxtaposition of the Potteries towns. The various towns could not come to agreement and borough status was missed. With this map the distances to the 6 town halls were compared from Basford, the Mount and the Etruria site - which are ringed. It is noticeable that the interests of Newcastle, Wolstanton and many other townships were totally ignored in making the decisions about the site.

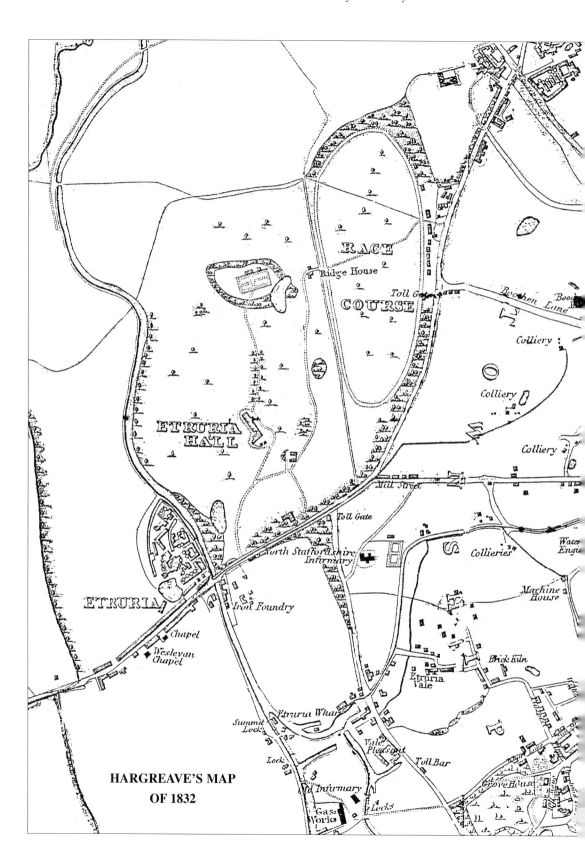

HARGREAVE'S MAP OF 1832

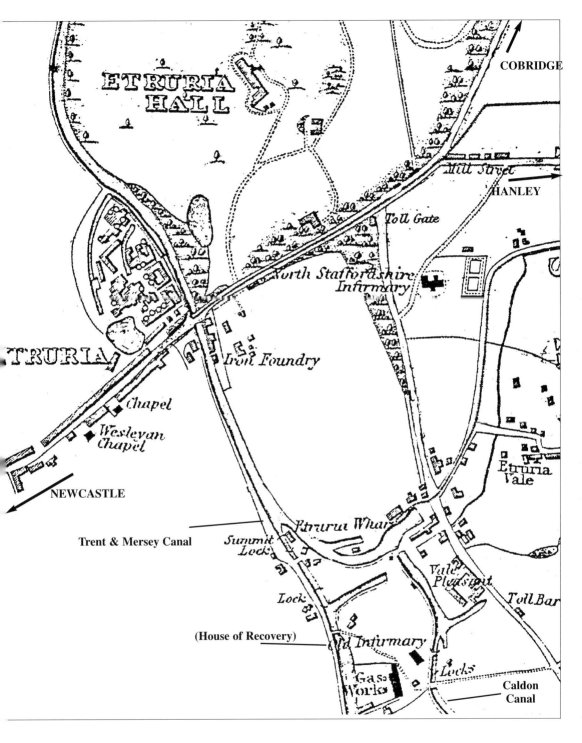

A detail of Hargreave's map of 1832 showing the House of Recovery labelled the 'Old Infirmary' at the junction of the Trent & Mersey and Caldon canals. The 'New Infirmary', the North Staffordshire Infirmary stands near to Etruria Hall and Wedgwood's works. The land on which both buildings stood was purchased from the Wedgwood Estate - the proximity of which made the Wedgwood's very personal involvement in the hospital possible.

CALL OF THE FIRST MEETING.

THE mortality among the Poor of the populous Parishes the Pottery, during the late severe times, which arose in a great measure fro epidemical fevers breaking out and spreading rapidly through each Workhous is well-known.—The distress also of the Poor, in procuring advice and med cines has been severely felt, notwithstanding the benevolent exertions of sever Medical Gentlemen. Impressed with these ideas, we have been much gra fied with the knowledge of the humane disposition of many of the inhabitar of this Neighbourhood, to encourage the establishment of a MEDICAL DI PENSARY,—such an institution will afford much heart-felt satisfaction fro the reflection of its saving the Lives, and easing the sufferings of many of o Fellow Creatures.

All those who are desirous of contributing their advice and assistance so salutary and beneficial an institution, are requested to meet on WEDNESD 28th July instant, at the SWAN INN, at HANLEY, at Eleven o'Clock in Forenoon.

EDWARD POWYS,

W. H. COYNEY.

The first pages of the first volume of Infirmary minutes (1802) were printed as seen in this copy of the call of the first meeting - they soon became a hand-written record. Edward Powys and W.H. Coyney were magistrates and no doubt would be well aware of the health problems and needs of the Potteries.

Stoke, Fenton, and Lower-Lane.

Mr. THOMAS MINTON,
JOSIAH SPODE, Esq.

Hanley.

Rev. R. E. AITKENS,
Mr. CHARLES MEIGH.

Newcastle.

SAMUEL BAGSHAW, Esq.
Rev. EDWARD CARLESS,
Rev. CLEMENT LEIGH,
THOMAS WARD, Esq.

Lane-End and Lane-Delph.

Mr. WILLIAM BAILEY,
Rev. THOMAS COTTERILL,
Mr. THOMAS HARLEY.

Shelton.

Mr. JOB MEIGH,
WILLIAM YATES, Esq.

Cobridge and Etruria.

Mr. RALPH STEVENSON
JOSIAH WEDGWOOD Esq.

Burslem.

Mr. JOSEPH MACHIN,
Mr. ENOCH WOOD.

Members of the Committee were recruited as stewards to solicit contributions from their own districts.
There are many famous names from the Potteries here, seen here working for the community.

CHAPTER 1
The formation of opinion: newspapers and word of mouth

Why was the Dispensary and House of Recovery founded in 1802, why not earlier, why at that particular time? This chapter considers why the moment was right for the initiative to succeed.

When we consider how and why an event occurs at a particular time, we need to know as much as we can about the people involved, their opinions and their knowledge of their world. In this case what was their vision of a hospital, what could it offer over and above the local Apothecary or Surgeon, how could one gain admission to it? How did the service it could offer compare with the Workhouse or the Parish doctor?

At a time when literacy was by no means universal, spread of news by word of mouth was important. We know that papers were read aloud in workplaces, coffee shops and inns by the literate for the benefit of the illiterate. Information was not yet universally available, it had to be gathered by whatever means were available. If we doubt the effectiveness of basic methods of communication, in our time everyone can recall fires lit on hillsides at times of national celebration, or in memory of events such as the Spanish Armada. Anyone who remembers the last War will recall the chilling sound of the siren signalling an air raid, or the silenced church bells, only to be rung in the event of an invasion.

For example, on December 27th 1814, John Tomlinson added a post-script to a letter addressed to Josiah Wedgwood II, relating to the Infirmary *'P.S. The Postman is decorated with ribbons and says the Mail (coach) came in covered with laurels on account of the peace being signed with America and that the Courier* (London newspaper) *contains the news.'* It was indeed true, the Treaty had been signed at Ghent in Belgium on the evening of December 24th, and peace with America was of vital importance for the trade of the Potteries and therefore the prospects for raising money for the Infirmary. The laurel-covered Mail coach and the be-ribboned postman are striking visual methods of the speed and effectiveness of communication available at that time, and that the papers had moved very quickly, even over Christmas!

Within the years leading up to the Napoleonic Wars newspapers had become more common. Local papers blossomed. The *Staffordshire Advertiser*, which first appeared in 1795, was the local paper in the years surrounding the founding of the Dispensary and House of Recovery and a study of its pages will tell us a great deal about the information available to the people of North Staffordshire. The paper was in a position to influence opinions, and the publication of letters to the Editor (or often in those days to the Printer) meant that a dialogue could be conducted by the public on matters of the day.

Anyone who studied the *Advertiser* would be surprisingly well informed, even by today's standards. The Napoleonic War dominated the news. It was reported very fully, naval heroes were great public figures. Parliamentary debates were reported in great detail and at length, Fox and Pitt would have been as real to their contemporaries as our leaders are to us, with all their media advantages. Local people would have had an uneasy familiarity with Napoleon; his speeches and his proclamations were readily accessible in the papers, as were reports of his military successes.

In the papers, we find all the elements of tabloid journalism, scandals, thefts and accidents, all replete with graphic descriptions. Staple items were murders, executions, and

At a MEETING *held at the* SWAN INN, *at* HANLEY, *this 28th Day of July,* 1802, *for the purpose of taking into Consideration the expediency of establishing a Medical Dispensary, and a Ward for the reception of Fever Patients.*

WALTER SNEYD, Esq. in the CHAIR.

IT WAS RESOLVED,

FIRST.   THAT such an Institution will be highly beneficial to the Neighbourhood.

SECOND. THAT it must be supported by the Subscription of Individuals, Parishes, and Societies.

THIRD.   THAT a Committee be formed of all the Gentlemen here present, to draw up Rules adapted to the intended Institution, and to make a Report of the eligibility of erecting, or hiring a building suitable for the purpose.

FOURTH. THAT any Five shall compose a Committee.

FIFTH.   THAT the Committee shall meet at this House, at eleven o'clock precisely, on THURSDAY the 12th, and MONDAY the 23rd of August.

SIXTH.   THAT a General Meeting for the purpose of receiving the Reports of the Committee, and entering into a Subscription for carrying on the intended Plan with as little delay as possible, be held at the same place on MONDAY the 30th of August.

THAT these Resolutions be inserted in the next Stafford Paper; and that a number of Hand-Bills be printed, and dispersed throughout the Parishes in the Neighbourhood.

(SIGNED)   WALTER SNEYD, Esq. in the CHAIR,

JOHN E. HEATHCOTE,	JOHN WARBURTON,
EDWARD POWYS,	JOHN TURNER,
W. H. COYNEY,	RALPH STEVENSON,
JAMES BENT,	W. H. SMALLWOOD,
JOSIAH SPODE,	THOMAS BRECK,
D. WHALLEY, junr.	THOMAS BYERLEY.
GREGORY HICKMAN,	F. H. NORTHEN,
JOHN ROBINSON,	GEORGE STEEDMAN.

THAT the Thanks of this MEETING be given to Colonel SNEYD, for his taking the Chair, and his able conduct therein.

The printed report of the minutes of the first meeting. Josiah Spode II is present and Thomas Byerley represented the Wedgwood family. Even though the three sons of Josiah Wedgwood I were living at this time in the south of England, surviving correspondence shows that Thomas Byerley wrote regularly to Josiah Wedgwood II keeping him fully informed about the early meetings.

The Swan Inn at Hanley c. 1802 at about the time of the first meeting to discuss a new infirmary. It was the venue for many of the important meetings held in the Town in the absence of a large meeting hall. The Swan was replaced by the covered market in 1849, and in turn by the Potteries Shopping Centre.

last words from the scaffold.   Trials were extensively reported. Frequently the paper reported actions for damages by injured spouses on account of adulterous behaviour or criminal conversation as it was called being cheerfully shortened to Crim Con in headlines. It was a tough world, footpads and highwaymen made regular appearances, as did duellists.   Prominent were local advertisements for cock-fighting, reports of bull-baiting, and of bare-knuckle boxing matches which could have a fatal outcome.   Open fires and candles meant that there were many reports of deaths from burning.   In the issue for April 13th, 1799 one would find *'Hints for females whose clothes have taken fire'*; suggested action included calling for help, getting some water and rolling oneself in the carpet, all of which seem entirely reasonable.   Newspapers were businesses, and a profit was necessary for their continued existence.   Therefore they could not afford to offend their readers sensibilities in politics, and had to reflect their fears as well as their hopes, interests and aspirations.

In most issues the *Advertiser* contained a substantial number of reports of hangings from all over the country. In addition to the wide variety of cases for which the punishment was administered, it is the way in which it was carried out and reported which must have coarsened the public attitude to death and physical suffering. To take an example, at one execution the paper reported that the prisoner's struggles were extremely severe, two and a half minutes elapsed before the prayer book was dropped, and four and half minutes before he appeared divested of life. People were accustomed to personal pain to an extent very different from our experience. Childbirth, toothache and the pain of fractured limbs had to be endured without any really effective pain relief.

How did the paper report on medicine and doctors? What could the man in the street know about the changes taking place in medicine, and how would that knowledge affect his decision on whether or not to support the proposed new Dispensary?

An inspection of medical textbooks and journals published in the early 19th century shows medicine slowly moving from an era of old wives' tales and a belief in the almost magical properties of ancient remedies into an era of scientifically based medicine. This was based on the new sciences that had developed during the Enlightenment of the latter half of the 18th century. The work of the great chemists, Priestley, Lavoisier and Davy, all incidentally personally known to the Wedgwood family, meant that the fundamental processes of life such as respiration were coming to be understood. In future new developments in medicine would have to be founded on observation and fact to command attention.

The *Advertiser* appreciated this trend in 1795, when the generous donations of the Wedgwood family to Dr Beddoes' Pneumatic Institute in Bristol were listed in a report. In fact, this list by no means completely expresses the Wedgwood's support for this, the first publicly funded research institute in the country. Tom Wedgwood was a patient of Beddoes, as were the son and daughter of their friend James Watt. The Pneumatic Institute searched for a therapeutic use for the newly discovered gases, particularly as a cure for tuberculosis. While no such cure came about, the Institute launched the remarkable career of Humphrey Davy, and hugely raised the profile of chemistry in Britain. *The Advertiser's* over-optimistic correspondent said that the experiments on the elastic fluids (gases) have been attended with a success in various diseases, beyond the power of any known drug.

These early therapeutic measures were entirely eclipsed as items of news by Edward Jenner's introduction of vaccination to prevent smallpox (1796-8). Smallpox was a disease that was commonly fatal and left those who survived with disfiguring facial scarring. Throughout the 18th century smallpox was inoculated into the arms of children and young people in the hope of preventing an attack of the disease. The matter from a previous patient's inoculation site was used for the next, the hope being that the infection would become attenuated, i.e. weaker as it passed from arm to arm while retaining its protective power. Josiah Wedgwood recorded the anxiety he and his wife felt when their elder children became very feverish after inoculation with smallpox, as well they might, seeing that a son of George III died soon after the procedure.

Jenner, a Gloucester physician, among others noted that milkmaids who had suffered naturally from cowpox, a disease of cows as its name suggests, were immune to smallpox. The cowpox produced skin lesions that were similar to smallpox, but much less dangerous. Jenner acted on this observation and demonstrated that a patient who had cowpox introduced into his arm was protected against smallpox. Inoculation of cowpox material, vaccination as it came to be called, would become a most powerful weapon.

The *Advertiser* took up the story very quickly, with a clear account of the process, which it followed up by printing Jenner's own instruction for the correct performance of the procedure. This included the advice that the lancet used for vaccination should be washed and wiped clean between each patient. The Academy in Paris, perhaps the pre-eminent scientific body in Europe, judged that vaccination was the greatest discovery of the 18th century. The *Advertiser* exceeded this when it said that Jenner's discovery was the greatest since William Harvey described the circulation of the blood. For the very first time the treatment of an infectious disease was tackled by a rational process based on sound scientific observation, and it is fitting that in the 20th century smallpox was the first infection to be declared eradicated by the World Health Organisation. Vaccination raised the wider hope that medicine could offer more than the palliation of symptoms. Vaccination was the first important treatment to be made available at the Dispensary; vaccination with the Cow-

Pock would have its own special ticket of recommendation.

At this time the medical profession was resolving into its three main branches, Medicine, Surgery and General Medical practice. The Apothecary was de facto a general practitioner, permitted to treat or advise a patient but not allowed to charge for advice, only for the drugs he supplied. Their standing depended on their personal qualities. Surgeons were seen as artisans, men who got their hands dirty. They traditionally performed amputations, opened abscesses, closed up wounds, and let blood for the physicians, who were not expected to shed blood. Physicians were the best educated and most esteemed members of the profession.

Surgeons frequently featured in the newspaper as a result of being called to attend the victims of accident or assault. In these cases they were called to give evidence; thus they were often associated in the public mind with the law. Unfortunately, by the historical quirk that confined the legal supply of corpses for dissection to those who had undergone capital punishment, the sentence of hanging became coupled with being delivered to the surgeon. The surgeon and dissection were associated in the public mind, leading to a desire to avoid post-mortem examinations in cases of natural death and paving the way for the resurrection men (body-snatchers), whose activities were regularly reported in the *Advertiser*.

Of the knowledge required by a doctor, particularly by a surgeon, the first subject to be extensively studied was anatomy, the structure of the body. It was studied and memorised with greater detail than any of the other subjects, which were at a very rudimentary level of development, and was the most esteemed part of the medical course. The importance attached to anatomy helps to explain the need to procure large numbers of bodies for dissection. Unfortunately, the route to medical progress was through the post-mortem examination of people who had died of disease. By this means the signs and symptoms shown in life could be compared with the changes found in internal organs. The association with the resurrection men held up research throughout the 19th century. As late as 1860 Dr Wilson Fox was only able to perform two post-mortem examinations during his stay in North Staffordshire, delaying the elucidation of the chest diseases that so afflicted pottery workers.

When the first hanging took place at the new Stafford Gaol on 1797, the *Advertiser* reported that the body was transferred to the Stafford General Infirmary and dissected by Mr Hughes the Surgeon, Mr Fawkes the Apothecary and others. Such persons as were desirous to view the proceedings were admitted through the gates of the Infirmary for that purpose.

Due to the importance attached to gentlemanly status and an exaggerated code of honour duelling reached epidemic proportions about this time. Two surgeon's apprentices fought a duel in Newcastle under Lyme in 1795; alas bathos set in when they fired and both missed. The affair concluded in a fist fight. Much more seriously, a doctor could become involved in duelling, either by being called to treat a duellist, or even being asked to be in attendance. Should one of the combatants be killed, the charge was murder, and the doctor could be charged as an accessory. A report of such a case would seriously damage any surgeons image in the eyes of the public.

Public attitudes to doctors are most important when money is being sought to build and maintain a hospital. At this time hospitals depended on public support, and as we shall see in North Staffordshire they depended on sustained support from the working people.

The early meetings of the supporters of the Dispensary and House of Recovery were reported in the *Advertiser*, and were the subject of an editorial article supportive of the new venture. So if the public were used to reading about doctors, how was the public reaction to the proposed Dispensary reported?

The number of letters to the Printer (as the Editor was called in those days) that were included in the *Advertiser* varied from issue to issue, often no letter at all was printed when other news was abundant. The foundation of the Dispensary and House of Recovery in 1802 occurred during an interlude of peace, so the Editor was able to find room for letters for and against.

On August 14th the paper published an open letter from Dr F.H. Northen, who was to become the first physician appointed to the institution, addressed to Messrs Coyney and Powys, the magistrates who had called the first meeting. He commended their proposal to found the Dispensary and House of Recovery, both for improving the health of the population at large, and as at other towns, ridding them of fever cases. The initial resolutions to found the House of Recovery speak of recent infections in the area overwhelming the workhouses, but Dr Northen's remarks look forward to something more ambitious, a proper general hospital, able to care for cases other than fevers - patients with acute medical illnesses or the victims of accidents.

He wrote: *Some of the diseases incident to your poor are local, that is they are connected with causes inseparable from the nature of their employment. I, in particular, allude here to the indispensable use in the manufacture of earthenware, of certain minerals, which are known to exert a virulent action on the human body, and ultimately to produce obstinate and dangerous disorders. To investigate these still further, to attempt to elucidate their nature, and, if possible to advance a step towards their prevention and cure, are objects much to be desired, and which may not, I think, be unreasonably expected to result from the opportunity offered by the proposed institution to the Medical man, of enlarging his experience and comparing with his professional colleagues his additional knowledge of such diseases.*

This letter is most significant because it recognised publicly that there were diseases peculiar to the pottery industry and that they should be researched.

Dr Northen, the first Physician at the Infirmary, wrote an influential letter of support which appeared in the *Advertiser* in 1802.

Bringing these cases together under one roof would permit their more detailed study, further, each doctor could gain a wider experience of the industrial diseases than he could if confined to his own practice. Discussion with professional colleagues, the doctors at a hospital, would add to the pool of knowledge. Clearly, Dr Northen is referring to flint dust and to lead under the euphemism of certain minerals. We know from Josiah Wedgwood's published letters that Dr Percival of Manchester had offended him by questioning and investigating the amount of lead in the glaze used on Queen's Ware, and perhaps Dr Northen did not wish to offend the Potters whose support for the new Institution would be vital. The harmful effects of flint (Silica) dust on the lungs were already well appreciated by the workers. The letter anticipates the essential features that we hope to see in today's modern hospital, one that not only treats patients but is also concerned with research and the dissemination of knowledge. This was an ambitious plan when we consider that the planned institution was starting completely from scratch, with limited finances and few traditions of corporate action existing in the district as a whole.

Other than Dr Northen's letter, those letters in favour of the Dispensary are much as we might expect. The replies of those opposed to the plan are much more informative. The most vociferous opponent signed himself *A Theophilanthropist*, a name which signified someone who loved God and Nature. This name was taken from a sect that originated in France in 1796 and suppressed in 1801 by Napoleon. It was intended to replace Roman Catholicism, combining the Christian religion with the officially approved cult of the Revolution, that of the Supreme Being.

A Theophilanthropist said that the House of Recovery would fail, that no one in North Staffordshire would contribute to its maintenance. In Manchester and Birmingham many workers had no family living in those towns, being migrant workers they would make use of such an institution. In the Potteries people were in contact with their families, and would not willingly leave them to go to a hospital, it was better to give them food and clothing. His most positive suggestion was that four schools should be opened to teach reading and writing to the poorer classes, which would enable them to appreciate the value of money, set up decent homes, bring up their children properly and become decent members of society. This would in turn enable them to become self-sufficient, and implicitly not perpetuate a cycle of dependency.

An Inhabitant believed that the existing parish system of free medical aid to the poor could not be improved upon, provided that the Parish would pay enough to attract decent doctors. This letter concludes with a puff for the Methodist Sunday Schools. Another letter contains a hint that self interest by a doctor could be behind the proposal that pay for Parish Surgeons should be increased.

A Subscriber replied that to read *A Theophilanthropist* it would be imagined a Bastille was to be set up, not a gentle asylum, and the patient dragged off against his will. This was an early use of Bastille to describe a hospital, it was famously used by Charles Shaw and later Arnold Bennett in *Clayhanger* to describe Chell Workhouse. Admission to the House of Recovery would not be indiscriminate, but the removal of the sickest people from the worst houses would save whole families from destruction. Referring to Manchester, *A Subscriber* reported that since the opening of the House of Recovery there, the cost of pauper coffins had fallen by a third, and pauper burials were down by 400, a startling statistic, but perhaps just as likely to be accurate as any other statistic relating to the poorest classes of that teeming town. Of all human activities, those involving money are usually most accurately recorded.

The following week, on November 6th, a further letter came from *A Theophilanthropist*. If the working class were to become sufficiently educated to bring their passions under the control of reason, they would appreciate the value of their labour, have sufficient to live on, have good homes etc. His attack on potential subscribers then became personal. Where were the benevolent gentlemen (supporters of the House of Recovery) in the recent times, when every poor man's home was a fever ward, bread was 5d a pound? Were they spectators of these miserable scenes? No one was bold enough then to propose fever wards and dispensaries. There was not even a solitary soup kitchen in the Potteries, though they were otherwise universal throughout the kingdom. This episode would form a memorable epoch in the history of our cluster of towns, should it ever reach the eyes of posterity.

On November 13th came the last shots in the battle. *A Journeyman Potter* opposed *A Theophilanthropist*. Teaching was of no use when food could not be afforded. *A Subscriber* said that by their support and contributions, the Artificers (workpeople) of the town had joined with others to subscribe sufficient money to secure the start of the Dispensary and House of Recovery and by so doing had given it public sanction, i.e. by subscribing they had already approved the plan and given it practical support. It was an insult to these people to conclude that they were too ignorant to have decent homes and families, but long and severe illness will reduce even such people to seeking relief at a public institution (hospital or workhouse). He conceded there were problems with labourers who were mainly passing through rather than settled in the community. Had *A Theophilanthropist* not noticed the many meetings held in the towns to raise money? There had been private distribution of this money, as the people had a feeling against soup kitchens, *'an unhappy prejudice was found to prevail against them'*. (One had in fact been opened in the Potteries, perhaps that at Newcastle, where a Ball had been held to raise funds for the Soup Institution.) Where were the benevolent gentlemen? Let me ask in turn, where was *A Theophilanthropist* (when money was needed)? This splendid parting shot closes the correspondence. War was resumed in 1803, and the papers had weightier matters to report.

Each side had right on its side. There would be those who could not be cared for in crowded homes, and isolation of the first case of an infectious disease might save the rest of the family. Equally education is still held to be the way to encourage the population to take care of the health of themselves and their families, to increase their prosperity, and help them to live more fulfilling lives. Plus ca change!

Judging from the correspondence there is less doubt expressed about the need for a hospital than there is doubt about its financial support by the community. As first steps the Dispensary and House of Recovery were sensible choices, being much cheaper to build and run than a full blown hospital.

A montage of signatures from the first years of the Infirmary minutes.
John Wedgwood, Josiah Wedgwood II, Enoch Wood, James Caldwell, John Ridgway,
Thomas Byerley, The Marquis of Stafford, James Bent.

CHAPTER 2
The Dispensary and House of Recovery

The story of the Dispensary and House of Recovery tells of the first years of our hospital from 1802 until 1814 - the year in which the decision was made to move into a brand new Infirmary. The original modest institution allowed assessments to be made of the needs of the district and the likelihood of adequate financial support. At the same time the Governors explored the response to a proposed Board of Health which would encourage and coordinate efforts to improve the health of the public. Despite the need to control expenditure we find the medical staff eager to undertake surprisingly sophisticated clinical research. Many useful lessons were learned regarding the management of the buildings, finances and staff.

The Dispensary and House of Recovery only existed for a dozen years before being superseded by the Infirmary in Etruria. It could be seen as a diversion, a waste of time and effort. Rather I believe it should be seen as an indispensable first step in establishing an institution that was outside the experience of most people in North Staffordshire at that time and that in its short life many useful lessons were learned. We know that the Staffordshire Potteries differed from older towns with their long established methods of government; it could not be taken for granted that the voluntary pattern for a hospital would flourish here. A tentative first step meant that medical needs and the likely financial support could be assessed along with the direction of rapidly changing requirements of the district.

As it happens those first years prefigure many of the concerns which were to last until the coming of the National Health Service in 1948. The first and the most important was the ever present question of finance, of capital to provide the buildings and equipment and revenue to pay for the running expenses. The next we may categorise as management issues and personnel or human resources issues. Though the staff was tiny in number, principally the Matron with a few nurses and the Apothecary, the doctor who also functioned as dispenser and secretary, this small group caused a remarkable number of problems to the Committee who were elected from the Governors; they had to learn some hard lessons. Other concerns related to the elevation of standards of medical practice, research and prospective methods of improving heath in the Potteries which we may call health education and public health.

The first step was to decide what sort of institution the Governors should build. It was agreed that it should be a voluntary institution, the principles on which the charity was set up differ little from those which governed voluntary hospitals across the land. Indeed, they closely follow the rules enunciated by the Governors of Westminster Hospital when setting up the first voluntary hospital in 1719. The medical staff would not be paid, apart from a resident doctor, the apothecary, or as he was later called the house surgeon; patients were limited to those who could not otherwise afford treatment, and while subscribers would have the privilege of recommending patients for admission they must not benefit from the charity themselves.

It was decided to begin with a dispensary rather than a complete hospital or infirmary. A dispensary was a most useful component of the voluntary system. It could be attached to a hospital, or it could stand alone. It 'dispensed' both free medical attention and medicines to the poor who were treated as outpatients. It had low overheads as it had no beds and no in-patients to house and feed and no resident nurses, so it was a most efficient means of delivering a basic level of health care. It could have its own doctor and dispenser (pharmacist), it could be served by doctors acting in a voluntary capacity, by paid doctors or a combination of both.

An alternative system was provided by the 'provident dispensary', where patients paid in a small amount each week, that covered medicines and treatment delivered by doctors who would be paid a salary. A dispensary was a natural first step for those who founded the Potteries first voluntary institutions. It was useful in scattered communities whose small populations could not sustain a hospital, and in teeming inner cities where the population were too poor to afford to establish one. Even though London was a very rich city, its voluntary hospitals were crowded together in the centre. As late as the 1880s 90% of all the hospital beds in the capital were to be found within a radius of $1^1/2$ miles of Charing Cross, while in North London, 1 million people had only 59 beds available to them. Dispensaries filled the gaps. Eventually, they were replaced by absorption into hospitals as casualty and outpatients departments, as in North Staffordshire, or into general practice. True, the ill patient had to get himself to and from the dispensary, and be nursed at home, usually by his family. It was not a perfect solution, but it did permit the poor patient to receive free treatment, treatment for which he would have to pay if received from a surgeon in the town.

The House of Recovery was the usual euphemism for the fever ward. The minutes tell us it was called the House of Recovery in order to prevent alarm to patients. The purpose was as much the isolation of a fever patient before he passed on the infection as his medical care. In the absence of specific treatments for infectious diseases, isolation of an infected case and simple nursing were all that could be offered.

Having decided to proceed, a Building Fund was set up and donations were solicited. In addition donors were invited to become regular subscribers and, provided their subscription reached an agreed value, to become Governors. Governors were eligible for election onto the Committee, thereby having a say in the running of the Charity. Alas, the donations were of a disappointing level. A committee of manufacturers known as the Anderton Committee, probably associated with canal interests, subscribed £50, as did the Marquis of Stafford, but no donation from the manufacturers of the area amounted to £50. Indeed the next highest donation of £20 for the building and £13 for revenue came from the workmen of Etruria. The initial sum raised was about £800. At this time the Stafford General Infirmary still attracted subscriptions from North Staffordshire families such as the Wedgwoods. Stafford had an established infirmary and Stafford was the County Town. The executors of Isaac Hawkins of Burton on Trent allotted a legacy of £800 to the North Staffordshire Dispensary and House of Recovery, even so we should note that they gave £1000 to a hospital in London, £3000 to the funds of the Staffordshire General Infirmary and more than £5000 to Derbyshire General Infirmary.

If we compare the financial support in the Potteries with that received by the Derbyshire General Infirmary, which was being set up at exactly the same time, 1804, the Derby donations make a staggering contrast to those in North Staffordshire. £500 was received from the Corporation of Derby, £2000 from the Duke of Devonshire, £1000 from his son and another £1000 from Richard Arkwright; more than thirty other individuals donated £100. When the Derby hospital was built their fund had reached £27,705, which meant that they could set out to erect a handsome building for 80 patients, not including provision for the fever patients. This was 'not intended to appear ostentatious', but it had a double staircase rising from the entrance hall and to avoid any lack of symmetry in the design, false doors were built against the side walls, in the best tradition of country house design. To put the difference between Derbyshire's wealth and North Staffordshire's poverty in perspective, when Derby was building on an aristocratic scale North Staffordshire was making the decision to allow no more than one nail in the stable for the attachment of the halter of each visitor's horse and telling Mr Coxon to build as cheaply as possible.

The Governors in North Staffordshire had looked for a building that could be adapted, *'one that would supply suitable rooms for the planned functions of the charity'*, and having found *'no building which would unite all the necessary circumstances'* decided it was best to build anew. They concluded that a building sited on the fields between Stoke and Shelton would be ideal. The site they chose, initially rented from the Wedgwood estate, between the Trent and Mersey and the Caldon Canals, was described as elevated yet secluded, having easiness of access, good water and dry gravel soil. By March 1803 the plan, for which Mr Bellhouse of Manchester was paid four guineas, was made available for inspection at the counting house of the treasurers, at Messrs Wedgwood and Byerley's works at Etruria. It should be noted that for the first nine years Wedgwood and Byerley were not only the treasurers but provided the business address of the new institution, and although many accounts passed through the works' ledgers, they made no charge for this service, but paid interest on the money they were holding on behalf of the charity.

When we consider the actual building of the Dispensary and House of Recovery, there were no really innovative features, certainly no evidence of display. It was a plain building with two parallel *'wings'*, a dwelling house for the Apothecary, conveniences for the occasional lodges (rooms) of two or more nurses and a shop, the surgery, which constituted the Dispensary. The other *'wing'* was detached from the Dispensary and contained some rooms which were for fever patients, the House of Recovery. This second wing was completed after the receipt of the legacy of £800. Among the necessary offices was a room for changing the clothes of the patients, and for washing and airing them. The House of Recovery was supplied with water closets and shower baths, which by this time the Governors considered a necessity in their own homes and therefore required in an institution caring for the sick. A minute thanks Mr (John) Wedgwood for *superintending* the installation of a water closet, a toilet that cost £20.

Only two pictures of the Dispensary and House of Recovery have survived. The first is a photograph of a painting made in 1828. It shows a gabled building with two parallel wings, rather like two houses that are joined together by common buildings at ground floor level. The general appearance is domestic rather than industrial or institutional and it is already somewhat marred by the close proximity of a gasworks with two gas-holders. The other is a photograph taken about 1860 that shows a neat brick building with no decorative features, and standing on somewhat bare ground, with houses and potteries in the surrounding area.

From the very first year, 1802, there is no way in which the Committee can be accused of rushing into building contracts without due consideration. One of the very earliest minutes refers to their having examined the plans adopted in other places. The evidence indicates that Manchester was the principal source of their information, probably via Dr Thomas Percival.

Mr Coxon, a builder of Hanley was appointed to erect the Dispensary and House of Recovery. The contract was drawn up, and financial penalties for delays were agreed. It is typical of the management of a voluntary institution that a member of the Committee, Mr

Miss Whalley,	-	1	1	O
Daniel Whalley, Esqr. Fenton,	-	2	2	O
Additional, upon making the Charity an Infirmary,	-	2	2	O
Daniel Whalley, junr. Esqr. Ditto,		2	2	O
Additional, upon making the Charity an Infirmary,		2	2	O
John Wedgwood, Esqr. Cote House, near Bristol,	-	5	5	O
Josiah Wedgwood, Esqr. Etruria,		5	5	O
Thomas Wedgwood, Esqr. Eastbury, Dorset.	-	5	5	O

1804. Josiah Wedgwood (II) is living in Etruria while John and Thomas are in the South of England. The subscriptions of Daniel Whalley, Junior & Senior show the pressure to establish an infirmary.

William Heath, was appointed to represent the Governors and oversee the contractor.

In July 1803 a site meeting was held, a first instalment of £300 was paid over to Mr Coxon, and ten shillings and sixpence was paid to provide drink for the workmen. Further instalments of £200 were paid in October and in January 1804. As the building work progressed, the tide of opinion among the Committee veered towards the provision of an infirmary where general and accident patients could be admitted, not just fever patients. As a result certain alterations were undertaken - the space between the Dispensary and the House of Recovery was enclosed, providing wash and coalhouses and *'necessary houses'* (toilets).

In April 1804 the Committee announced that they were satisfied with Mr Coxon's work as the buildings were nearly ready. Despite some delays *'because of the workmen'*, it was decide to open such parts as the finances would stand. Having some money in hand, the Committee wished to begin the fitting up of *'such a part* (of the House of Recovery, the Fever Wards) *as they think proper for the purposes of a General Infirmary'*. They were also aware that they were losing subscriptions by failing to open an Infirmary.

Eleven beds arrived from Manchester of the pattern used there. Two of these beds had adjustable backs. Providing a rare splash of colour some blankets were dyed blue to provide coverlets. But despite determined frugality, it soon became clear that the Committee were heading for a serious overspend, and the proposed move to provide an infirmary was put on hold.

Having raised some money and recruited staff they opened their Dispensary in 1804 and began the task of treating patients. At this time, a start was made with the provision of inoculation against smallpox and the regular attendance of a surgeon between 10 am and 1 pm each Tuesday. So important was the provision of vaccination it was seen as deserving its own recommendation form. They were in business, but were again concentrating on the Fever Wards rather than any general wards. In January 1806, the Committee sought information about the price of a sedan chair with a moveable washable lining for moving patients to the House of Recovery - perhaps the Potteries' first ambulance. A *'proper tub'* (whether for washing patients or their clothes is not made clear) was to be provided for the use of infected patients.

It must be admitted that the next few years saw little progress in the facilities or

GENTLEMEN,

I Recommend to your Examination, *Elijah Machin* of the Parish of *Stoke-upon-Trent* who (I am well satisfied) is a real Object of Charity, and desire *he/she* may be admitted an *IN/OUT* Patient of the Dispensary and House of Recovery, if duly qualified.

Your humble Servant,

AGE, ...

DISTEMPER, *(illness)*

HOW LONG ILL, ----------

N. B. A Subscriber of One Guinea per Annum is entitled to have one Patient constantly on the Books of the Dispensary.

A very early 'recommendation' for the Dispensary and House of Recovery. A subscriber would fill in the form if he felt that the person needed the treatment and could not afford to pay for it - ie a 'real Object of Charity'. The dotted lines and the italicised entries are additions for clarity.

COW POCK INOCULATION.

INOCULATE

SIGNED,

N. B.   Attendance will be given every Monday from Ten till One.

Vaccination, ie inoculation with cowpox to prevent smallpox, had its own form of Recommendation.

Medical Difpenfary & Houfe of Recovery,
FOR THE USE OF THE
POTTERIES and NEIGHBOURHOOD.

AN APOTHECARY is wanted to refide in the Houfe, and to give up his whole time to the charity, commencing at *Lady-Day* next. Perfons difpofed to accept this Office, are requefted to fend their teftimonials and propofals, *poft-paid*, to the Treafurers, Meffrs. *Jofiah Wedgwood & Byerley*, at *Etruria*, in *Staffordfhire*, on or before the 15*th of February* next, in order that they may be laid before the *Committee* at its meeting on the following day ; which is all the trouble that candidates will need to take in the firft inftance.
January 6th 1804.

The first advertisement for a doctor at the Infirmary, 1804. Note that the application was to be sent to Wedgwood & Byerley at Etruria, and that the post was to be pre-paid - until the Penny Post the recipient was liable for postage.

services provided in these buildings. The country was in the middle of the Napoleonic Wars and trade was severely disrupted. We know that the Committee and the Medical Staff were anxious to develop further the services available in North Staffordshire but financial concerns held up the decision about the development of an infirmary. The development would not become possible until the inception of the 'Establishment Schemes' which would provide a reliable income. The activity of the House of Recovery was low, indeed no cases of fever at all were admitted in the year 1812 and four in 1813.

Plans were drawn up for the provision of inside and outside staircases, together with a stable, which cost £29, and a scullery at a cost of £16. The land in front of the building was enclosed, and potatoes, gooseberries and currant trees were planted. Benches and a stove for the comfort of waiting patients arrived. Small scale improvements continued year by year. Alterations to enlarge the waiting room, to move the entrance door and re-roof the stables were undertaken. In 1810 the Committee embarked on the keeping of pigs, fattened on kitchen waste It was *'Resolved: That a pig stye be immediately erected on the spot pointed out by the Committee'*. In practice the keeping of Infirmary pigs continued for more than a century. The pigs were a sought after commodity in Newcastle market, and produced a substantial and regular income for the Infirmary.

Having achieved these limited goals, the Governors began to think about their wider ambitions for the district: research, education and a *'Board of Health'*. There is no doubt that Dr Percival of Manchester was an inspirational figure for the Committee. He was particularly involved with the Fever Hospital and the Board of Health in Manchester. His example and his writing about the establishment of a Board of Health, together with the issuing of instructions on cleaning houses affected by infectious diseases, clearly inspired the new Committee to get their teeth into a practical problem. As early as 1802 Dr Northen had quoted Percival as an authority when he wrote his supportive letter to the *Advertiser*. It is not surprising that Manchester was the source of much advice to the infant Committee in North Staffordshire.

The Board of Health was proposed to extend the usefulness of the Dispensary into the community, indeed into public health. It was recognised that infectious diseases were the most obvious threats to the health of the people. It had long been appreciated that poorer people living in crowded accommodation were the most susceptible and at the same time the least equipped to control its spread. The idea that health of the public was a public responsibility did not sit easily with the contemporary ideas of the rights of property, or the idea that a man should be able to do whatever he liked in his house - or to his family. Indeed in 1802 such thoughts of public responsibility encroaching on people's private affairs may have seemed downright dangerous in the aftermath of the French Revolution.

Independent of the arguments for attention to the health of the Poor, which result from a sense of duty, or from a benevolent disposition, there appear to the Committee, others, which powerfully apply to the personal feelings and safety of every one. It is known that the diseases incident to the poorer classes are more generally contagious than those which are common to persons in an easy condition of Life, and if neglected, become more highly so, and the infection is long retained in their cloaths and dwellings : It is therefore not unlikely that such diseases in spreading may reach the most opulent, and severely revenge their insensibility to the wretchedness surrounding them.—

1802 minutes - Arguments in favour of a Dispensary and House of Recovery.

The Governors addressed the public in terms likely to appeal to their sense of personal safety and enlightened self-interest, and simultaneously appealed to their feelings as ratepayers. When they spoke of the need for fever wards they pointed out that *'infectious diseases could multiply among the poor, if neglected become more contagious and be long retained in their cloathes (sic) and dwellings'*. Now comes the crunch: *'it is therefore not unlikely that such diseases may reach the most opulent and severely revenge their insensibility to the wretchedness around them'*. The concept that wealth may not be a guarantee against infection, and the reminder that good quality housing was often surrounded by slums, was unsettling. Having waved the stick, the Governors appeased the ratepayers with a carrot. *'....There is reason to believe... that the Dispensary and House of Recovery will be of advantage to the Parish funds for the relief of the poor and of those of Friendly Societies in as much as subscriptions on their behalf will afford the most economical way of procuring medical relief'*, in other words it will keep the rates down.

It was felt to be necessary to explain the Board of Health to the public and potential subscribers. *'The Committee are aware that the idea of a Board of Health is novel in this neighbourhood, and its utility may not be very obvious at first. Their views extend only to the forming of some public body that shall consider itself bound to watch over all those circumstances which are likely in any way to affect the general health of the Poor and report the same to the magistrate, for removal or amelioration...'* They were careful to avoid the suggestion that compulsion might occasionally have been in order - that would have been a matter for the law as administered by the magistrate. Of course many of the Committee were magistrates, but we can see that it was necessary to keep the Dispensary at arm's length from being seen as an arm of the Law. We may recall the letter to the *Advertiser* about the sick being carried away to a bastille. The setting up of a Board of Health could only be done by agreement, and it needed the continued permission of the public. Throughout the 19th century much of the public health legislation was permissive, such a law might say you could, for example, should you so wish, put sewers into your town, it did not say you had to put in the sewers. The permissive legislation was therefore often the only legislation that Parliament would accept; it was a gift to those local authorities (including some of the Potteries towns) that opposed any avoidable expenditure, and delayed the provision of public works in some towns for many years.

Having decided to set up a Board of Health, the Committee endeavoured to follow the Manchester pattern, and tried to find men in Newcastle and in each of the Pottery towns who would be taught the method of cleaning and purifying houses which had infection in them, and who would be rewarded for their work by the Committee. It was agreed to print and circulate instructions for the cleaning of houses and clothes, but a month later they reported that they were unable to recruit any men prepared to do the work, so they decided to hire in casual labour, or to offer rewards to families for cleaning their own infected homes. The active functions of the Committee as a Board of Health soon seem to falter in North Staffordshire; it then operated more as an out-reach service offering help and advice from the Dispensary.

Dr Percival's account of the Board of Health at Manchester showed that it had powers of which North Staffordshire could only dream. In addition to its powers to cleanse buildings whose inhabitants were suffering from fever, i.e. infectious disease, in Manchester the Board had powers which went far beyond infection control. They examined the buildings of the poor, prohibited the construction and use of buildings which could not be made salubrious, removed improperly sited privies, and saw to the cleaning of the streets and the removal of dunghills. Further they wished to enter factories and examine the working conditions, especially those of pauper apprentices who were not under the immediate direction of their family and friends. The example of Manchester's Board of Health inspired the first Sir Robert Peel's pioneering Bill of 1802 which gave some protection to these pauper apprentices, and was the first instance of employment legislation to be enacted. The provision of outreach activities, such as securing decent lodgings for men who had come to Manchester looking for work, and the inspection of the House of Recovery were to be undertaken by the independent Strangers' Friend Society.

Why was it so difficult to set up a Board of Health in the Potteries, why was there such a difference between Manchester and the Pottery towns? Manchester was in law still a village, as it was until after Peterloo in 1819, but it seems to have acted much more nearly as a single unit even at this stage, while the Pottery towns and Newcastle went their own way, even failing to find people willing to put these relatively simple reforms into action. These ideas for an integrated system of public health and hospital care in the whole of North Staffordshire under one united Board of Health as planned by the Governors antedate the first Improvement Act in Newcastle by 17 years, and by many more years those of the Pottery towns. If taken up, could such a unified organisation have led to earlier integration of the Pottery Towns? The establishment of a Board of Health in the Parish of Stoke was fought off in 1851, despite the report of Rawlinson in 1850, in language and with arguments that reflect no credit on those involved locally.

An early aim of the Governors was *'to furnish attention to the mass of the people about those things in common life which require their attention for the preservation of health. They continued with their intention to distribute among the poor instructions as to the most probable means of securing themselves from infection, and what ought to be their conduct in all cases of fever, accident and suspended animation, and to circulate cheap publications relating to these important subjects.'* The early years of the Dispensary coincide with the spread of Sunday Schools, and the foundation of the two societies which provided day schools, the British and Foreign Schools Society, originally supported by Quakers, and the National Society, the Anglican Society which grew out of the Society for the Propagation of Christian Knowledge (SPCK). Another significant step in the history of self help was the foundation of the very first of all Mechanics Institutes in Chester in 1810. All this presumes a considerable degree of literacy in the population, but it should be borne in mind that this was a period in which many would consult a self-help book (if necessary with the help of a literate neighbour) before consulting a doctor. A pirated edition of the most popular book on home medicine, Buchan's *Domestic Medicine*, was published in Burslem in 1812, along with John Wesley's book, *Primitive Physic*.

Research was not forgotten. Less than ten years had passed since the introduction of vaccination and there were many potential detractors, especially those who felt it interfered with nature. Many articles in the medical press proclaimed its usefulness and compared the infection rate where it had been used with where it had not. We cannot underestimate the importance of vaccination in the mind of the public and the medical profession. Its success was vital for the progress of medicine. Apart from its immediate benefits, successful vaccination justified the profession's claim to offer reliable and rational treatment and offered the public a means to judge the claims of this *'new'* medicine.

Vaccination was a treatment that could be offered at the Dispensary to the poor as outpatients; smallpox was a terrifying scourge at the time. We know from correspondence between Dr James Bent and Josiah Wedgwood II that the fee for a private vaccination was half a crown (two shillings and sixpence), a sum far beyond most working men with a family. A supply of lymph, containing the cow-pox virus which was introduced into the skin, came from a Central House in London, and could be passed from arm to arm of vaccinated persons to make it go further.

Thus the success of vaccination was bound up with the success and good name of the Dispensary; moreover it was capable of scientific investigation. Therefore in July, 1806 it was a matter of great concern when rumours began to circulate that people in the district had contracted smallpox even though they had been vaccinated. The physicians and surgeons met to consider the action they should take. On 15th July Mr Cleavin, as Apothecary and Secretary, was told to send a letter to the Medical Practitioners of Newcastle and the Potteries:

Sir,

Rumours having prevailed that some instances of Smallpox have occurred in this neighbourhood after the Cowpox (i.e. Vaccination), which appear to have prejudiced the public mind and to have diminished the number of applications for Vaccination at the Charity, the medical committee have thought it their duty to make an enquiry into the truth of such reports, and for that purpose will be much obliged to you to inform me whether any such cases have occurred in your practice, and what number of patients have been inoculated by you since you have commenced the practice of Vaccination.

Signed by Dr Cleavin

The meeting further *'Resolved'* in a minute signed by J.H. Northen, Physician:

A late 18th century engraving showing Etruria village and the Wedgwood works running along the centre of the picture. Etruria Hall stands on the rising ground to the left. Above on the higher undulating hills is seen Hanley Church and the Windmill. Along this high ridge lies Stoke, to the right and hidden by the tree, and

The view from Etruria Hall in the 1850s.
Cows still graze, the Wedgwood Etruria works is alongside the canal, but smoke rises ominously from the chimneys of the Shelton Iron Works.

'that a certain number of those who have been Inoculated for the Cow Pox at this Institution be Inoculated for the Smallpox by the Apothecary, that those so inoculated be selected from different parts of the Potteries, and the progress of the test be occasionally examined by the Committee'.

Sadly we do not have any further information. Vaccination continued to be an important part of the work of the Dispensary, and the prevalence of smallpox appears to have been reduced in the neighbourhood. Nonetheless, the letter to the General Practitioners of North Staffordshire is a postal survey, a form of enquiry that is still in use today, and this must be a very early example.

The resolution is also of exceptional interest as an example of the research interest of the medical staff. In this it was proposed that there should be a clinical trial of the effectiveness or otherwise of vaccination. Some of those who had been vaccinated (using cowpox) were to be inoculated with smallpox. If these patients showed signs of smallpox, then vaccination would have failed to protect them, if the smallpox did not produce an infection, then vaccination had been successful. We cannot claim it as a double blind trial, but the reference that those inoculated should be selected from different parts of the Potteries showed the Committee had an appreciation of the randomisation necessary to minimise local effects which would affect the result.

As I have said, we have no evidence of a response to these initiatives, though they may be connected with the minute of August 5th when the two physicians, Drs Bent and Northen were requested to report on *Contagious fever which has appeared in Penkhull.*

In 1810 the Medical Staff adopted another innovative scheme for quality control. Concerned that mothers would not bring children back to the Dispensary so that the success of their vaccination could be checked, they proposed that the mother should leave a deposit of one shilling at the time of vaccination, which would be returned at the follow-up visit. This would also ensure a supply of lymph for the next candidates for vaccination.

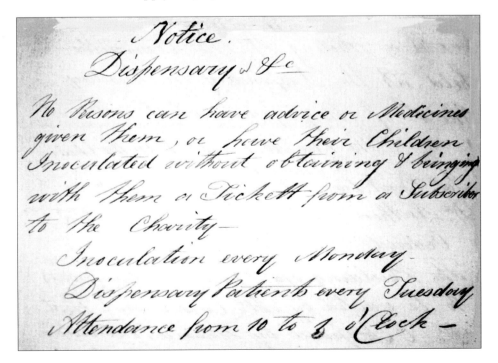

Notice copied into the Minutes regarding the need for a 'Tickett', and the hours of attendance, 1804.

Etruria works   Etruria Hall   Infirmary   The House of Recovery

Three increasingly enlarged images of the same painting showing Etruria and the House of Recovery in 1826. The two tall blocks are immediately behind the Gas Works that dominates the foreground, with the Trent and Mersey Canal immediately in front of that. To the right of the picture the Bedford Street Bridge crosses the Caldon Canal. *The Warrilow Collection*

A photograph from Ernest Warrilow's Collection (Keele University) showing the obvious two block building of the House of Recovery to the left of the picture, about 1860.

Etruria Vale in the mid-19th century. Taken from Basford looking east (where the chimneys of the Iron and Steel works are seen in the trees). The white building (ringed) seen through the trees is the Infirmary.

From the surviving records we can see that the spirit of research was soon constrained by the necessity of raising money and developing the services available. Nonetheless, the most active Governors were supportive of research. We have a note made by Josiah Wedgwood II on a piece of scrap paper, an aide-memoire for a planning meeting for the new Infirmary in 1815. Writing about the Mortuary, he made a note about the need for double doors and the possibility of dissection taking place. Were the double doors to contain any offensive odours, or to keep prying eyes away from that which was best concealed? Opposition to post mortem examination of patients was encouraged by the idea that the poor were to be dissected so that operations could be more successfully performed on the rich, i.e. by practising on the poor.

Dr Percival in his book of 1803, pointed out that even if a surgeon used what he had learned (by dissection of the poor patients) in the course of treating a rich patient, the ultimate benefit was eventually much more advantageous to the poor. Medical knowledge always percolates through the profession, and as there were many more poor people in the population than noblemen, ultimately far more poor people would benefit from this growth of knowledge.

The question of cost was ever present from the earliest days of the Dispensary. As early as 1805 the size of the drug bill was causing alarm. The Apothecary was not to order any drug without the signature of a physician, 'ESPECIALLY not Burnt Sponge for patients with Bronchocele'. If patients were admitted with this complaint, they were to be moved on as soon as possible, and admissions were not encouraged for this treatment 'which the finances of this Institution cannot afford'. Bronchocele is the name for a goitre, a swelling of the thyroid gland common in places distant from the sea, often known as Derbyshire neck and due to a dietary deficiency of iodine. It had been known empirically that sea sponge and sea-weed could cure this form of goitre, though the active principle that they contained, iodine, would not be isolated until 1814. Quite why burnt sponge was so expensive is not stated. Whether the Napoleonic War had made imports difficult and expensive, or whether the market had been cornered by a Dr Bate of Coventry who was known to have used sponge as a secret ingredient in a patent medicine, is not clear. It was an effective but expensive treatment for a common condition, a 'NICE' dilemma one might say.

The duties of the Apothecary were increasing. He had to attend to much of the work of the Dispensary, visit potential cases of fever and look after them in the House of Recovery, and, as we have seen, write letters and circulars. He was also responsible for the preparation of medicines, for looking after the money and for the collection of subscriptions. He was allowed two days each week to go about the district collecting subscriptions, and during his absence his duties were to be covered by the surgeons. The physicians were held in too much awe to be asked to fill in for the Apothecary, though it was thought a quite proper activity for the surgeons, who were still perceived as having the lower status at this time.

The Committee had to learn the hard way about the management of their medical staff. The first three Apothecaries all left under a cloud. The first was Mr Wilde who on July 2nd 1805 approached the Committee with the demand that unless he be permitted the privilege of private practice for his own emolument, he would resign. The prospect of the Apothecary being allowed to conduct a private practice was quite unacceptable. He was already paid a salary and being on the premises he would be well placed to poach private patients from the consultants who depended on private practice for their whole income. This was not a wise action on the part of Mr Wilde, as the Committee immediately accepted his threatened resignation and declared the post vacant.

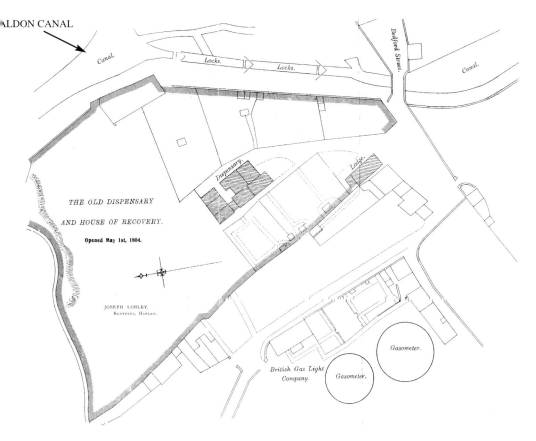

Plan taken from Hordley's 1902 History of North Staffordshire Royal Infirmary.

Earl Granville's blast furnaces, built in 1850.

Mr Cleavin was appointed as Apothecary in August 1805. The following year he received an additional payment of five guineas for extra attendance on fever patients. He appears to have given satisfaction, coping with the vagaries of the nursing staff levels of those early days, and dealing with new arrangements for the management of cases of fever. The Board of Health seems to have been delegating most of its remaining functions by January 1810. Regulations for dealing with fever now involved the referral of an infectious case to the Resident Apothecary who was to visit the affected household and report on the circumstances to the physician of the week, but where a house needed fumigation the assistance of a member of the Board of Health was still to be sought.

A bombshell fell later that month. Mr Cleavin was required to put a notice in the newspapers calling a Special Meeting of the Committee on a matter of importance. The matter of importance was a charge that had been preferred against Mr Cleavin himself accusing him of indecent and improper conduct towards Mary Forster on December 2nd, 1809 when attending at the Dispensary for medicines. After a full investigation of the circumstances of the case, by examining witnesses in support of the charge and also in behalf of the accused, it was resolved that:

(1) the Charge was fully proved
(2) Mr Cleavin should be removed from his office
(3) A Special meeting of the Committee should be called to confirm the decision.

This meeting confirmed the decision. Mr Cleavin was told to make up his accounts before he left.

Although this sorry little tale may seem of little importance in view of the then current military and social upheavals in Britain and Europe it is an illustration of the practical morality of the time. Nearly fifty years would pass before the formation of the General Medical Council, and the establishment of the principle of a doctor being struck off for inappropriate behaviour with his patient. In this case of 1810 the plaintiff was a female patient, and, significantly, a poor patient, as she was attending the Dispensary for medicines, in the words of the ticket of recommendation she was *'A real Object of Charity'*. Mr Cleavin had offended thrice over, he had made unwanted advances to a female person, he had abused his position in respect of his patient, and the position that he had abused derived from the Charity, bringing it into disrepute. The Committee had taken the matter very seriously. The enquiry had been held under the Chairmanship of John Tomlinson of Hanley, solicitor to Josiah Wedgwood II and to the Dispensary. The minutes record that the *'Thanks of the meeting be given to the Chairman for his indefatigable and impartial actions during a long and painful investigation'*. No doubt they could have swept it under the carpet; this trial illustrates the Committee as a strict and upright body, willing to support the impecunious patient against the doctor, whose status as Apothecary was well above that of the patient.

The next Apothecary was Mr Richard Heath, appointed in February 1810. He seems to have been well thought of, until in August 1814, the minutes record that Mr Heath had unfortunately been attacked by a *'phrensy'* (sic) brought on by excessive drinking. They noted that Mr Heath was not a habitual drunkard, but he had in the last month used spirituous liquors in great excess. The minute continues that *'in the consideration of Mr Heath's former habits of strict attention to his duties and sober conduct ...it was proposed that he should retire to the care of his friends... and that his salary could be continued for at least one month and at the most two.'* If his habits and intellect were perfectly restored he could resume his post. Alas, no reply was received from Mr Heath's brother, therefore the Committee could not adduce any satisfactory proof of Mr Heath's convalescence. Sadly worse was to come, when the accounts were made up it appeared that there was a shortfall of £26-5-0, a sum nearly equivalent to eight months salary and that the deficiency preceded his unfortunate malady.

This was too much, it was resolved that Mr Heath was unfit for his situation, and it was recommended that he be removed from his post as Apothecary and Secretary. It seems that in this case the Committee had been remarkably tolerant. It may be that Mr Heath was a very popular member of staff, the Committee certainly gave him every opportunity to recover, even offering two months paid leave. They could have felt that Mr Heath's drinking was an internal matter for the Committee provided that the medical duties were covered, but in the case of a default in public funds they had no choice but to act as they did. Later a communication was received from his family offering restitution of the money.

After this stormy beginning, the house surgeons caused the governors little trouble for the next 30 years. Thomas Woolrich succeeded Richard Heath, serving from 1814 to 18, and during his term of office he oversaw the interim arrangements prior to the transfer to the new Infirmary in Etruria in 1819. Mr Lamb was house surgeon in 1818 and 1819. The most remarkable period of tenure was that of Joshua Seddon who served from 1820 until 1836, returning as Surgeon from 1839 to 1845, when he retired to the South of England for his health.

The governors therefore had plenty to occupy themselves in the early years of the Dispensary - as we might say today, they faced a steep learning curve. As they raised the money for the new Infirmary in Etruria they would have been fully employed, and would realise that they had moved up into a different and more strenuous league.

When the patients and staff of the Dispensary and House of Recovery removed to Etruria to occupy the new Infirmary in 1819 the old building remained. There was frequent discussion about selling it, but it always seemed that any offer the Governors received was less than that which had been hoped for. They had rather hoped that the encircling industrialisation would cause a demand for land and so inflate the selling price. The building was converted to housing, nine dwellings in all, in later years often used by men working on the canals. In 1832 concern about the first cholera epidemic, which occurred in that year, provoked a hasty search by the Stoke Vestry to find accommodation for sufferers from that disease. The tenants were summarily ejected and the building became an isolation hospital for the Parishioners of Stoke-upon-Trent. It was used for this purpose for six months, and then reverted to its role as housing for nine families. It was eventually sold to the Gas, Light and Coke Company in 1868 to provide room for an extension to the gasworks, for £1000, selling for the price that was originally asked in 1818.

The present day site of the old Dispensary and House of Recovery. Messrs Shirley's bone mill and the Etruria Industrial Museum are to the left. The first two locks of the Caldon Canal are in the foreground.

TO THE PUBLIC.

The COMMITTEE for promoting the establishment of

A MEDICAL DISPENSARY

AND

HOUSE of RECOVERY,

make known the following at the request of some well-disposed Persons, who think it may tend to promote the Interests of this very useful Public undertaking.

The WORKMEN in the MANUFACTORY at

ETRURIA,

have subscribed, in the Book appointed for their District,

TWENTY POUNDS

towards the *Building*, and also the Sum of

SIXTEEN GUINEAS

to be paid yearly for the support thereof, and this last money they will raise by a *very small* weekly Contribution from each Person, to be paid into the Hands of their Employers.

HOW MUCH GOOD MAY BE DONE, WITH A VERY LITTLE MONEY!

They will be entitled hereby to recommend EIGHTEEN Persons every Year to the *House of Recovery*, and to have besides EIGHTEEN Patients *constantly* on the Books of the *Dispensary*; and supposing these EIGHTEEN should be changed once in every Month, they will then have it in their power to procure good advice and Medicines, for TWO HUNDRED AND SIXTEEN Persons within the Year. Other Sums will be entitled to proportional advantages.

GO, AND DO THOU LIKEWISE.

The Consideration that appears to make this voluntary, and highly praise-worthy measure of the greater Importance is, that in case the Manufacturers should generally adopt it, a support so extensive will enable the Projectors of the Institution to increase its benefits far beyond what has hitherto been thought of.

The Book for the District of *Lane-End*, &c. is left with Mr. WILLIAM TURNER,

	Stoke, &c.	-	-	DANIEL WHALLEY, junr. Esq.
	Hanley, &c.	-	-	EPHRAIM CHATTERLEY, Esq.
	Burslem, &c.	-	-	Rev. Mr. RICHARDSON,
Sept. 18th. 1802.	Tunstall, &c.	-	-	Mr. KEELING.

Smith, Printer, Newcastle.

The over-optimistic poster of 1802.

CHAPTER 3
Raising Money

This chapter looks at a voluntary hospital, how it provided hospital care for the large mass of the population who could not afford to pay for their medical care and offered an alternative to those who would have had to declare themselves to be Paupers, and dependant on the Poor Law and the Workhouse. It looks at the peculiar and innovative methods found of financing the Infirmary in North Staffordshire.

Until the 20th century, if you had enough money you were treated and cared for at home, for there was little a hospital could offer that could not be provided by family and servants in a good home. There was however a need for a middle ground between the ideal of care in the home and the dread and stigma of the workhouse. In 1719 Westminster Hospital in London opened its doors to address just this problem; it was the first voluntary hospital.

In 1716, a group of men meeting in a London coffee house had proposed a new form of charity. The book in which they recorded their decisions at that first meeting has survived. Their *Charitable Proposals* provided for free medical and nursing care for the sick who could not otherwise afford them, in addition the charity would pursue the parish authorities to ensure the payment of any money due to a sick person. Others who attracted their attention were poor honest women with child who were often turned out of their lodgings when the birth was due, losing their own and their infant's lives, sick prisoners, and poor strangers from different parts of the world, who would be helped to reach their homes.

Led by the banker Henry Hoare the charity they founded became in 1719 Westminster Hospital, the first voluntary hospital. This form of charitable hospital became the model for more than 200 others across Britain, and they served until the coming of the National Health Service in 1948 when they became an integral part of that service. In Stoke-on-Trent the principal voluntary hospital was the North Staffordshire (Royal) Infirmary.

The essential principle of the voluntary hospital was that it was a charity. It was there to care for those who could not afford to pay for medical treatment, and provide a place where they could receive the attention and nursing care that they could not find at home. The charity was supported by the well to do, but it was clearly understood that they personally were not to benefit from it, nor indeed use it to obtain free treatment for their servants. Those who subscribed did have the privilege of issuing the tickets or *'recommendations'* which were needed to allow the admission of a patient. The more money they subscribed the more tickets they had. It was understood that they would only recommend deserving cases to the hospital and, in issuing the recommendation, the subscriber was confirming that the prospective patient was unable to pay for his treatment, or, as the ticket put it, was a *'real object of charity'*.

The doctors gave their services free of charge. They would gain their income from their own private patients treated in the patient's homes, or in the doctor's surgery. It was an honour to be a surgeon or physician at the voluntary hospital; such an appointment was a validation of their skill and status, and this in turn would increase their own private practice. These voluntary hospitals were usually the leading hospitals in the town and many grew into teaching hospitals.

The first voluntary hospitals were founded in London, but after 1730 they spread across the country to the major centres of population. They were first developed in the county towns, for example Shrewsbury in 1746 and Stafford in 1767. They spread later to major centres of population associated with industrialisation, for example, to Manchester in 1752, and to North Staffordshire in 1802.

In general, the provision of money for voluntary hospitals was from the upper and middle classes. It soon became quite clear that in North Staffordshire there would not be sufficient financial support for the Infirmary. Why this should be, in comparison to other parts of the country is not absolutely clear. Most towns that were the seat of a voluntary hospital were the county towns, like Winchester, Salisbury, Shrewsbury and Stafford. Providing the legal, financial and shopping facilities for the surrounding country estates, and with an established social circle drawn by the regular Assizes and Quarter Sessions, these towns were a natural centre for fund-raising activities.

Charitable motives were many sided. Many people were driven by genuinely philanthropic impulses, some were appalled by the poverty around them, while some no doubt felt that they should make a thank offering for their own good health, in the hope that it would continue. Some may have felt they were setting a good example to their fellows, especially to the lower orders. The organisers knew that publishing the subscription lists complete with details of the amount subscribed by each person provided a dual stimulus, a desire not to be outdone by one's neighbours and a sense of satisfaction if one could head the list. It was part of life and accepted as such. Sadly this could descend into petty snobbery when the real object of the charity was forgotten. In 1869 that most astute observer of society, W.S. Gilbert, proposed in a play that there should be a *'Universal Agent for all Charities'*, whereby a small donation could be distributed between 867 charities, the truly charitable preferring this course, for their names being printed 867 times, they have the advantage of setting 867 good examples at a very modest outlay. Half a crown was suggested as an appropriate contribution!

A striking feature of the records is the absence of a significant contribution to the running of the Dispensary and in due course the Infirmary by the Borough of Newcastle-under-Lyme. Of course there were subscriptions received from Newcastle, though many were from industrialists who lived in that borough but whose factories were in the Potteries. For this reason the actual sources of the money given are difficult to pin down. Newcastle had a smaller working population than the Pottery towns, so the preponderance of the working men's contributions came from the latter source.

I refer rather to the lack of a distinctive Newcastle voice in the Infirmary's affairs. It is an unexpected vacuum in the moral leadership one might have anticipated. Having noted the tendency for voluntary hospitals to be founded in county towns, it is surprising that Newcastle, being the county town of the hypothetical county of North Staffordshire did not provide the inspiration or the driving force behind the new institution. Although it did not have the Assizes, Newcastle was the market town of a prosperous agricultural area and the legal and financial centre of North Staffordshire. It had its race meeting which provided it with a mini-season, when balls and theatrical entertainments were held. It is true that the early years of the Dispensary overlapped the withdrawal of the Trentham interest from the town. This was a period when the activities of the oligarchy that ran the town would come in for criticism, as in 1827 for its undemocratic elections open only to a handful of burgesses. The incidence of cholera in the town in 1832 and especially 1847 struck hard at the poor, crowded into the town centre at a time when the Burgesses were

The original book in which signatures were collected at the Swan Inn in November 1814
Signatures of Sir John Heathcote, Josiah Wedgwood II and John Tomlinson.
Josiah Spode has signed for his family and also the Fenton Park Colliery in which he was a partner.
The small ticks and crosses record the payments in fulfilment of pledges made in this notebook.
The notebook has a very homemade appearance. We can imagine it being carried from person to person by John Tomlinson at the meeting, those present being 'invited' to sign the book and enter the amount of their donation.

slow to release land for the building of new homes. Perhaps this is all of a piece with the absence of a hospital foundation in Newcastle.

We shall see in another chapter how the House of Recovery was found to be inadequate for the purpose of a general infirmary and its site and construction were unsuitable for expansion. It was recognised that the new building would be expensive to build and operate and more money would be needed. Equally, the finances were already stretched, and, while special appeals would probably pay for the new building, there was no prospect of raising all the running expenses from the small middle class who lived in North Staffordshire.

There were serious misgivings about the development of an Infirmary. James Caldwell, partner of Enoch Wood and Recorder of Newcastle-under-Lyme sent a Memorandum to the Committee in which he asked some searching questions. How many patients was the Infirmary to hold, how many came from the mines, how many went to Stafford? £1500 was spoken of as an estimate of the annual running costs; was this for the infirmary AND the Dispensary? How many patients would go to the Fever Wards? How could the Governors ensure a continuance of the money? What if there were bad times, wages low and provisions dear? Compulsory powers were out of the question and the contracts with Masters were difficult to enforce. How could they rely on collections from Churches or from those who were already subscribing? He now put forward his major concern; would they endanger the existing Dispensary, *'affect the great and certain benefits now derived from that salutary and excellent institution?'* This early business review reveals the quality of thought on which the Governors could call.

Clearly the need had arisen for some creative thinking. The masterstroke, as is so often the case, was incredibly simple. It consisted of the synthesis of the weekly personal contributions, by which many self help societies operated, with the voluntary hospital system of annual subscription by better off donors. At a meeting attended by all the manufacturers of the area (none of the famous names are missing) held in 1814, it was agreed that an *Address to the Working Classes* should be printed. It was signed by Josiah Wedgwood II as President of the Infirmary, and stylistically probably written by him. All the manufacturers who were present countersigned the Address. The Address recognised that it would not be possible to provide adequate facilities for hospital care without tapping a new, and even more important, a reliable and sustainable source of funding.

What was proposed was that the existing nationally understood voluntary system of support by well-off subscribers who did not themselves benefit should continue, as in other towns, but workers were invited to contribute by a deduction at source from their wages that became known as an Establishment Contribution. Those who earned above 18 shillings a week should contribute 1 penny a week, those earning between 7 and 18 shillings should contribute a halfpenny, and those below 7 shillings a farthing.

This money would be collected at source by the Master, by the addition of an extra column in the account book, and, hopefully augmented by a contribution from the Master, would be transmitted to the Infirmary. This money then earned pro-rata the same privileges in numbers of patients who could be recommended at a given level of subscription, as those granted to an Individual Subscriber for the same sum. In contrast to Individual Subscribers, whose recommendations were available to anyone in need in the community at large, the recommendations earned by Establishment Contributions were held by the Master solely for the benefit of those in his employment who subscribed. The Master would then issue tickets of recommendation to those workers who needed

AN ADDRESS

TO THE

WORKING CLASSES

OF

NEWCASTLE, THE POTTERIES, AND NEIGHBOURHOOD.

TEN years ago the Dispensary was erected. The sole object of those who established and have supported it was your relief in the day of sickness. You all are witnesses of the solid good which it has produced. More than 5000 of your number have been essentially benefited by the gratuitous advice of able Physicians, and other Medical Gentlemen, and by adequate supplies of expensive medicines; the progress of infectious disease has been arrested, and that scourge of man, the Small-Pox, has nearly been banished from among us. But these blessings, great as they are, may be still farther extended. Our Institution cannot reach to cases of the severest calamity. Many instances must have fallen within your observation, in which the unhappy sufferer was unable to profit by the healing hand extended towards him; his sickness was of such a nature as to render a weekly walk to the Dispensary impracticable: it required the daily, the hourly attention

But we chiefly look to you for such a fixed and important addition to the *Annual Income*, as may enable the Institution to meet the great increase of expence which must necessarily be incurred: and this may be obtained by means of a small payment, in every *working* week only, on the following plan. That

Each person who earns upwards of eighteen shillings per week, contribute not less than one penny weekly;

Each person who earns upwards of seven shillings, and not more than eighteen shillings, per week, contribute not less than one half-penny weekly: and

Each person who earns not more than seven shillings per week, contribute not less than one farthing weekly.

The manner in which these easy contributions will be collected, should be settled with you by your respective Masters. It may, without difficulty, be done by means of a

The opening page of the 'Address to the Working Classes'.

This extract of the 'Address to the Working classes' details the scale of contributions.

Although subscriptions by working people became common elsewhere at the end of the 19th century, the North Staffordshire Infirmary's 'Establishment Scheme' is remarkably early, and unusual in the extent of support, providing the great majority of its income until 1948.

John Ridgway
Thomas Cotterill
Thomas Yeoman
Robert Hamilton
Thomas Wolfe
William Adams
William Arrowsmith
Josiah Spode, jun.
William Kentwright
Thomas Lakin
Joseph Mayer
John Daniel
John Rogers
George Rogers
Thomas Slade
John Wood
John Meir
Thomas Knight
Hugh Williamson
Joseph Knight
Thomas Toft
Jacob Baggaley
Thomas Goodfellow
William Rhead
John Robinson
Christopher Robinson
Joseph Machin
Enoch Wood
James Caldwell
John E. Heathcote
John F. Boughey
George Tollet
Francis H. Northen, M. D.
Edward Powys
Josiah Spode
Job Meigh, jun.
Henry S. Belcombe, M. D.
Clement Leigh
Bernard Coombe
Josiah Wedgwood
Henry Dobbs
Thomas Horwood
Thomas Butt
Richard Bent, M. D.

John Davenport
Benjamin Adams
J. H. Clive
James Davenport
Job Meigh
Thomas Harley
George Forrister
Robert Garner
John Harvey
Thomas Hewitt
Richard Barker
Thomas Stirrup
Charles Harvey
Charles Meigh
John Glass
Richard Hicks
John Riley
Richard Riley
Thomas Heath
William Bourne
Thomas Godwin
Benjamin Godwin
John Hall
Ralph Hall
William Bathwell
Thomas Bathwell
John Blunt
John Carey
William Bailey
George Wood
Robert E. Aitkens
John Hales
William Adams
Ralph Stevenson
John A. Prowse
Edward Carless
John Tomlinson
Thomas Griffin
Thomas Allbut
James Whitehead
William Yates
Thomas Minton
Robert Griffin
W. H. Smallwood

Pages 7 and 8 of the *Address to the Working Classes*. Some of the names endorsing the Establishment Scheme of Contributors. Every major name in the Pottery industry appears, together with many of the leaders of North Staffordshire.

treatment at the Infirmary. It is most important to recognise that unlike Friendly Societies which imposed embargoes on groups of subscribers, e.g. dippers and miners, membership of the Establishment scheme was open to all subscribing employees. There were medical conditions which were not admitted, because the Infirmary feared being totally bed-blocked with chronic untreatable cases, but these conditions applied to everyone who sought admission.

It must be emphasised that in 1814 the Governors knew they were breaking new ground. Draft letters from Josiah Wedgwood II set out their claim to originality '...*on a plan which we believe to be new and which is an extension of the Benefit clubs which have proved so generally useful. The principle is that (some) of the annual income for the support of the Infirmary is the Voluntary contributions of the working classes. The efforts of the Committee have been directed towards the raising of a fund for erecting a Building and for the necessary original expenses, in which they have met with the cordial support of the neighbourhood, and several gentlemen resident in other parts who are connected with the Potteries by commercial dealings and the supply of materials, or by the benefits derived from their estates'*. The better off would supply the Capital for the new building, while the running costs, the Revenue would be provided by the new Establishment Contributions.

Another draft letter written in January, 1815 reads.... '*The plan for raising the necessary annual income is an extension of the principle of the Friendly Societies, which have been found so generally beneficial, and it has been taken up so readily by the working classes, as to afford the greatest probability of its success*'. Finally, a draft letter to the Duke of Devonshire says '...*One circumstance distinguishes this from all other Infirmaries... working classes have contracted to furnish an annual income for its support.*'

We can see that the promoters of the Establishment Contributions were quite clear that this was an original scheme, being an extension of the principles of the Benefit Clubs which have been found so generally beneficial. Josiah Wedgwood II, in whose hand we have the draft letters extolling this system, certainly had experience of both Sick Clubs at the Etruria factory and the voluntary hospitals in London where he was a subscriber to Westminster Hospital.

It was in the expectation that the Establishment Schemes would be supported that the Governors proceeded with the new Infirmary in Etruria. There must have been some anxious moments when the contributions did not flow as readily as had been hoped. It took time to convince workers of the benefits that would accrue. Not until 1822 when it was decided to include non-working wives and children as beneficiaries, and when people could see the Infirmary was actually dealing with injured patients, that its future became assured.

Of course, any scheme which offered relatively expensive benefits to patients in return for relatively small contributions depended on there being a large number of non-claiming subscribers; it was in fact a form of insurance. The Governors having pointed out the benefits - the advice, medicines, vaccination and care of fever patients - already conferred by the Dispensary and those new benefits that could be hoped for from the new Infirmary, laid out a scale of privileges and the number of recommendations that were granted in respect for a particular contribution. They then inserted a clear caution, one that applies to every insurance scheme, that if every member claims for every possible benefit, the scheme will either fail or become prohibitively expensive. Again and again one is impressed with the clear and hard-headed thinking of these men, their experience in business being placed at the disposal of the Infirmary. Without it, the Infirmary would not have survived, there was no great landowner prepared to pick up the pieces and no contribution from the state in the event of financial disaster.

The Address concluded with this warning:

The Institution cannot depend on casual and uncertain bounty, the expence (sic) is permanent and recurring. We would not awake unreasonable expectations as if for such sum every case of sickness may be provided against and all prudent preparations for a rainy day rendered unnecessary.

Your good sense will show that such a thing is impossible, a much larger sum of your earnings would be required for that purpose. But we can do much, though we cannot do all we wish.

There was to be provision for every accident but if there were too many applications to be inpatients, the members of the medical staff were to decide on priority.

It was pointed out that while Establishment Contributions were to be made by workers, they should continue to pay their subscriptions to other clubs (friendly societies). These could include benefits for sickness at home, for sick pay or the benefits of a Burial Club. The Address concluded with a final exhortation:

Should you be blessed with uninterrupted health, your money was not thrown away. Christian charity was the duty of all, cheerfully made contributions are accepted like the widows mite - Go then and imitate the Good Samaritan and do likewise.

Not everyone understood the principle of insurance. It is always helpful to have an exception that proves the rule, and who should that be but Thomas Byerley. It is perhaps typical of him that his heart overruled his head in charitable work as well as in business, he was a kind but not a firm man.

In the excitement of the initial fundraising for the Dispensary in 1802, when you will recall Josiah Wedgwood's sons were living in the South of England and Byerley was the family's representative in North Staffordshire, the action of the workers at Etruria was held up as an example before the Public. They had subscribed the sum of £20 towards the building and £16-16-0 (16 guineas) towards the support of the Dispensary. This sum had been subscribed in small amounts by the workers, foreshadowing the larger scheme of 1814. In 1804 an advertisement that drew attention to those contributions was issued by the Committee, *'at the request of some well disposed persons who think it may tend to promote the Interests of this very useful Public undertaking'*. So far, so good, but it went on to give examples of how much good may be done with very little money. Based on the numbers of patients a subscriber could possibly recommend in return for their contribution, it was demonstrated that *'the workers would be able to recommend 18 (inpatients) to the House of Recovery each year, and to have besides 18 patients constantly on the books of the Dispensary (out-patients); and supposing each patient is changed once a month, they will have it in their power to procure good advice and medicines for 216 patients in a year'*. Thus less than £17 would pay for 18 inpatients and 216 outpatients in a year.

I conclude that Byerley was at least party to this advertisement. During the period when the Wedgwood brothers were living in Southern England, Byerley was in charge at Etruria, the firm of Wedgwood and Byerley were treasurers to the charity, so Byerley would know all about the finances and the need to raise money, and finally he was the person most likely to know of the contributions of the Etruria workmen. The projected outgoings as outlined would have exceeded the whole activity of the Charity in any of the early years. A take up of benefits on this scale was just not economically possible. Byerley wrote regularly to Josiah Wedgwood II about business and about the Dispensary. When

Wedgwood heard of this circular it may have reinforced his decision to return to North Staffordshire, to take over the running of the business (and the Dispensary) and send the soft-hearted Byerley back to London to run the shop.

It has to be said that there was not an immediate rush by working men to join the scheme, nor by their employers to play their part. We note later Thomas Butt, the Vicar of Trentham's anxiety about including mention of the Establishment Contributions in the Inscription on the Portico of the new Infirmary. In fairness, in the first years they would have seen few tangible benefits until the scheme was extended in 1822 to wives and children, and the Infirmary was being used and was of obvious utility. It was only then that the Scheme became more widely supported, indeed it never looked back. Now, for a maximum contribution of one penny a week, a working man and his family could receive free treatment as outpatients, or be admitted as inpatients and receive treatment, nursing and their keep. Further, as Establishment Subscribers they did not think of themselves as objects of charity, and socially were unquestionably distanced from the state of being a Pauper. Some of the larger companies, for example Mintons, would make a willingness to be an Establishment Subscriber a condition of employment, which by the 1890s caused the authorities to wonder whether this condition of employment transgressed the Truck Acts.

If the original voluntary principle was to remain, then only those who were truly poor should benefit from the charity. However, the Establishment Subscriber could not, by definition, be destitute if he earned enough to be a subscriber. At the same time there was no ceiling imposed on wages above which one could no longer be a subscriber. If a worker earned eighteen shillings a week he paid his penny a week, but if he earned five pounds a week, there was nothing to stop him benefiting for the same contribution.

When someone became a subscriber, even an Establishment Subscriber, he had rights, he did not see himself as an object of charity, and he said so. This early letter brilliantly encapsulates the whole dilemma. It is dated 1818.

To Josiah Wedgwood (II)
Sir,

It is with the greatest respect I wish to call your attention to the case I will lay before you. I know that of itself it is of no consequence, but as Liberty and Independancy is the Birth right of an Englishman, so I hope you will not overlook what I have to say, for if persisted in I believe it will be of very great consequence, for I think I hav a better oppertunity then you (sic), to know the spirit of the people.

The reason I have for choosing you to address on this subject before others, is, from the General Character that you have for the good of the Community at large, and from the Office you sustain in the management of the North Staffre. Infermary.

I am a man with a wife and three small children, and had the misfortune to stand in need of Medical aid, and to my great disgust, as well as many others, found that in my Note of recommendation that I was a real object of charity tho I am a subscriber of 4s per year, this expression a real object of charity is a palpable insult to the feelings of them that subscribe, to think that they must be called objects of Carity (sic) to pertake of that that they work for. I know what can be said of the Rich subscribing but that is no weight with the people to convince them of the propriety of the expression, and I know a many that will not subscribe if that is not altered, and I can assure you that all that I have heard speake repprobate (sic) it in the most violent manner.

Now sir, if you have a real wish for the real prosperity of the Institution, I entreat you to use all the influence you have to get them altered before the consequence is more great than it is -- as perhaps you may hear from me again on the same subject, I shall subscribe myself.   E

Any letter from a working man of this period is to be valued for its rarity. The clarity and organisation of the letter is impressive, but the depth of resentment wells over that he who had subscribed his four shillings a year (a penny a week, 48 old pennies, the highest subscription - so he was earning over eighteen shillings a week) had taken care to insure himself against hospital treatment and yet was called a real object of charity. He repeats the phrase three times with quotation marks, with a decreasing command of his spelling as the words spill forth. In this, a most moving social document, one can feel E's frustration. We should also note that the letter is signed only with an initial. The year 1818 is in the period 1799 to 1824 when the Combination Acts operated. Passed during the height of fear of the spread of Revolution from France, they forbade the combination of workers in trade unions. The caution displayed by E might indicate a previous brush with the law, or even a link with a trade union. After all, many Friendly Societies were, rightly or wrongly perceived to be a cover for a Trade Union or even more Radical activity.

So we see that this financial arrangement was satisfactory for the patients and for those responsible for the finances of the Infirmary. What about the other parties to the contract on which the institution depended? It will be recalled that the physicians and surgeons who formed the Consultant Staff of the North Staffordshire Infirmary gave their services free to patients on the understanding that they could not otherwise afford treatment. It is clear that, at least in times of good trading conditions, some skilled workers could earn substantially more than 18 shillings a week, and there was no ceiling on wages above which these workers became ineligible for free treatment (until 1936). Had they applied for a ticket to an individual subscriber, these relatively well off workers would have been properly refused, not being deserving objects of charity. Now they were contributors and felt they had a right to receive treatment. Equally the Consultant might feel that he was giving free attention to a group of people who could well afford to pay, and that he was not only damaging his own income, but also depriving his colleagues in general practice of paying patients. General practice was by no means highly remunerative in industrial towns. Contributory schemes were often decried in the medical press as being unfair to doctors, and the term 'Hospital Abuse' appeared in letters and articles from all parts of the country and throughout the 19th century.

When he arrived in North Staffordshire, Dr J.T. Arlidge wrote an article on the State of Health in the Potteries in 1862 and in it he commented that the North Staffordshire Infirmary was to all intents and purposes a subscription hospital, a view he held until he retired. As the employer held the recommendation tickets specifically for those of his workers who subscribed, it was felt that the Establishment Subscribers could get treatment or even inpatient care much more easily than those who had to convince an individual subscriber, a member of the public, that he was a real object of charity. Arlidge was among those who felt that deserving cases from the public at large could be squeezed out by Establishment Subscribers suffering from less pressing conditions. These would find it much easier to obtain a recommendation through their employer than a poor member of the public, who might scour the town to find a subscriber willing to give him a ticket.

The Annual Report of the Infirmary published in 1881 stated that the Outpatients department 'functions as a Provident Dispensary grafted on to the Infirmary, but none is paid to the Medical Men'. In a true Provident Dispensary the patients pay towards their treatment, and it was accepted in these Dispensaries that the doctor could be paid. Again, the Infirmary was steering a course between the voluntary and the paying system. The Governors recognised that as the doctors were giving their services as if the Infirmary was purely a charity, it was unwise to presume too much on their good will, especially by packing the Outpatients Department with minor ailments. They appealed to Establishment Subscribers not to push their demands too far, *'if Providence and your own honourable industry have given you good work and good wages ...Do not lay on* (the doctors') *charity the burthen of your small ills which you have ample means and opportunity to relieve at your own cost. Be content to do something by your contributions for the general good of your poorer and more suffering fellow creatures'*.

At this time the number of patients attending for (free) dental extractions exceeded 1500 in a year, and the number had to be severely curtailed. It was suggested that those turned away could have their teeth extracted by a chemist for a small sum, which tells us a lot about dental services in the Potteries in 1881.

However, the Consultants must have been persuaded to stay with the system as it developed, for the honorary principle of unpaid consultant service remained essentially unchanged until 1948.

In addition to the never-ending activity of collecting regular subscriptions, there were other activities which we might term occasional. These might be the proceeds of a benefit performance at the local theatre, for example, Mr Staunton of the Newcastle and Potteries Theatre regularly offered benefits for the Dispensary, which could bring in £20 or more, then enough to pay the Matron's salary for a year. In 1805 the public saw a comedy *Everyone has his Fault* together with a farce *The Quaker*. Another source of money was a donation from travelling shows that passed through the Potteries. On one occasion the proprietor of a *Mechanical Exhibition*, perhaps an exhibition of mechanical dolls or automata, sent a contribution; on another the library received 3 guineas from Madame Tussaud, again from a travelling exhibition. This donation was placed wrongly in the general fund and the committee had to apologise to Madame Tussaud for their error. This was the original Madame Tussaud, who had been seated beneath the guillotine and modelled heads of the executed during the French Revolution

Another source of revenue was entertainment arranged by the local people. In 1826 a bazaar organised by Arthur Minton at the National School in Newcastle raised £960 that paid half the cost of a new fever ward. In 1833 a concert held in the recently rebuilt Stoke Parish Church raised £795 after expenses, a sum sufficient to pay off the substantial debts of the Infirmary. This concert has added interest in that an article on music in the Potteries in the *Grove Dictionary of Music* states this was the first major musical event in the Potteries.

The Governors were not always willing to accept offers to put on a concert. The offer by Mr Ashley of an Oratorio, for which he wished to be guaranteed £1000, any profit to come to the Infirmary, was declined as there was not sufficient prospect of success, indeed though they did not say so there was every prospect of making a loss. Even where there was no financial risk to the Infirmary the Governors did not always approve the use of the Infirmary's good name in association with a fundraising event. At times they declined desperately needed offerings on the ground that they would not have the Infirmary's name associated with public entertainment, although this attitude softened in the 20th century.

The next really major fundraising event was another bazaar held to raise money in aid of the building Fund for the new Infirmary in Hartshill. This Bazaar held in 1868 raised £3,600. It is particularly remembered for the display of electric lighting given by the young Oliver Lodge, the first ever demonstration of this phenomenon to be seen in the Potteries.

We know that there was an institution called the Infirmary Tea at this time. A letter in the records of the North Staffordshire Branch of the Manchester School for the Deaf and

The following alphabetical List of Stalls and Stall Keepers, with the amounts received from each of them, is taken from the "Staffordshire Advertiser" of October 10th, 1868.

STALLS	STALL KEEPERS	Receipts for first Three Days		
		£	s.	d.
Burslem	Mrs. Lamb, Mrs. Shirley, Mrs. Sutton, Mrs. Harley, Mrs. W. Bates, the Misses Walker, the Misses Shirley, Miss Till, Miss E. Sutton, and Miss Collinson ...	180	15	10½
Cheadle and Tean	Mrs. J.W. Philips, Mrs. Cotton, Mrs. Hallows, Mrs. Hutchinson, Mrs. Wilson, Mrs. E. L. Philips, Mrs. Edwards, Miss Buller, and Miss Bromhead ...	102	15	8½
Chesterton	Mrs. Jackson, Mrs. Haslope, Mrs. Cadman, and the Misses Melville ...	25	17	3
Hanley	Mrs. Nevill, Mrs. Jackson, Mrs. Folker, Mrs. Piercy, Mrs. Sergeant, Miss Baker, Miss Robinson, Miss I. Daniel, Miss E. Daniel, the Misses Llewellyn, Miss A. Stephenson, and Miss Brandon ...	148	4	4
Keele and Betley	Mrs. H. Sutcliffe, Mrs. J. Sutcliffe, Mrs. Harvey, and Miss Harvey ...	67	7	9
Kidsgrove and Mow Cop	Mrs. Kinnersly, Mrs. Robinson, Mrs. Hogg, Miss Gemmell, the Misses Chadwick, and Miss Vaudrey ...	58	17	8
Leek	Mrs. Worthington, Mrs. Cooper, Mrs. Ward, Mrs. Pidduck, Mrs. Stepney, Mrs. Sleigh, the Misses Worthington, the Misses Bamford, Miss Russell, Miss A. Sleigh, and Miss Fenton ...	163	5	0
Madeley	Mrs. Stanier, Mrs. Daltry, Mrs. T. Stanier, and Miss Stanier ...	53	1	0
Newcastle	Mrs. Litchfield, Mrs. Heath, Mrs. Knight, Mrs. Broad, Mrs. de Vine, Mrs. Tomkinson, Mrs. Orton, Mrs. W. Hallam, Mrs. J. Hallam, Mrs. Baildon, the Misses Heath, Hallam, Hall, Broad, Baildon, Lewis, de Vine, Astle, Tomkinson, and Reade ...	140	2	9½
Officials of the Old Infirmary, and a few friends at Etruria	Mrs. Kirk, Mrs. Hordley, Miss Ball, Miss Brown, Miss Taylor, Miss Derry, Miss Hordley, and Miss Beardmore ...	49	9	4
Silverdale	Mrs. Stanier Broade, Mrs. Armitage, Miss Justice, and the Misses Prendergast	66	11	0½

The list of stallholders for the 1868 bazaar gives a good idea of where the infirmary was gaining its donor support

A HOUSE OF MERCY.

In the year 1802 was called a meeting by circular, dated Trentham Inn, for establishing "A dispensary and a house of recovery," for the use of the Potteries, to be held on the 28th July, at the Swan Inn, Hanley. Those who have seen the Infirmary at Hartshill may be tempted to smile, not at the humble origin, but at the progress and development. And smile they may if they know its first location, and even so in relation to its second home. Still the latter place, called "Wood Hill," at the time of its erection, situated near to a large refuse heap from Slippery Lane Pits, no one can recall how pleasant it was many years ago. Near to was once a little valley, the highest land in the extremity of which is still called Mount Pleasant. Through this vale ran a clear brook, rising at the Birches Head, and, centuries ago, turned the water mill for Bell, the miller, whose timely services to the first of the Tudors, Henry VII., was rewarded by grant from that monarch, by his "holding" the mill and grounds to be freehold to him and his heirs, &c., for ever. The mill pool has just been filled up. It was situate by the footpath half-way down Etruria Road. This little brook ran its course close by the grounds of the first and second Infirmary, too. The first Infirmary was at the bottom of Bedford Street, just over the Bedford Street canal bridge, and near to the large gas-holder of the British Gas Company. The building was demolished about 1878, and although it was pointed out as the old Infirmary, I must say that I had some doubt, so small and mean were the buildings, but I was wrong.

From Wm Scarratt's *Old Times in The Potteries*, 1906.
The *'first Infirmary'* here refers to the House of Recovery. It is an eyewitness account of the House of Recovery, and how insignificant it seemed against the Infirmary at Hartshill.

Dumb written by the Rev E.J. Edwards, Vicar of Trentham, advised anyone seeking funds for a charity to attend the Infirmary Tea, as it was a place where charitable people were likely to be found. Trivial in itself, perhaps, but it sheds light on a private world of mid-Victorian charity. The men dealt with the finances, ladies sewed and made articles of clothing for patients, and gave papers, books and flowers. Those with extensive gardens and greenhouses sent fruit and vegetables.

Companies gave money, goods and services. When the Victoria Wards were being built in 1881 suppliers gave materials at cost, and sometimes below cost. The Staffordshire Potteries Water Company gave water without charge to the Infirmary in Etruria, and at a reduced price when it removed to Hartshill. The North Staffordshire Railway put a box on the down platform of Stoke station so that gentlemen travelling from London could leave their London papers there when they left the train; they were taken to the Infirmary for the patients. In 1902, at the time when the electrical department was set up with the encouragement and support of the Duchess of Sutherland, the Potteries Electric Traction Company's tramway had reached Hartshill. From a point near the Church, a cable was laid to the Infirmary to transmit a gratuitous supply of electricity for that department, and later the supply was extended to the operating theatre. Particularly in Wartime, great efforts were made for the comfort of the patients, especially the wounded soldiers. Free trams would run to Hanley where the troops were entertained in free seats at the theatres. Always at Christmas time there were great efforts to entertain the patients by choirs and concert parties, both professional and amateur.

The Infirmary also made efforts to help itself. The Infirmary pigs appeared in 1810, and were a much sought after item at Newcastle Market for more than 100 years. Fattened on the waste from the kitchens, they brought in a steady and by no means insignificant income. In 1934, when the Milk Marketing Board was introduced nationally, the Governors were convinced that this was a development that would raise the price of milk to the substantial disadvantage of a large user like the Infirmary. Accordingly, they rented a farm near Whitmore, put in a manager and produced their own, selling the surplus. When it was given up in 1940 it had always made a modest profit, and though not as successful as had been hoped, the farm had provided good milk and fresh vegetables for the patients - and a supply of good, clean and safe milk was by no means guaranteed in the 1930s.

After 1910 there was a great acceleration in the need for expansion of the buildings and facilities, and for the staff to improve the services offered to patients. The First World War bequeathed a waiting list of 1600 patients. This is a heavier burden than it might appear today. Many patients were treated in bed for long periods in the hope that rest and good food would allow the body to heal itself. In surgical wards patients with a condition such as a hernia would be in bed for four weeks; today they can be day cases. This meant a vastly longer stay for each patient than today, and proportionately fewer patients were treated per bed.

We have seen how in the Edwardian era, over ten years £5000 was spent on capital works. In the next five years before the War, £35,000 was raised to bring the buildings, especially the Outpatients Department up to date. Immediately after the War the President was asking if £150,000 was too little to ask for, wouldn't £300,000 be better. If we recall that the average wage in the Pottery Industry in the 1920s was about £3 a week, whereas now the average wage in Stoke-on-Trent is £360 a week. If we say £300 a week, it is reasonable to multiply the £150,000 by at least a factor of 100, £15,000,000 today, a vast amount for working people to raise in the 1920s. This sum was for capital projects, buildings and equipment and was in addition to the running costs that were largely provided by the Establishment Contributions.

There were many components involved in meeting these challenges. Leading Governors such as Mrs Harrison, Miss Twyford, Mr Cornes, the Johnsons and later the Haughtons gave sums of money large enough to pay for whole wards, a lasting benefit of the civilised way in which the reforms of 1910 (q.v.) had been carried through. Equally, by the success of those reforms a great wave of goodwill was generated towards the Infirmary, leading to great increases in the Establishment Contributions and fundraising initiatives. When it was satisfied that the 1910 reforms were in place, the management of the Sentinel went out of its way to support and organise schemes such as a million shillings and raffles of cars given by local garages. At the same time there were a myriad schemes from the Hospital Cup Competition involving Stoke City, Port Vale, Crewe and Macclesfield to whist competitions, capable of raising thousands of pounds, down to many smaller local schemes. Schools raised money, for example many bought eggs for the patients. It was vital that the Annual Report should acknowledge every one of these initiatives, and after the large sums of money we can find an entry: *Anonymous, two dozen eggs.* The great virtue

Eggs :—

Allin & Williams, Longton (720).
Alton C. of E. School, per Mr. H. Bra
Anonymous (26).
Anonymous (60).
Anstey, Miss, Hanford (12).
Banner, Miss (24).
Barry, Mrs., Oakley Folly (30), (52).
Bloor, Mrs. J., Longton (170).
Bould, Mr. F. G., Tunstall (89).
Boulton, Mrs., Oakamoor (24).
Bradbury, Mr. J., Loggerheads (1080
Bradbury, Mrs., Mucklestone (78).
Bridgett, Mr. E., Newcastle (120).

NO GIFT TOO SMALL

A certificate records a girl's efforts on behalf of the Infirmary. Eggs were a regular and welcome gift, and all such gifts had to be acknowledged in the annual report.

HOSPITAL SATURDAY, LONGTON

JUNE 15TH, 1895.

This Memento

IS PRESENTED

To .... *Emily Nixon* ....

in recognition of her services as a
Member of the

Longton Little Girls' Hospital Brigade

and as a reward for having worked to aid the funds of that noble Institution, the North Staffordshire Infirmary.

GEO. E. FARMER, *Mayor.*

HUGHES, MARKET, LONGTON.

The miscellaneous receipts were a wonderful mixture, from the collected donations in the Plough smoke room at Bignall End, to the profit on the sale of the Infirmary pigs and dripping from the kitchen. Little was wasted.

MISCELLANEOUS.

	£	s.	d.
The Managers of the N. S. Infirmary Coffee Stall, per Mrs. Samuda	10	10	0
Payments with Trainers, Nursing Department...	25	4	0
Collected in Smoke Room, " Plough Inn," Bignall End	0	7	0
„ at a Xmas Party, Heugher Wall, Audley	0	10	0
Contents of Charity Box, N. S. Infirmary ...	2	19	2
„ „ Queen's Arms Inn, Hanley	0	9	9
Payments with Children's Ward Patients ...	0	18	6
Fines	0	3	8
Rent of Land	39	3	3
Hay sold	11	0	0
Dripping sold	68	4	6
Bones sold	3	4	1
Ice and Swill sold	1	1	0
Profit on Pigs	144	0	0

On TUESDAY MORNING, NOVEMBER 12, *1833*

WILL BE PERFORMED,

IN STOKE CHURCH,

A Grand Selection of Sacred Music,

From the Works of Handel, Mozart, Haydn, Beethoven, King, &c.

Part I.

Overture .... HANDEL.
Recit. and Air, Mr Pearsall, "Comfort ye."
Chorus, "And the Glory of the Lord."
Air, Mrs Knyvett, "Holy, holy."
Air, Mr Machin, "The fall of Zion."
Air, Miss Hardman, "But thou didst not leave."
Chorus, "Lift up your heads."
Air, Mr Mathews, "Thou shalt bring them in."
Quartetto, Mrs Knyvett, Mr Knyvett, Mr Pearsall, and Mr Machin, "Their sound is gone out,"
Air, Mrs Knyvett, "Rejoice greatly."
Chorus, "For unto us a child is born."
Air, Mr Pearsall, "O Liberty," accompanied on the Violoncello by Mr Giles.
Recit. and Air, Mr Machin, "He layeth the beams."
Chorus, "How excellent thy name, O Lord."
Air, Miss Hardman, "Angels, ever bright and fair."
Anthem, Messrs. Mathews, Pearsall, and Machin, "When the Son of Man." .... KENT.
Grand Chorus, "Hallelujah."

Part II.

Overture .... BEETHOVEN.
Recit. and Air, Mrs Knyvett, "With verdure clad."
Air, Mr Knyvett, "Return, O God of Hosts."
Chorus, "Fix'd in his everlasting seat."
Recit. and Air, Mr Bloore, "Lord, what is man."
Trio, Messrs. Mathews, Pearsall, and Machin, "Disdainful of danger."
Chorus, "Lead on."
Air, Miss Hardman, "From mighty kings."
Air, Mr Pearsall, "Sound an alarm."
Chorus, "We hear."
Concerto, Violin, Mr Mori.
Duetto, Mrs Knyvett and Miss Hardman.
Chorus, "Hallelujah, Amen." .... KING.
Recit. and Air, Mr Machin, "Honour and arms." ..SAMSON.
Solo, Miss Espley, "Sing ye to the Lord."
Grand Double Chorus, "The Horse and his Rider."
Recit. Mr Pearsall, "When David was old, &c.
Grand Coronation Anthem. .... HANDEL

TICKETS.

For the Morning Performance,—7s. 6d. for the Galleries and the Pews in the Middle Aisle; and 5s. for the Pews under the Galleries.
For the Evening Performance,—3s. 6d. for the Galleries and the Pews in the Middle Aisle; and 2s. for the Pews under the Galleries.

Instead of having, as is usual, a Collection at the Church Doors, it is respectfully requested that all Persons who may be pleased to present Donations on this occasion, will transmit the same to "The Chairman of the Oratorio Committee, at the North Staffordshire Infirmary;" or to "The Treasurers, Messrs. Kinnersly and Sons, Bankers, Newcastle,' a separate account of which will be published.

The Doors of the Church will be Opened at Ten o'Clock in the Morning, and the Performance will commence at Eleven.—And in the Evening, the Doors will be Opened at Six o'Clock, and the Performance commence at Seven.

The Patrons will enter at the South Vestry Door.—The Galleries to be entered by the North and South Gallery Doors.—The 7s. 6d. Tickets for the Body of the Church, by the North Vestry Door.—The 5s. Tickets to enter by the Tower Door.

BOOKS OF THE PERFORMANCE

will be Published, which, together with Tickets, may be had of the Booksellers in the Neighbourhood; and no Person will be admitted into the Church without a Ticket.

ALLBUT, PRINTER, HANLEY.

Nett Proceeds of Oratorio £395. 6. 7. B4

The concert held in Stoke Church in 1833, the proceeds from which were sufficient to clear the existing debts of the Infir
A similar programme was performed in the evening - note the charges, 7/6 would be more than a workman's weekly wa

of this was that it wove the worthy and necessary efforts of self-help into a community based activity which included so many strands of society. By 1935 the Annual Report ran to more than 200 closely printed pages, so numerous were the contributions that had to be acknowledged.

In addition to the Establishment Contributions the Infirmary began, from the 1870s, to encourage the development of two further schemes in response to the increased costs of running the new Infirmary. Beginning in the 1850s other towns had organised collections in order to tap their localities' working-class support in two parallel initiatives, Hospital Saturday in works and in towns, and at Churches and Chapels on Hospital Sunday. Community based activities were not totally confined to one day but on a series of Summer weekends communities would hold fêtes, carnivals, sports and entertainments with the aim of raising money for the local hospital. It was often **the** major local event.

In 1936 the four voluntary hospitals, the Infirmary, Haywood and Longton hospitals and the Cripples Guild in Hartshill, joined together in one fund-raising organisation, the North Staffordshire Voluntary Hospitals Contributory Association which absorbed the Establishment Scheme, eventually having more than 150,000 contributors. It was intended now that the subscribers should not be confined to those employed in factories, but be gathered from a wider spectrum of businesses. An upper earnings limit, £4 a week, was applied for the first time.

Had the War not intervened, it was hoped to introduce an insurance scheme that would supply the needs of the white collar poor. There was widespread concern that while the very poor and those receiving low pay were catered for in the voluntary hospitals and to an extent by the municipal hospitals, and the wealthy could become private patients, those earning relatively modest salaries were excluded. These people, clerks, teachers and shopkeepers, were not eligible for membership of the Contributory Association, earning a little over the income limit of £4 a week for a single person. They had the choice of scraping together the money required for private treatment or facing the hated means test before admission to the City General Hospital. These members of the middle class who had become caught in a poverty trap welcomed the coming of the National Health Service in 1948.

The collections for the Contributory Association were pooled between the four voluntary hospitals, the Infirmary being far and away the largest hospital received the largest slice of the income. Money was raised through company collections as before, while individual members could join, paying by purchasing stamps. The Staffordshire Nursing Association provided benefits such as home nursing to members of the scheme, and there were reciprocal arrangements for those suffering from acute illnesses to be admitted to municipal hospitals such as the present City General Hospital. Gradually the old antagonisms were being overcome and replaced with cooperation, well in advance of the coming of the National Health Service in 1948.

As a tail-piece, we have seen how the Establishment Scheme was theoretically and practically in conflict with the purely voluntary principle of charitable giving by the rich to the poor. When the new arrangements for the new Contributory Association was being discussed in 1936-37 it was feared that the expansion of the number of people who could participate would alienate the Honorary Medical Staff, who were still giving their services without charge to the patients of the Voluntary Hospitals. In the event they raised not a single objection to the change, and no one opted out.

This Wedgwood plaque is the only known
picture of Thomas Byerley 1747-1810.

Josiah Wedgwood II 1769-1843.

Godfrey Wedgwood 1833-1905

Francis Wedgwood 1800-1888

The four generations of the Wedgwood family who were immensely influential in the affairs
of the Infirmary throughout the 19th century

CHAPTER 4
The First Voluntary Institutions in North Staffordshire
The start of the Wedgwood family's involvement with the Infirmary

Two hundred years ago there were several methods of financing the provision of care for the less fortunate and those who were in need of assistance. The Parish, the administrative unit of England, was the area surrounding a Parish Church together with its inhabitants who held the ultimate responsibility for assisting their destitute neighbours. Burial clubs and Friendly Societies were essentially savings clubs with an element of mutual insurance against a rainy day. The club's contributors and their families were those who benefited, ie only those who were members.

A voluntary organisation is organised differently, existing to serve people who were not members. The word *'voluntary'* here may well include a donation of time and service to the organisation, what we mean today as a volunteer, but formerly it meant that the usual contribution was of money. Here the money was given voluntarily, in contradistinction to money raised by a tax or the local Poor Rate which was compulsory.

The first organisation I have found in North Staffordshire that conforms to this pattern is a Society which made its first appearance in the *Advertiser* in November 1797. It was announced that *'under the Patronage of Mr Byerley and several other respectable gentlemen... a laudable plan... a subscription has been set on foot ...affording Medical Aid to the poor of Hanley, Shelton, Cobridge and Etruria.'* The scheme was wished success by the *Advertiser*, and *'commended to the support of Philanthropists'*.

We know no more until a Notice appeared in the *Advertiser* of January 5th, 1799, calling for the renewal of subscriptions, a subscription of one guinea allowed four patients to be recommended in a year. The Notice ended with a report of the first year's activities. In that year 53 persons had been relieved, mostly married women in childbed, truly objects of compassion, because many of them were destitute of that assistance and comfort necessary in that situation. Some cases of obstinate disease had been relieved, others through timely aid had in all probability been saved from the calamity of a lingering disease, and in some cases of extreme difficulty small sums had been advanced.

At the end of the year the Charity had £8-18-6 in hand. This was after paying the Medical Practitioners, according to agreement. The poor Patients have the privilege of *choosing to which of the Practitioners, who have acceded to the plan of the Institution* (an unusual privilege) and they are required to bring back to the Recommending Subscriber, a printed letter of thanks, when discharged by the Doctor. This would encourage the Subscriber to continue his support, but also gave a simple means of auditing the delivery of services.

The statement goes on to propose that there should be a permanent Public Fund, under proper regulation, in addition to the Medical Institution. This probably refers to this existing scheme, but the notice speaks of permanence, and we may wonder if this is the first stirring of a plan to build a hospital or at least a Dispensary. Certainly Thomas Byerley attended the first Public Meeting of the Dispensary and House of Recovery in 1802 and served on its Committee. The first Treasurers of the new Charity were Messrs Wedgwood and Byerley, the Etruria Works provided the business address of the Dispensary and House of Recovery until its own building had been built.

Thomas Byerley was the nephew and partner of Josiah Wedgwood I, and has not had an entirely favourable press. His early career was rather wild, but he settled down, and became one person on whom his uncle could rely. At times he carried a heavy burden, running the Wedgwood works in Etruria, and being responsible for the London operation. His sons were a source of worry to him, and later to Josiah II, but his daughters were successful in running a boarding school, their most notable pupil being the novelist Elizabeth Gaskell. He was, in the years we are considering, the chief representative of the Wedgwood family in North Staffordshire after the death of Josiah I in 1795. He continued the family tradition of philanthropy, he was recorded in 1798 as organising a collection for the wives of the Herefordshire Militia who were accompanying their husbands as they proceeded along the Trent and Mersey Canal on their way to serve in Ireland. They were entertained by the people of Etruria, and by the munificence of Mr Byerley.

In 1800, during the food riots, Byerley was noted attending a meeting to support the suppression of forestalling of corn and flour, to fix butter prices, and to standardise Weights and Measures across the towns of the Potteries, and to alleviate suffering. Forestalling was the practice of buying up goods, especially foodstuff, before it got to market and then selling it at an inflated price. Observe also that all the towns in the Potteries used different standards of Weights and Measures. One month later he attended a meeting at which it was proposed that a co-partnership should be set up to erect a Public (Corn) Mill, the Hanley and Shelton Flour Co. Its purpose was to provide unadulterated flour at lower prices; it was to have a capital of £2000, in shares of £1, with a maximum of 20 shares per person. It was modelled on the London Flour Mill Company, but it seems to have failed for lack of support.

After his death, the sons of Josiah Wedgwood I moved away to estates in the South of England, but in the early 1800s John and Josiah II returned to North Staffordshire and took up the reins of the business. Of the sons of Josiah I, John was the eldest. He was not a good manager of money, personally or in business, his life style was expensive and exceeded his income. In his favour we should remember him as the founder of the Royal Horticultural Society. He was widely respected for his knowledge of plants. Thomas was the youngest son, perhaps the most able of the three. He was engaged in experimental science, and was certainly an important pioneer of photography, having published a paper with Humphrey Davy in the Journal of the Royal Institution in 1802. His health was poor: it is difficult now to disentangle his problem. A guess based on his doctors' letters would suggest an inflammatory bowel disease, perhaps colitis. Sadly, he was prescribed large and continuing courses of opium. The effect was disastrous, and worse, he became addicted to his prescribed medicine. He played very little part in the family firm, and died aged 35 in 1805. He was a very generous supporter of charities and remembered with great affection especially by his brother Josiah II and by many friends.

The unsuitability of John and Thomas for practical business meant that Josiah II had to return to Etruria, much against his inclination, and take over the running of the firm. The problems are well dealt with in *The Wedgwood Circle*. Suffice it to say that Josiah II sent Byerley to London having bought him out. Josiah then went into partnership with his brother John, but then this partnership was dissolved to prevent John's financial liabilities bringing down down the whole business. Josiah II was now in charge. He made sure John and his family were provided for, and even extended his father's will to include children who had been born into the family after his father's death. He was thoroughly honest, and having set a project in hand he poured his energies into it. He was happy to take financial advice and help from his brother in law Dr Robert Darwin, whose son Charles would marry

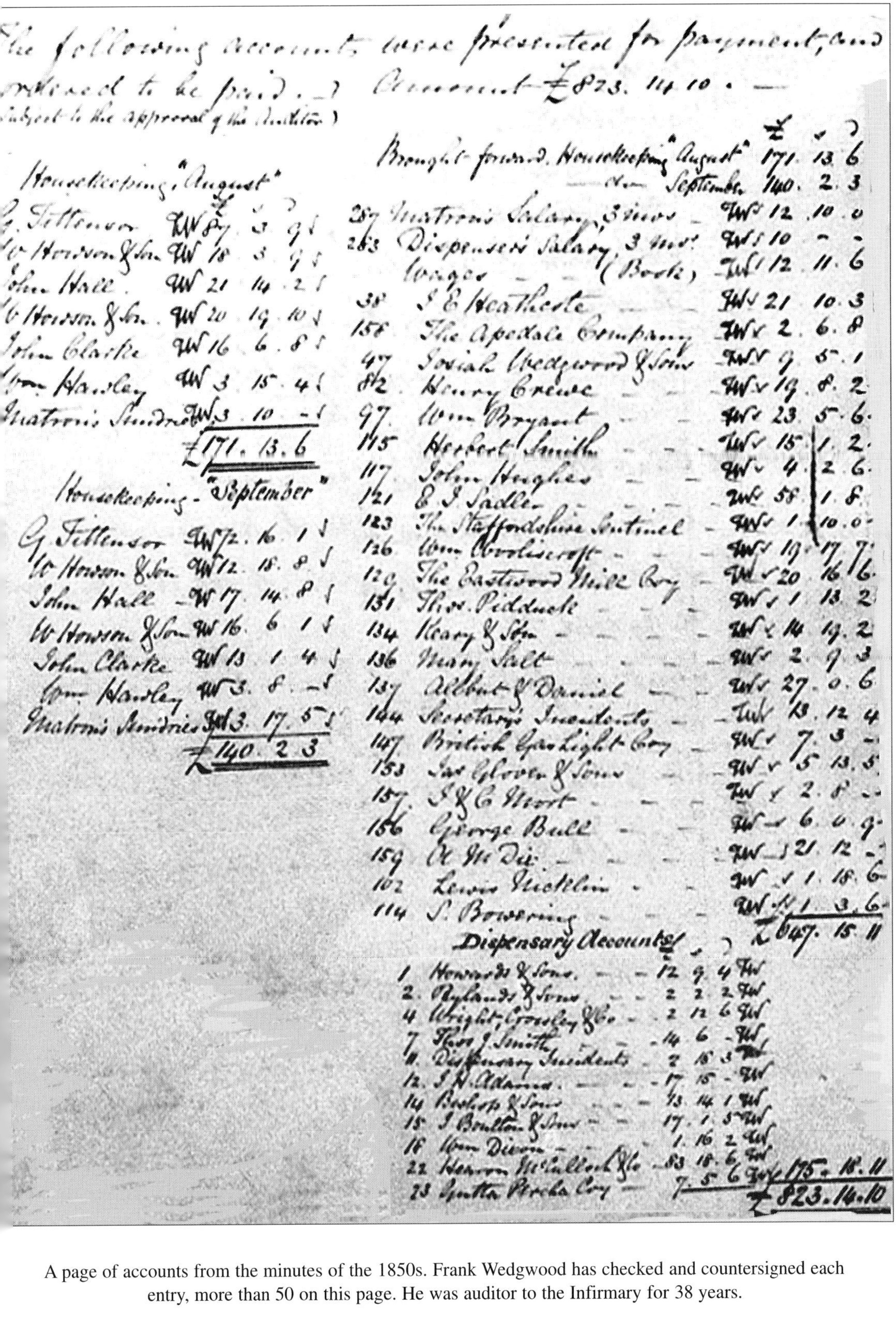
The following accounts were presented for payment, and ordered to be paid. – Amount £823. 14. 10. –
(subject to the approval of the Auditor)

Housekeeping "August"

		£	s	d
G. Tittensor	W	87	3	9
Wm Howson & Son	W	18	3	9
John Hall	W	21	14	2
W Howson & Son	W	20	19	10
John Clarke	W	16	6	8
Wm Hawley	W	3	15	4
Matron's Sundries	W	3	10	–
		£171.	13.	6

Housekeeping – "September"

		£	s	d
G. Tittensor	W	72.	16	1
Wm Howson & Son	W	12.	18.	8
John Hall	W	17	14.	8
W Howson & Son	W	16.	6	1
John Clarke	W	13	1	4
Wm Hawley	W	3.	8.	–
Matron's Sundries	W	3.	17.	5
		£140.	2.	3

			£	s	d
	Brought forward Housekeeping "August"		171.	13.	6
	do September		140.	2.	3
287	Matron's Salary, 3 mos	W	12	10	0
283	Dispenser's Salary, 3 mos	W	10	–	–
	Longe (Books)	W	12	11.	6
38	J E Heathcote	W	21	10.	3
158	The Apedale Company	W	2.	6.	8
47	Josiah Wedgwood & Sons	W	9	5.	1
82	Henry Crewe	W	19.	8.	2
97	Wm Bryant	W	23.	5.	6.
115	Herbert Smith	W	15	1.	2.
117	John Hughes	W	4.	2.	6.
121	E J Sadler	W	58	1.	8.
123	The Staffordshire Sentinel	W	1.	10.	0
126	Wm Wooliscroft	W	19.	17.	7
129	The Eastwood Mill Coy	W	20	16	6.
131	Thos Pidduck	W	1	13.	2
134	Keary & Son	W	14	19.	2
136	Mary Salt	W	2.	9	3
137	Albert & Daniel	W	27.	0.	6
144	Secretary's Incidents	W	13.	12	4
147	British Gas Light Coy	W	7.	3	–
153	Jas Glover & Sons	W	5	13.	5
157	J & C Mort	W	2.	8.	–
156	George Bull	W	6.	0.	9.
159	A McDie	W	21.	12.	–
102	Lewis Nicklin	W	1.	18.	6
114	S. Bowering	W	1.	3.	6
			£647.	15.	11

Dispensary Accounts

		£	s	d	
1	Howards & Sons	12	9.	4	W
2.	Rylands & Sons	2	2.	2	W
4	Wright, Crossley & Co	2	12	6	W
7	Thos J Smith	14	6	–	W
11.	Dispensary Incidents	2	16	3	W
12.	J H Adams	17	15	–	W
14	Bishop & Sons	43.	14	1	W
15	J Boulton & Son	17.	1	5	W
16	Wm Dixon	1.	16.	2	W
22	Hewson McCulloch & Co	53	18.	6	W
23	Gutta Percha Coy	7.	5	6	W
					175. 18. 11
					£823. 14. 10

A page of accounts from the minutes of the 1850s. Frank Wedgwood has checked and countersigned each entry, more than 50 on this page. He was auditor to the Infirmary for 38 years.

Josiah II's daughter; Robert Darwin was a most astute investor. Throughout the early 19th century trade was poor, and Josiah II would have sold up the business if he could, but he soldiered on, out of duty to the extended family that depended on it for its income.

Just at the time of the foundation of the Dispensary there were health problems within the Wedgwood family that caused Josiah II to seek medical advice from London. Tom was declining, and Elizabeth, Josiah II's eldest daughter, suffered from a severe curvature of the spine. This brought him into contact with the leading members of the London medical establishment as he sought the best care for his family. In 1797 he subscribed 30 guineas to Westminster Hospital, the first voluntary hospital, and as a consequence he became a Governor. There are surviving letters that were exchanged between Josiah II and Anthony Carlisle, Surgeon at Westminster Hospital and later President of the Royal College of Surgeons, and Matthew Baillie, President of the Royal College of Physicians.

Thus he was in contact with the leaders of the medical profession and already familiar with the role of a Hospital Governor when he became involved in the development of hospitals in North Staffordshire. He was not passionately absorbed by the Pottery industry as his father had been, but for more than thirty years he worked unstintingly for the Infirmary, perhaps finding there a satisfaction not provided by the Works. This was the start of an association of the Wedgwood family with the Infirmary which would last into the 20th century.

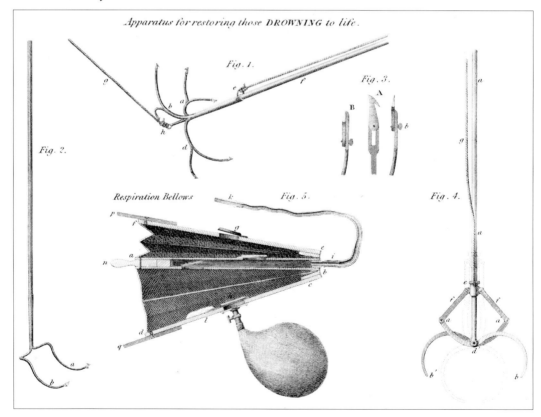

Apparatus prescribed by the Royal Humane Society 1804.
The Governors were proud to have acquired this equipment and issued posters to inform the public of the fact. Here we see bellows to inflate the lungs of a drowned person and drags to draw a the person to the bank. Canals were a frequent cause of fatalities in the unlighted Potteries.

CHAPTER 5
Treatment

The records of the treatment available in the first sixty years of the Infirmary's existence are fragmented. We have to make use of any material that has survived in order to obtain a picture of the nature and standard of the work being done in the early years, namely those spent in the Dispensary and the 'Old Infirmary' in Etruria, culminating with the move to Hartshill in 1869.

From the beginning, the diseases related to North Staffordshire's local industries were a concern of the Infirmary's staff. They well understood the connections of disease with lead and with dust in the pottery industry. Other industries had their own particular problems. Mining caused chest disease, but far more feared were the explosions from inflammable gas, and crushing injuries due to falling rock. Iron smelting, and particularly puddling, which involved the manipulation of streams of molten metal, were regular sources of severe burns.

There was little or no legislation to control risks in these industries, but the Governors did recognise that they had an opportunity and a duty to give a lead to efforts to minimise these injuries. In 1817 a letter was sent to all the coal owners of the area, which was copied into the minutes. It advocated the use of the very recently invented Davy Safety Lamp in all the mines of the area. Davy of course was well known to Josiah Wedgwood II, for Davy had started his career at the Pneumatic Institute in Bristol to whose funds the Wedgwood family were major contributors. It must be a very early example of a 'Health and Safety' notice:

ADDRESS

The Committee of the North Staffordshire Infirmary feel themselves strongly called upon to recommend to the serious attention of the Proprietors of Collieries the late invention of safety lamps by Sir Humphrey Davy, their humanity has been deeply wounded by the sight of a miserable object lately burned in a coal pit in Hanley who died soon after his admission into the Infirmary. They beg leave to refer to the managers of the respective collieries of the Marquis of Stafford, Thos. Kinnersley, Esq, and the Fenton Park Company, where the lamps are now used with perfect success.

Another form of death peculiar to industrial towns was drowning in canals, reservoirs and flooded marl pits. While the main streets of a town might have some form of lighting, canal banks did not. Early in its existence, situated as it was between two canals, the Infirmary had purchased a set of apparatus of the type recommended by the Royal Humane Society. The bellows, fitted with a tube to be placed in the larynx, which provided the air to inflate the lungs, appear identical to the bellows found in any domestic coal fired hearth. In 1822 the Governors provided a set of drags to draw a body to the side, and drew attention to their possession of this useful apparatus by publishing circulars.

In 1825 the Committee decided that they would pay for the purchase of such medical books as the Medical Committee should *'wish to recommend as serviceable to the increase of science in the Medical Officers of this institution'*. Thus the Medical Library was formed: it has a continuous history of service to the present day as the Library of the North Staffordshire Medical School. It still holds books from the earliest days, and may claim to be the oldest library in continuous use in North Staffordshire. In 1829, it was expanded by the donations

In 1930 the dipper still has his hands and arms covered in glaze. Although by this time the amount of lead used was much reduced, the photo shows the time honoured process.

There was still much heavy labouring work in the pottery industry in 1930.
The man seen here is loading the grinding pans by shovel.

Courtesy of Barbara Hobson

A smoky scene over Longton at the end of the 19th century.

Courtesy of Barbara Hobson

Marl hole and pot banks at the beginning of the 20th century.
These pictures are typical of the industrial landscape of the Potteries at the turn of the 20th century.

The blackened form of the Hanley Meat Market prior to cleaning and its conversion to the Reginald Mitchell pub, is a clear testament to the smoke-polluted atmosphere enjoyed by the area's inhabitants.

BELOW
A detail from an illustration in the London Illustrated News of 1873 depicting the scene following an explosion at a coal mine in Talke. Women and children often suffered great deprivation when they lost the breadwinner of the family. Coal mines were usually out of sight and out of mind until there was a disaster, but miners were frequent patients of the Infirmary.

Minutes of a monthly meeting. Ralph Bourne of Fenton is the Chairman. Also present are Herbert Minton and three Wedgwoods - Josiah II, III and Frank. This minute records support for the Medical Library. It illustrates the great attention given to the regular working meetings by the Wedgwoods and other pottery owners. The degree of commitment transcends any financial donation.

of Governors and Medical staff, and to it was added a Museum. The Governors confirmed their appreciation of the importance of a good library by continuing to finance it. The need to house the library, which by then served most of the hospitals of the area. was one of the motivating influences behind the setting up of the North Staffordshire Medical Institute in 1960. From the Institute grew the School of Postgraduate medicine, and it may make some claim to be a parent of the Medical School at Keele University. The bulk of the library moved to its new home in the Medical School on the City General site in October 2004.

Although the foundation of a 'medical school' has been an underlying ambition in North Staffordshire for very many years, as part of the training of surgeons, the pupil system was in operation through much of the 19th century. In order to become a surgeon, young men would pay a premium to an established surgeon, and as an apprentice would observe and assist in the consultant's practice before going to a Medical School, often in London, to complete their education and satisfy the requirements of the Royal College of Surgeons. This system operated in North Staffordshire. In addition to those attached to the Honorary (consultant) Staff, there might also be a pupil in the Infirmary attached to the House Surgeon.

This explains how, in 1834, when the Government conducted a survey of the Hospitals in England offering training, the North Staffordshire Infirmary was included as

A letter from Joshua Seddon, House Surgeon and Secretary to Josiah Wedgwood II, asking him to 'admit' patients - ie check their eligibility for admission. It shows the level of personal commitment required of the committee members taking their turn as Chairman of the month.

a Hospital that had pupils attached to it. The survey was part of an overhaul of the whole system of medical training, practice and examinations. There were those who worked for reform, led by Thomas Wakley, Editor of the Lancet, and those in the Colleges of Physicians and Surgeons, who feared a loss of their privileges and were opposed to reform. When in that year the old Houses of Parliament caught fire from an overheated chimney, the replies to the questionnaire which had just been returned to Parliament were in the building and being analysed. It is said that the reformers rushed in, tore down curtains and bundled the papers wrapped in the curtains out of the window to safety. The unkind say that those opposed to reform were outside throwing the papers back in! Whatever the truth, the draft of the return from North Staffordshire, in the handwriting of Joshua Seddon, long serving House Surgeon and later Surgeon to the Infirmary, has survived in the Infirmary records.

The return of information is in the form of answers to questions; even by modern standards the form was exhaustive, having over 60 questions needing reply. The first questions concern the founding and financing of the hospital, the Voluntary and Establishment contributions, and the invested money, in this case the Accumulating Fund. The number of beds, 100, the numbers of patients treated in the three preceding years, and the number of patients in the hospital on January 1st were given in each of those years. This last figure is relatively constant, just above 50, which gives a bed occupancy of just over 50%. A breakdown of the Medical and Surgical cases follows. Of the Medical cases treated in 1833, 105 were described as acute, while 172 were chronic, while of the Surgical cases 42 were due to accidents and wounds, the remaining 159 were put down as acute and chronic.

Question 8 asked about Capital (major) Operations in the years 1830-33. During these four years there had been 33 Capital Operations, 14 were amputations of the leg, 6 above the knee, 8 below. Of amputations of the arm, 1 was at the shoulder, 7 above the elbow and 2 above the wrist. The remaining Capital Operations were 3 extractions of cataract, 1 tying of an aneurysm of the popliteal artery behind the knee, 1 lithotomy (removing a bladder stone by operation), 1 removal of bladder stones by dilatation of the urethra in a female, and 1 hernia repair.

Question 9 dealt with Minor Operations. There were 26, made up of amputations below the wrist or the ankle, the excision of dead bone or of 'tumours', operations to secure wounded arteries and to repair hare-lip.

What can we make of this? Firstly operations were relatively rare events, undertaken as matters of necessity in those pre-anaesthetic days. Next, no attempt was made to enter the three main body cavities, the head, chest or abdomen. In the 'pre-aseptic' era such an operation was a recipe for disaster. Eye surgery for the removal of cataract had an ancient history. Removal of dead bone would have been required to promote the healing of a chronic sinus due to bone infection, osteomyelitis. The repair of a harelip was not a cosmetic procedure but a necessity, because the open gap in the child's lip would prevent it from sucking, and render it unable to feed and survive.

The answers continue with a summary of the numbers of patients treated as in and outpatients. Usefully we are told that outpatients were not treated in their own homes, but could be seen at the Infirmary on two days a week. All the Physicians and Surgeons lived in Newcastle-under-Lyme. Their qualifications and the Medical School that they had attended were all spelled out, for example both Physicians were Edinburgh graduates. They were required to attend the Infirmary every Tuesday and Friday at 11am to examine the patients in their care, receive those who were to be admitted and discharge those cured, relieved or incapable of further benefit. We know that one of the Governors, the Chairman of the Weekly Committee, was required to attend with the doctors on these days to 'admit' the new patients, his function was to make sure that they had been properly recommended, and were eligible for admission. A note requesting the presence of Josiah Wedgwood II for this duty has survived. All Physicians and Surgeons were required to meet in consultation in difficult cases, to attend their respective patients as often as they judged necessary or if called by the House Surgeon. The Tuesday and Friday visits usually lasted for two or three hours.

The House Surgeon had three major duties. Firstly, he attended the patients of the Physicians and Surgeons in their absence, secondly as Apothecary he (with the aid of his assistant) dispensed such medicines that were prescribed for both in and outpatients, and thirdly as Secretary he entered all proceedings of meetings and took charge of all books and documents committed to his care. He actually resided in the Infirmary. He was not required to be of any particular religious persuasion, nor rejected on account of any.

The Infirmary obtained its drugs from two wholesale druggists in London and two in Newcastle; already the drugs bill was substantial, £233 in 1833.

There appears to be at times a class distinction between the Physicians who had pupils, and Surgeons who had apprentices, though later the terms appear to be interchangeable. The fees to be paid were a matter of individual agreement between Pupil and Physician. The House Surgeon was the only paid doctor, £125 per annum plus board and lodging.

The apprentices could not treat a patient, but could do the dressings of the patients in the absence of their Masters under the supervision of the House Surgeon (The title dresser for clinical students on a Surgical Ward persisted into modern times). On proof of a pupil's improper behaviour the Committee could prohibit his future attendance. In the 1860s this rule was tested by a Pupil who got the Housemaid with child: he was dismissed and his indentures were cancelled, though the Committee later relented and returned his indentures, allowing him to resume his career elsewhere. Pupils still appeared in the minutes until the early years of the 20th century.

The death rates among inpatients were given in the return, though outpatients presented a problem, as the relatives of many outpatients did not inform the Infirmary of their decease, as the answer put it, *'the friends of patients who die frequently omit to apply for discharge'*. Quite!

Remembering that this questionnaire was issued in 1834 and referred back to years since 1830, just before the introduction of the Anatomy Act, any reply on the matter of dissection of the dead had to be answered carefully. Theoretically, such postmortem examinations were illegal, thus the reply: 'anatomical examination of patients who die in the Infirmary are not **formally** (my emphasis) sanctioned by the Governors'. Such examinations were therefore only made in particular instances, as when the deceased person was without friends, or when the consent of friends could be obtained. On these occasions one of the Physicians or Surgeons or the House Surgeon attended to display the diseased or injured structure to the students.

Having detailed the Committee structure, the last questions led on to the matter of record keeping. A General Register of the in and outpatients was kept by the House Surgeon, who also acted as Secretary, in which were stated the name of the patient, date of admission, residence, disease, under whose care, by whom recommended, when and how discharged. (The keeping of this register is the origin of the rank of Registrar in the hierarchy of junior doctors.)

There were also casebooks for the Physicians' and Surgeons' inpatients, kept also by the House Surgeon in which were entered name, age, employment residence of patient, and date of admission, followed by a Record of the Disease, a report of the case, the Medical Treatment and the Result of Treatment. This is much more important than simple book keeping. Now, in North Staffordshire, large numbers of patients were being seen together. Only by properly recording all these details about the patient could cases be considered and analysed, and figures used to assess the results of treatment. They represent a humble but vital step on the road medicine was taking from an 'art or a mystery' to a rational and scientific subject.

Our next view of the work of the Infirmary comes from a casebook compiled by R.C. Garner, son of the Surgeon Robert Garner, covering exactly the years of the Crimean War, 1854-6. It gives us the opportunity to compare the practice of the Infirmary with the received impression of a civilian hospital promulgated by Florence Nightingale.

No account of a hospital in the Victorian era can escape mentioning the influence of Florence Nightingale. Her reputation is currently undergoing a revaluation, and it is becoming clear that the reforms for which she is remembered were not purely her invention but were in large measure a response to doctors' needs for a new type of nurse able to understand and contribute to changing treatments. Equally, she was not as single-handed as she presents herself as being. She undoubtedly did contribute to the improvements in the care of the sick, and by raising the problems then current in hospitals brought them into the public debate. Unfortunately, in order to make her points she cast such a dark picture of the Victorian hospitals, those who worked in them and those who ran them, that this gloomy view is now beyond argument, the received truth.

From a study of the Archives of the North Staffordshire Infirmary, I was aware of a disparity between the condemnation of hospitals and doctors contained in Florence Nightingale's writing and the story unfolding in the archives. Here I found a group of men who appeared to be doing their best to provide the best care that the district could afford, men who were cultured and familiar with the London teaching hospitals, and with the leaders of the medical profession. It has been claimed that Florence Nightingale was one of the first to make use of statistics to prove her points and as ammunition for her campaigns. She certainly did use statistics, but whether or not they were used properly is open to doubt. Abel Smith in his classic book on hospitals points out that she demonstrated figures of mortality for hospitals which were five or even ten times worse that those of other observers, and this also applies to the statistics of the North Staffordshire Infirmary. These, in common with most other hospitals showed a death rate of less than 10%, figures confirmed by another statistician, Fleetwood Buckle. The Nightingale figures approached 90%. One set of figures produced by one of her co-workers showed the mortality in Manchester exceeded 100%!

Miss Nightingale, in the Hospital, at Scutari.
The Lady of the Lamp - the iconic view of Florence Nightingale.

How did this come about? How did Florence Nightingale find a mortality almost 10 times higher than Buckle's? The answer lies in the calculations. Buckle divided the number of deaths which occurred in a year by the number of patients admitted in the year. Florence Nightingale took the number of deaths for the year and divided that number by the beds in use on a particular day. For example, if we take a 100 bed hospital that had 80 deaths, Florence Nightingale's computation would indicate a mortality of 80%, 80 deaths in 100 beds. Buckle recognised that there was a turnover of patients, that each patient's stay was about 35 days, each bed would thus have 10 occupants a year, therefore the hospital would admit 100x10 =1000 patients in that year. Therefore 80 deaths among 1000 patients is a mortality of 8%.

The figure of 5.9% mortality shows that in North Staffordshire the Infirmary was well within the 'norms' for its time. It is true that if we look at specific operations, such as the early attempts at abdominal surgery, which were pioneering efforts, the death rates were appalling, in some series there were no survivors, a death rate of 100%. Nonetheless, the numbers involved in these operations were but a small proportion of all those who passed through a hospital, and usually involved those for whom there was no other hope of survival. It is very wrong to confuse those figures with the overall mortality of the hospital.

To be fair, it must be admitted that Governors massaged their figures by insisting that after two months in hospital all in-patients had to be reviewed, and if they were allowed to remain in hospital, they had to have another recommendation ticket, and effectively be readmitted. Thus one patient could be in hospital for a year, by no means impossible in a case with severe burns, and this one patient could count as several admissions, thus increasing the activity figures, while being only able to die once he/she would not do disproportionate damage to the mortality rate. The Governors of the Infirmary did do just this, improving the mortality by perhaps 20%, say reducing a true 7-8% to a published 5.9%. It was a nationally recognised way of attracting the essential subscriptions by showing the results of treatment in the best possible light.

R.C. GARNER'S NOTEBOOK

R.C. Garner was a pupil at the Infirmary and son of the Infirmary surgeon Robert Garner, though not attached to his father's firm. The notebook consists of detailed accounts of the patients in the wards who came into young Garner's care, and I believe was compiled for his own education, rather than as a part of the hospital record. Because this is a pupil's work, it is remarkably detailed. The task of recording these cases was still a pleasure to him and had not become a chore wherein only the essentials were recorded in shorthand. It is of exceptional interest because the years covered are precisely the years in which Florence Nightingale formed many of her opinions. (1854-56)

Garner's book lists a wide range of patients. Some were medical; there is a diabetic, with his urine input and output chart recorded in pints; there are patients with heart and kidney disease, and many with venereal disease. We find that sexual abuse caused the death of a ten year old girl in a Potteries' home of the 1850s. Many patients had infectious diseases, often abscesses. Analysis of the casebook suggests that Potters were more frequently afflicted with skin infections than the ironworkers and the colliers. Could this imply that the clay became ingrained in the skin and promoted boils, while the dirt of the ironworks washed off more readily, or that the phenols in coal exercised antiseptic properties?

Many patients were under the care of the Surgeons, often admitted as the result of accidents. The unlit urban night would be much darker than any we are accustomed to. One (drunken) man was struck by a train as he crossed the railway line, while another fell into a marl hole while being chased by the police. Traffic accidents were not uncommon, the practice of riding on the shaft of a cart and falling under the wheel was a regular cause of injury. Mines, with rock falls and explosions, were productive of crush injuries and burns. Molten metal at the ironworks was a frequent cause of burns, especially among the Puddlers.

A very common cause of death, especially of women of all classes, was burning due to their clothes catching fire from an open fire or naked candle flame. A girl of 18 fell asleep before the fire, a coal ignited her dress, and her clothes were all burnt away, including her stays (corset). She died two days later. Another patient fell into the fire in an epileptic fit, while yet another perished from burns received while dead-drunk. Men did suffer from burns, most intriguing is the case of the young man with six ounces of gunpowder in his pocket. No explanation is given for its presence. A spark ignited the gunpowder. He did not survive.

There are no examples of surgical intervention other than in cases of injury, ie there are no examples of 'cold surgery'. The notes give an account of the circumstances of the precipitating event, the occupation and condition of the patient and of the particular that had caused admission to the hospital. There is little or nothing about the wider physical state of the patient, no routine examination of heart and lungs unless they were particularly involved. The pulse was noted and recorded, as was the rate of respiration, and the urine examined but at that time clinical blood pressure recording was unknown. We have details of specific treatments, of analgesics and stimulants, of treatment undertaken and dressings applied. Comments made by the patient were recorded, and in general the treatment was well reported, and the outcome, at least as far as the patient's time in hospital was concerned was recorded in the notes.

The advent of anaesthesia has been described as a defining moment in our history, signifying a total change in attitudes to the infliction of pain. Were surgical operations always conducted under anaesthesia at that time? Well, yes and no. There is no doubt that it was the usual practice to anaesthetise patients for operations, but there are operations described in which it was not used - see the detailed account on the next page of a patient with a compound fracture whose condition was so poor that it was not felt safe to give him chloroform. His pulse was barely perceptible throughout the operation. He was put to bed, fell into a deep sleep, and when he woke said he had no recollection of his leg being taken off.

Patients at this time could have endured hours of pain in an open cart as they came to the hospital, causing substantial blood loss and shock. For this there was no treatment, no intravenous fluids, morphine (opium) for pain and alcohol as a stimulant. Patients readily lost consciousness as a result of the shock. The idea of alcohol as a primitive anaesthetic is one beloved of popular fiction. Unfortunately, alcohol, if consumed in the quantities required to produce anaesthesia renders the patient in real danger of death. Lesser doses would remove his self-control, presenting the surgeon with a fighting drunk. Any reader who has had the doubtful privilege of sewing up such a patient in casualty would not recommend alcohol as a preoperative preparation. Alcohol is always referred to as a stimulant in the notebook.

We can explore the attitudes of the staff through this notebook. In their use of language we can try to enter the world of their hospital. Some of the phrases they used are strikingly modern: *'a consultation was held', 'it was decided to try to save the limb', 'an operation was decided upon', 'he was watched carefully through the night'.* These phrases suggest a decent, considered and caring approach to the patient.

It is certainly true that reality fell below these high aims from time to time, usually from shortage of money and lack of staff with sufficient ability and training. I believe we must distinguish between failure to care about the bad conditions and failure to achieve rapid improvement. The Governors and Staff acknowledged the problem and did all they could at the time. There is a difference between the old Infirmary being a bad institution and, in newspeak, being 'institutionally bad'. The persistent picture of a Victorian hospital as a death trap from which a patient had little of hope of emerging and where they were wilfully mistreated was a product of propaganda, however benign the intention. Our local records suggest that the more spectacular images of Victorian hospitals were not universally true.

A method of illuminating the throat before the electric torch

Other sources of information come from outside assessments by visiting authorities, Dr (later Sir) Benjamin Ward Richardson in 1864 and Sir Henry Burdett in 1909. Richardson was touring English hospitals and writing articles about his findings in the *Medical Times and Gazette*. He was the great friend and biographer of Dr John Snow, the first professional anaesthetist and pioneering epidemiologist. Indeed he saw Snow's last book, unfinished when he died suddenly, through to publication. Therefore his account of the giving of anaesthetics in North Staffordshire at this time is of special interest. He described a simple method being in use, pouring chloroform on a towel through which the patient breathed, 'rag and bottle' as it was known, but he records that the person giving the anaesthetic was a doctor, and that he had no other duties in the operating theatre than the care of the patient. The evil of the single handed operator/anaesthetist, the same person giving the general anaesthetic and doing the surgery and thereby dividing his attention, caused many disasters. It would be well over a hundred years after Richardson's visit that this practice was finally rooted out nationally and it is satisfying to see it had been abandoned at the Infirmary at such an early date.

Richardson described the unsatisfactory state of the building and its surroundings and the battle to get it moved. He was very intrigued by the paradox of the poor health of the population and their relatively good pay. In his research of the towns he visited he shows himself to have been very thorough. He quotes from Pitt's *History of Staffordshire* (1819), Scrivens' *Review of Working Conditions* (1842) and Dr Greenhow in 1860, all sources which we rely on today as the best available account of their time. Despite their apparently good pay, (in relation to workers in other towns) he says *'There are many advantages pertaining to the potters; but, in spite of these, no one can pass even a few days in the district without being assured that there is something wrong. The men are unhealthy in aspect, the women cadaverous, the children small,*

[Handwritten case history — first entry]

Richard Jackson. — — — — — — Mr Ball.

A miller, æt 15, a very strong healthy looking lad admitted under Mr Ball. Comp: fracture of Leg. States that at four o'clock this afternoon his clothes got entangled in some machinery, he was dragged in and got his leg crushed between two cog wheels. Had a good deal. A surgeon who was called in bound up tightly the limb.

[Handwritten case history — second entry]

On admission he was quite sensible but very low. The man was admitted to day under the care of Mr Ball with a compound fracture of the thigh.

The accident was occasioned by the man sitting on the shaft of a cart which he was driving and falling off and the wheel passing over his thigh. The cart contained about 12 cwt of iron, he had been jolted in a cart ...

Robert Garner, Surgeon to the Infirmary. He was father-in-law to Charles Lynam, the architect to the Hartshill Infirmary, and his son wrote the notebook of cases between 1854 and 1856.

Extracts from case histories in R.C. Garner's notebook - now to be found in the Staffordshire Records Office, Hanley.

The top entry is a classic example of the danger of unguarded machinery - clothes caught in the cogs dragging the leg between them.

The lower entry is an apparently common form of road traffic accident in the 1850s.

On the opposite page we have a 'real-time' account of the amputation in a shocked patient. No chloroform was given because of the risks in such a shocked patient. After he had fainted he was administered brandy and wine as a stimulant.

It is interesting to note that exactly this time, Sir James Clarke, heading the medical services in the Crimea, was severely criticised for his 'cruelty' in advising caution in the use of chloroform in the severely injured. His opinion was clearly not unusual in practice.

put in a cart and brought here. He was very much shaken in the cart. His leg was not looked at before he came in. State on admission. The leg about three inches below the knee was completely smashed. There was a wound on the outer side through which the flesh was pushed, another underneath. The ends of bone were felt sticking almost through in several places. There was also alarming haemorrhage, the tourniquet was immediately applied, but it did not stop the haemorrhage, which must have been from the blood collected in the leg. He was exceedingly low and soon became insensible, he had immediately 2oz of brandy, and during the next hour and a half 8oz of brandy and 8 of wine. An hour and a half after his admittance amputation was performed above the knee, no chloroform was given, as he was so very low, four vessels required ligatures, the flaps were only laid together and strips of wet lint & plaister & a bandage put over them. During the operation his pulse was hardly perceptible. Very little blood was lost during the operation. The patient was laid in bed and Carb. Ammonia gr v every half hour or hour. His pulse gradually became better, although still rambling, he got several good sleeps in the night and towards morning was quite sensible, he had not any recollection of his leg being taken off. There was but little oozing from the stump.

The stump was done up this morning with ointment and strips of plaister & bandage. Tongue & pulse good. Cal. gr iij Pulv Ohii gr ¼ 6th Clk hs. Pretty good night. Pulse good. To have a little broth or beef tea and Mist. Effervesc tr indie. Morph Acetatis gr ⅙ h.s.s.

1) Note the ill effect of being 'very much shaken in the cart'.
2) Haemorrhage leading to reduced blood flow to the brain caused him to become insensible. His pulse was 'hardly perceptible' during the operation.
3) No chloroform was given 'as he was so very low'.
4) By morning he was sensible, but he 'had not any recollection of his leg being taken off'.
5) He was now given broth or beef tea, and morphia for his pain.

Joseph Crowther. ———— Mr Turner

Joseph Crowther, at 38, a smith at the railway works, was admitted to day under Mr Turner. Compound Comminuted Fracture of the Humerus. His friends state that he was drunk and as he was crossing the line an engine ran him down; the buffer striking his chest and the wheel passing obliquely over his arm. There was violent hæmorrhage at the time. A Surgeon was sent for who put a tourniquet on and sent him here. When brought here he was rambling although conscious of what was going on. He was very low. Carbonate of Ammonia in wine was given. The Elbow joint and the Humerus to within three inches of the head was literally smashed. There is fracture of one or more ribs with Emphysema. None of the Surgeons being able to come, the House Surgeon Mr Folker determined upon removing the limb at the shoulder joint. The Operation was commenced by an incision commencing over the Acromion

---

Sedation ———— set
20   Easier. Ung oxdearg on lint to be but lightly round the hand. Is losing strength.
25   Painful. Cont Cat Lin. Pot Belladon.
5   There being no chance of saving the hand, amputation was decided upon, which accordingly was performed about two inches above the wrist, in the double flap operation, the patient being under Chloroform. Three vessels required ligature and the flaps were brought together by four sutures. Cold water dressing. But little blood was lost. About three quarters of an hour after the operation there being considerable hæmorrhage the wound had to be partially opened and a vessel tied. Shortly afterwards, bleeding returning, the wound was left exposed and a wet rag put over which effectually stopped it. Towards evening the two stitches which had been removed were reinserted.

The upper extract refers to an emergency where the operation was performed by the House Surgeon without waiting to consult senior staff because no one was available.
The lower extract describes an injury to the hand. Some days of conservative treatment were allowed before 'there was no chance of saving the hand', when amputation was performed under chloroform.

A 'mutton chop' was a sign of progress, after a 'light diet'.

stunted and though not mis-shaped, ill-shaped'. He quotes approvingly the famous passage written by Dr Arlidge, which achieved immortality by being included in Volume I of Karl Marx's *Das Kapital.* *'The potters as a class... represent a degenerated population, both physically and morally...'* He goes on to speak of the illnesses to which the potter was especially prone, chest disease, especially potters' asthma.

Richardson visited the Potteries at the time when the extension of the Factory Act to young people engaged in earthenware manufacture was being debated. He agreed with the prevailing view that the excessive carrying of heavy weights when young undermined the health of the pottery worker, and aggravated by the constant severe changes of temperature.

Whatever the causes, there does seem to be agreement by doctors who came to the area permanently or as visitors that the population were strikingly unhealthy in appearance. Richardson reported that he had been told that Dr Thomas Addison, a truly great physician of Guys Hospital in London in the first half of the 19th century, had visited the Infirmary. Addison had described failure of the adrenal glands as the cause of the then untreatable disease which still bears his name, and which killed Jane Austen. He had been so struck with the variety and severity of the conditions he saw in the wards here that he expressed the thought that he could wish to end his days as a *'retired student in North Staffordshire observing the clinical experience of the hospital'.* Richardson agreed with this view of the vast number of cases of great clinical interest to be found in the wards of the Infirmary!

Richardson was extremely complimentary about the Medical staff: *'any inquiring stranger will find in the North Staffordshire Hospital as united and energetic staff as could be met anywhere. Possessing a magnificent field for observation and research, the members of the staff compete only in striving to gather together all the new facts of the day, and in subjecting proposed and reasonable methods of novel treatment to immediate and rigid trial'.* In modern terms, they worked together to observe their patients, kept up to date with the medical literature, and while introducing the latest treatments, observed them carefully to see that they were indeed improvements.

His only criticisms were that they should publish their cases more widely, and that they suffered from the very few post mortem examinations undertaken. *'Such is the extreme prejudice of the people against the examination of the dead that an autopsy is a rare occurrence. Until a more enlightened attitude prevails pathology as deduced from morbid anatomy will have a poor chance of original development in North Staffordshire'.* When Dr Wilson Fox was briefly a Consultant Physician in North Staffordshire from 1858 to1861 before being 'headhunted' to become Professor of Pathology at University College, London, he only managed to get permission to perform two postmortem examinations in his entire stay. When we consider Wilson Fox was the most distinguished member of the staff in the 19th century, a leading pathologist whose interest was in diseases of the chest, how much more could have been done for the Potters' chest diseases if conservatism had not prevented research.

Richardson was impressed with the medical treatment; he observed several operations,

A patient with syphilis, who was doing well but was expelled for smoking.

and reported that three operations had been successfully undertaken for the removal of large ovarian cysts, known as ovariotomy. The real jewels of these accounts are in the small details. The ovariotomy cases which frequently proved fatal, were at risk in the poor conditions prevailing in the Infirmary. He says that 'To avoid risks, the cases have been isolated, and attention to the minutest details in the after treatment had been rigorously pursued'. The reference to the avoidance of risk clearly refers to infection; the fact that they were isolated successfully indicates that in 1864, before Lister's earliest papers, the danger of cross infection was well understood. A further detail concerns pain relief before the days of hypodermic syringes. The effectiveness of a pain-killer given by mouth was often defeated by post operative vomiting, so here the pain relief was given by suppositories containing opium.

Midwifery was not considered a 'proper' part of medicine, indeed, at the Infirmary at least as late as 1877, should a Physician be in practice with a person practicing midwifery he would have to resign his post at the Infirmary. With a relatively low standard of obstetric care across the country, prolonged, frequent and often traumatic deliveries were common, so we cannot be surprised that damage to the pelvic tissues plagued many women who had borne children. Damage to the bladder and the lower bowel could form false passages or fistulae that made these women incontinent of urine and/or faeces, an appalling fate that ruined their lives. One of the operations Richardson observed was the repair of a tear between the bladder and the vagina. Frequently, the prolonged labours had the effect of so weakening the pelvic ligaments that the uterus descended into the vagina, a prolapse, or 'fallen womb'. Before operations to repair prolapse became common, a large internal device known as a pessary was commonly used to support the womb. Richardson reported that the firm of Pinder, Bourne and Co of Burslem (later absorbed by Doulton) made pessaries for Mr Walker's patients from highly glazed earthenware, either oval or round and in three sizes. Being very smooth, they were recommended for the ease of keeping them clean.

Richardson's visit occurred in the midst of the battle to remove the Infirmary to Hartshill. He had no illusions about the state of the Infirmary as it stood in Etruria; he said it was 'a blot on the map of sanitary science'. He also clearly understood the inter-urban battle then taking place within the Potteries. If the Governors wished to see a falling death rate 'they will allow no tradition, no idea of expense, no temporary agitation to prevent them from razing the old building to the ground and erecting a new pavilion Hospital in some new and more favoured spot, where the air is unpolluted, where there is rest for the sick, and where a surrounding healthy vegetation tells the story that life is there respected, and held at its prime worth'.

Richardson's account is the last independent account to survive until Sir Henry Burdett's articles in 1909 (see ch. 17). Fortunately, the Annual Reports 1860 to 1910 contain a complete analysis of the numbers of patients treated, with lists of operations performed, and most importantly, the outcomes. The most spectacular advances of the later 19th century were in surgery, and using the Annual Reports, we can watch the changes unfold, progress which is also recorded in chapter 12.

CHAPTER 6
The Etruria Infirmary 1819-1869

Nowadays, when a new hospital is built there are agreed guidelines and standards to which it must conform. Two hundred years ago there was no general agreement on the layout, contents or facilities that a hospital should offer. While large Voluntary Hospitals had been built in the 18th century, which could be visited, local circumstances dictated what could be achieved. In North Staffordshire a group of well-educated businessmen were determined to go their own way in order to overcome particular local circumstances and to enlist the help of a broad based group of advisers.

In 1812 the Committee purchased the site of the Dispensary from Josiah Wedgwood II for £370 on independent valuation. The purchase of the land on which the building stood put the Institution on a permanent footing, and was an important statement of confidence in the future as the Governors had every hope that they would soon be able able to extend their existing building. The income of the Dispensary was improving, and there was pressure from a rising population who were involved in mechanised industry, a continually growing source of accident victims. Moving injured patients to Stafford in an ironstone cart was no longer an acceptable option.

The next steps were taken in November 1814 when a committee was appointed to look into the practicality of adding an Infirmary to the Dispensary. The members were Josiah Wedgwood II, Josiah Spode II, Thomas Butt the Vicar of Trentham, R.E. Aitken Curate of Hanley and John Tomlinson Solicitor to the Governors. The initial proposal was to add a new wing to the existing building. It was estimated that an income of approximately £1500 a year would be needed, which could not be provided by the existing subscribers. The committee looked to the miners for support, they offered the most numerous group of patients, a numerous, wealthy and respectable class.

This acknowledgement of the difficulties to be expected in the raising of an increased level of income culminated in the publication of the 'Address to the Working Classes'. By December it was believed that the majority of works would agree to participate in the Establishment Scheme, indeed £860 had already been subscribed. On this basis it was agreed to proceed; the excellent example of the working class meant that the more opulent would follow. Subscriptions were solicited, the neighbourhood was divided into local districts and representative Governors organised collections in their own district.

In January 1815 a Building Committee was appointed, Sir John Heathcote, Josiah Wedgwood II, Josiah Spode II, John Davenport, John Tomlinson, William Yates and William Bent. The Marquis of Stafford was invited to be President. He had presided over a Public meeting in Hanley, thereby giving a seal of approval to the new Infirmary, an act of great symbolic importance.

Mr Winks surveyed the existing structure of the Dispensary and the House of Recovery: he recommended a new building, the present one not being fit for enlargement. The present building was too slight to have the internal walls taken down, a new floor and roof trusses would be needed, even so, the building would be weak and imperfect, it would be best to take down the building and reuse the materials. The problems of the restricted site could never be overcome, it would be best to seek a new site and start again.

A Building Fund was begun, and soon the financial account showed that £4600 had been subscribed and that £6000 was hoped for. It seemed best to keep the existing building

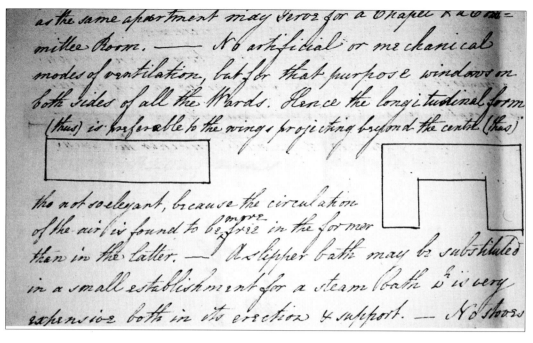

Part of a letter (1814) from Rev. RE Aitken to Josiah Wedgwood II reporting on the fact-finding visit to Birmingham. The left hand sketch and description is essentially that of a pavilion or Nightingale ward.

The only item surviving from the old Infirmary (1817-1869), this copper plate marks the laying of the foundation stone on July 3rd 1816 by Sir John Edensor Heathcote, as proxy for the Marquis of Stafford.

of the Dispensary and House of Recovery in operation while the new Infirmary was built. Continuity of service would be maintained and more time would be available to complete the new building. Josiah Wedgwood II was willing to sell land from the Etruria estate, initially 6 acres at £200 per acre, and rent out another 3 acres at 6 guineas per acre.

The water supply was tested and found to be satisfactory, the local clay was suitable to allow the common bricks which would be needed to be made on the site. Enquiries were made regarding the mines in the area, the Committee was advised that no inconvenience was foreseen as the main coal seam lay at a depth of 200 yards or more, a considerable depth at that time. The land was purchased. The Prince Regent graciously authorised a royal donation of £500 to the building fund - although it actually came from sums paid by the owners of encroachments (land that had been enclosed or appropriated from the Common land) in the Manor of Newcastle-under-Lyme.

As they had done when erecting the Dispensary and House of Recovery, the Committee went to considerable trouble to investigate current practice. Information gathered included the cost of maintaining the buildings, and the cost of feeding the patients. The Rev Robert Aitken, the Curate of Hanley, travelled to Birmingham to investigate the cost of building and running cost of the hospital there. This had been built 20 years previously at a cost of £10,000, and accommodated 130 patients. Howard's book on *Prisons and Hospitals* had been a key reference source in its planning. The provision of large wards was advised, with a few smaller rooms; and a hospital should have large sewers to cope with the filth from the water closets.

In view of the Florence Nightingale's claims of priority in the design of the Pavilion or Nightingale ward, it is interesting that a ward corresponding exactly to the pavilion pattern had been advised by the Birmingham Governors in 1814. The description and an outline sketch in Aitken's report to Josiah Wedgwood II showed long narrow wards with windows on opposing sides, and heated by open fires rather than artificial or mechanical ventilation. The sketch in the letter may be one of the earlier depictions of a Pavilion ward. The advice given included that slipper baths rather than steam baths should be provided. The Birmingham governors also advised that a working drawing should be obtained from an architect, only then should a working surveyor be employed to avoid the expense of a contractor.

At the same time, the committee received alternative advice from Derby where a new Infirmary had recently been completed. The communication with the Derby Committee came through the agency of Josiah Wedgwood II. The Derbyshire General Infirmary had been designed by William Strutt, the son of Jedediah Strutt who had designed an early mill building, one of the earliest fire proof buildings to be erected. Jedediah Strutt had been a partner of Sir Richard Arkwright, and through him was well-acquainted with Josiah Wedgwood I. Another link with Derby was through Dr Thomas Bent, a Physician at Derby for many years. He was a son of Dr James Bent, a founder member of the staff of the North Staffordshire Infirmary, and the man who had amputated the leg of Josiah Wedgwood I.

Thus there were many family links with the Derbyshire Committee and their views were taken seriously. When Dr Thomas Bent was describing William Strutt in a letter to his uncle William Bent the brewer of Newcastle-under-Lyme, he referred to Strutt as the oracle in all Infirmary matters. He reported that the Derby Infirmary had been designed largely with the use of an architectural model, which had been so effective in spotting problems that it was estimated to have saved £600 in avoiding errors in planning. Said to have cost £100, it was so large that a house was taken in Derby to display it to prospective contributors. Strutt offered to sell it to North Staffordshire for £50, then offered it as a loan which was accepted, but there is no record of it ever coming to North Staffordshire.

The model illustrated a building that was the antithesis of the pavilion wards. Instead of long narrow wards with natural ventilation this was a square block of a building, with wards of 8 beds, others of 1,2,3 and 4 beds. It was a very sophisticated design that included day rooms and convalescent wards. The smaller wards were designed for occupation by patients who *needed quiet, or for groaning noisy complaining ones or those with ill-smelling sores.* It was felt that so many small wards, if each were provided with an individual fireplace, would produce an excessive amount of work for the staff, while producing a fire risk, a long held concern of the Strutts. The Derby method of heating was designed to use a stream of air warmed by a single central stove. By this means the Derby plans overcame the lack of cross ventilation inherent in the square design.

While ventilation itself did not perhaps have the health giving benefits claimed for it, it made a great contribution to the dispersal of smells. In the search for further improvements in the atmosphere of a hospital, the water closets designed by Strutt were described as the *ne plus ultra* (or last word) in toilets. They possessed a door which fitted closely to the arc of a curved wall, and as the door was closed after use this door swept out the foul air, while at the same time a system of levers caused the closing door to automatically flush the toilet. We have no evidence of such toilets being installed in North Staffordshire, but they indicate the level of sophistication available to designers of a Georgian hospital. At the time, William Strutt's designs attracted attention from across Europe.

In any event, the Derby Infirmary appears to have had more influence on the choice of a design for an Infirmary in North Staffordshire than did the advice from Birmingham. Plans were invited from Thomas Sherwin of Hanley, Mr Wincks of Trentham and Mr Haycock of Shrewsbury, whose design was preferred. The Committee asked for estimates based on several alternative versions:

(1) *the complete plan*
(2) *with the attic floor as a shell only, for completion at a later date*
(3) *plan with an attic in the centre only, leaving out the Fever and Lues (syphilitic) wards*
(4) *plan without an attic storey.*

A separate subscription was set on foot to provide the Portico, with Doric columns, without which no building of the time could have any pretension to academic status, and to supply other improvements to the architectural style of the building. The Infirmary building as we see it in a photograph of about 1860 shows a white two storey building plus a basement, with sash windows, two low pitched, almost Italianate gables at each end. New wards can be seen extending to the right of the picture as we see it. We cannot yet see any evidence of the damage due to subsidence, but another photograph taken at the same period but from a different angle shows the Infirmary dwarfed by a forest of chimneys of the Ironworks.(see page 100) These offer testimony to the pollution of the site though the lack of smoke suggests that these photographs were taken during the Wakes. In the centre of the Infirmary a flight of steps rises to the level of the front door, over which was the Portico, surmounted by an inscription, *The North Staffordshire Infirmary, Erected and Supported by Voluntary Contributions.*

In June 1815, four days before the Battle of Waterloo, the Committee announced that *'wishing to be well advised* (they) *have submitted the same* (plans) *to Mr Potter of Litchfield, the County Architect of Staffordshire'.* From correspondence between Messrs Spode and

Wedgwood it would seem that the advice to involve Mr Potter came from Josiah Spode II. At any rate, while Mr Haycock was working on his estimates, the plans were subject to the scrutiny of Mr Potter. Josiah Wedgwood II suggested that the attic storey should be abandoned and the Derby method of heating should be employed. By August 1815 Mr Potter prepared the estimates; they were accompanied by the usual wrangles over what was and what was not included in the contract. Ominously, while writing to Mr Potter confirming the deletion of the attic storeys, Wedgwood referred to the need to rearrange the rooms as the plan was still *'too extensive for our resources'*.

Josiah Wedgwood II was involved in every stage of the planning, and in every decision. The Record Office in Stafford holds an aide-memoir, a to-do list in which we can watch him at work. Would dissection be undertaken in the dead room? (mortuary), would an outer door be required as well as an inner one? Should the Operation wards be moved from West to East? Should the Operating Room have a skylight? Should it give a North light? This snapshot of the man in action has to suffice, otherwise the catalogue of detail becomes tedious, but we could note that business letters on behalf of the Infirmary were written even on Christmas Day, as he wrote on that day in 1815 to remind Mr Potter of the conditions of the contract which was to be entered into for the building work.

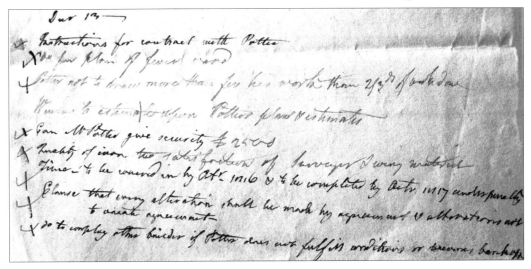

These are the working notes in Josiah Wedgwood II's hand - in ink and pencil. Among the points are the requirement of Mr. Potter to provide a security for £2500 in the event of bankruptcy. The notes also refer to rates for completion of various stages of the work, that no alterations be undertaken without agreement and agreement to employ another builder if Potter *'does not fulfil conditions or become bankrupt'*.

The Committee were particularly concerned to protect themselves against the possibility of bankruptcy on the part of Mr Potter. As part of the contract they insisted on a security of £2500. An inspecting surveyor was to be appointed, the roof was to be completed by October 1816, and the building completed by October 1817. The quality of materials, the timber, iron and lead were to be approved by the surveyor. Mr Potter affected to be unconcerned by the appointment of a surveyor, a proposal which had originated in Mr Aitken's report of his visit to Birmingham. He implied that if the Committee wished to waste their money that was their business. Mr Haycock disappeared from the scene, having been paid 20 guineas for his original plan, though he insisted that his were the accurate estimates. He expressed surprise at the lightness of Mr Potter's

The Etruria Infirmary - a watercolour painting by Lucy Lynam, wife of the architect of the new Hartshill Infirmary.

1860. The Infirmary in Etruria - with its inscription above the portico. The photographer was Mr Alfieri, a schoolmaster and President of the North Staffordshire Photographic Society (*People of the Potteries*, Keele.) Although it is difficult to see, there are 9 figures in this old photo: 2 top-hatted men peer out from the bushes on the left, 3 men are on the grass, a top-hatted porter stands on the steps, another figure stands just below the end of main frontage in the distance, and a man and lady in a crinoline walk away towards the right end.

An engraving of the Etruria Infirmary from the 1859 Annual Report.

An engraving of the Derbyshire General Infirmary from 1817.
There is an obvious resemblance between this and the Etruria Infirmary.

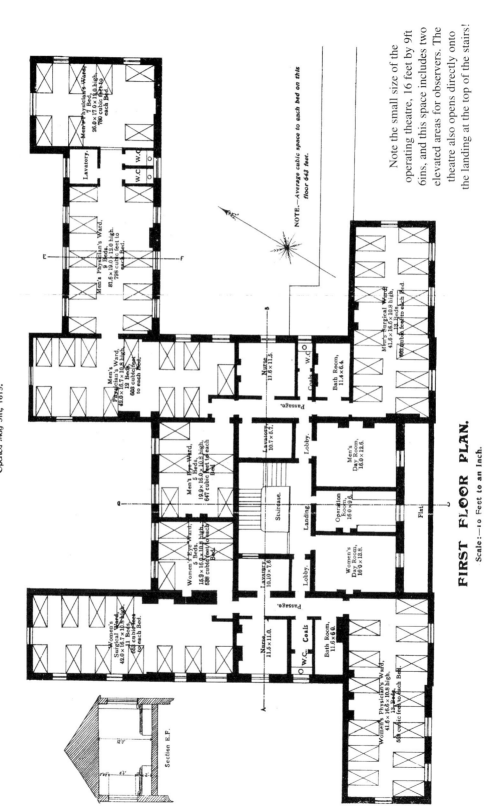

NORTH STAFFORDSHIRE INFIRMARY, ETRURIA,

Opened May 5th, 1819.

FIRST FLOOR PLAN.

Scale:—10 Feet to an Inch.

NOTE.—*Average cubic space to each bed on this floor 643 feet.*

Note the small size of the operating theatre, 16 feet by 9ft 6ins, and this space includes two elevated areas for observers. The theatre also opens directly onto the landing at the top of the stairs!

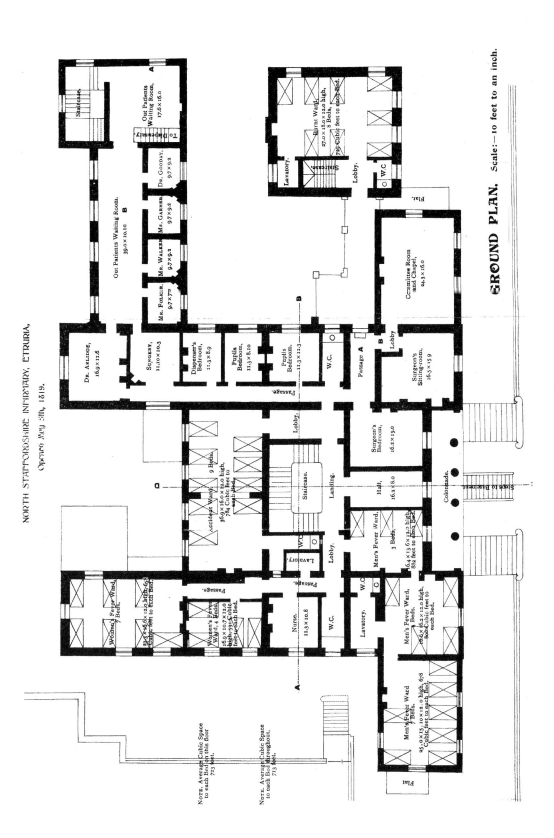

NORTH STAFFORDSHIRE INFIRMARY, ETRURIA,

Opened May 5th, 1819.

GROUND PLAN. Scale:— 10 feet to an inch.

Staircase.

Out Patients Waiting Room, 17.6 × 16.0

Out Patients Waiting Room, 39.0 × 10.10

To Dispensary

Dr. Gooday, 9.7 × 9.2

Mr. Garner, 9.7 × 9.2

Mr. Walker, 9.7 × 9.2

Mr. Foden, 9.7 × 7.7

Dr. Arlidge, 16.9 × 11.6

Surgery, 11.10 × 10.3

Dispenser's Bedroom, 11.3 × 8.9

Pupils Bedroom, 11.3 × 8.10

Pupils Bedroom, 11.3 × 11.3

Passage.

W.C.

Passage A

Burnt Ward, 27.0 × 18.0 × 12.0 high, 8 Beds, 729 Cubic feet to each Bed.

Lavatory.

Staircase.

Lobby.

W.C.

Committee Room and Chapel, 24.3 × 16.0

Flat.

Lobby.

B

Surgeon's Sitting-room, 16.5 × 15.9

Accident Ward, 9 Beds, 36.9 × 16.0 × 12.0 high, 784 Cubic feet to each Bed.

D

Staircase.

Landing.

Surgeon's Bedroom, 16.2 × 13.0

Hall, 16.2 × 8.0

Colonnade.

Steps to Basement

Lobby.

W.C.

Lavatory.

Men's Fever Ward, 3 Beds, 16.4 × 13.6 × 12.0 high, 882 feet to each Bed.

Women's Fever Ward, 7 Beds.

Passage.

33.4 × 46.6 × 12.0 high, 653 Cubic feet to Each Bed.

Women's Fever Ward, 4 Beds, 16.0 × 10.7 × 12.0 high, 513 Cubic feet to each Bed.

Nurse, 11.3 × 10.8

W.C.

Lavatory.

Men's Fever Ward, 16.0 × 16.4 × 12.0 high, 860 cubic feet to each Bed.

Men's Fever Ward, 7 Beds, 35.0 × 15.10 × 12.0 high, 678 Cubic feet to each Bed.

Flat.

Note. Average Cubic Space to each Bed on this floor 723 feet.

Note. Average Cubic Space to each Bed throughout, 713 feet.

successful bid, and said that the *Governors were indeed fortunate if they could get the Infirmary built at that price.* Mr Haycock later built the Infirmary in the centre of Shrewsbury.

Although any inner struggles within the Committee are decorously hidden in the formal minutes, a letter from Thomas Butt to Josiah Wedgwood II lifts the curtain and shows how important Wedgwood was to the success of the whole scheme. Butt wrote *'...The more anxious I am that you may be induced to undertake the command. In that case you must be Chairman of the Building and Infirmary Committee. I think your acceptance would give satisfaction to all parties.'*

The decision having been made to build on the agreed plan, the most contentious matter needing resolution was the question of the system of heating to be employed. As the style of the North Staffordshire Infirmary bears a marked resemblance with the Derbyshire General infirmary and none with the Pavilion style, it is not surprising to learn that the Strutt system was adopted.

Basically the principle of this system was that air entered via a very large pipe, one end of which was arranged to face constantly into the wind by a large weather vane. The air then blew along the pipe through the foundations, around the outside of a large hot stove, and having been heated it passed through a system of pipes and vents to all parts of the building before escaping to the outside, hopefully taking the noxious odours with it. It required specially designed stoves, and the correct construction of the vents was crucial for success. The system was most likely to be efficiently installed if put in as an integral part of the original building work. In North Staffordshire it was certainly planned to heat the Infirmary by this method.

A long correspondence survives between Josiah Wedgwood and William Strutt's assistant, Charles Sylvester, who travelled the country installing these systems. Clearly Mr Potter was not keen to cooperate with Mr Sylvester. The main air duct was installed in North Staffordshire's Infirmary *after* the building of the foundations had been completed. It is not clear that the system ever gave satisfaction. References to its operation in North Staffordshire are scanty, and pictures of the Infirmary show a building well provided with chimneys, suggesting a move back to conventional grates. We know from a letter that Josiah Wedgwood II considered using the system for boiling plaster at the Etruria works and he stated that several stoves were working well in the Etruria works. It was explored as a heating system at the National School in Etruria, and there is a reference to its employment in Leek Parish Church.

Charles Sylvester was on good terms with Josiah Wedgwood II, having met him when he came to collect material for an article about the pottery industry for the 1815 edition of the *Encyclopaedia Britannica*. Sylvester, an excellent mathematician, was one of the generation of engineers of the early 19th century who were at the cutting edge of the Industrial Revolution. In addition to his work with Strutt, he worked with George Stephenson on the trial that proved that smooth wheels would haul trains on smooth rails provided gradients were not too steep. This trial secured the future of high speed railways against the rival schools which favoured cable haulage or cogwheel propulsion, both of which were inherently slow.

Sylvester wrote a book, published in 1819, about the Derbyshire General Infirmary with particular reference to its heating, hot water provision and sanitation. He referred to the North Staffordshire Infirmary, giving it as an example of the *failure of the system due to the incompetence of the builder.* Sylvester also received a letter from Wedgwood, as a Committee member at the Stafford Asylum, complaining that a heating system that Potter had acquired from Sylvester for the Stafford Asylum had failed. Sylvester replied forcefully to the charge. It seems that Potter had used Sylvester's ideas but not his equipment, *'I have no doubt that the great mischief is in the flues, which having, I suppose, been made by Mr Potter, who has exercised his own opinion as he did in those of the North Staffordshire Infirmary'.*

Sylvester was clearly furious with Potter, but he had the last word - his book is still quoted 200 years later and the Strutt/Sylvester system was a very important experiment in the heating of large buildings and hospitals in particular. Eventually it failed, the variability of the wind and therefore the airflow meant that when the original Infirmary building at Derby was replaced later in the century, the Strutt/Sylvester system was not repeated. Indeed, the pipe itself had become a source of smells and a home for rats, as no arrangement had been made for cleansing it thoroughly. Today such hot air heating systems rely on electric motors rather than the vagaries of the wind.

Perhaps this flirtation with innovation was North Staffordshire's final attempt to be at the cutting edge of hospital design. There is no evidence of anything but the most conventional in additions to the Infirmary for its remaining years. In 1828 £985 had been contributed for fever wards. A bazaar organised by Mr Arthur Minton raised a further £960 to allow building to proceed. Two other blocks were added to the Infirmary in the 1850s to ease overcrowding even though the presence of subsidence on the site had led to an embargo on further building. One was a ward for burned patients, largely paid for by money raised by Daniel Ball, Surgeon, and another ward was paid for by money collected by Mr Charles Kinnersley. The troubles that befell all these buildings are described in another chapter. A final legacy from the Derby design was that the central staircase functioned as a chimney to bring smells from the kitchens, the broken sewer and elsewhere throughout the whole building.

The one distinctive architectural feature of the Infirmary was the Portico. The new Infirmary was to be built on rising land in a prominent site, overlooking the road from Newcastle to Hanley. Although the building had been reduced in size to match the available funds, its appearance was of some importance and it was agreed that there should be a Portico over the front entrance. In order that it should not absorb money needed for patient care a separate fund was set up to pay for it. It raised £119-9-0. Every building with academic pretensions built in the early 19th century had a portico. The National Gallery, the British Museum and the Colleges of Physicians and Surgeons, each had a Portico, though Sir John Summerson in his book *Georgian London* observes of the latter pair, *'neither has any particular purpose except to signalize the academic status of the corporation behind it'.*

A portico demanded an inscription, to be read by every visitor or passerby who would hopefully become a subscriber to the Infirmary. This was a matter of some importance and a sub-committee was appointed to recommend an appropriate form of words. It consisted of John Tomlinson, Josiah Wedgwood II, and the Rev. Thomas Butt, the Vicar of Trentham. John Tomlinson favoured an inscription that recorded both a Royal connection, through the donation from the Prince Regent, and the Establishment Contributions. Josiah Wedgwood favoured an inscription that recorded the gifts of all sections of society, the opulent and the working class. He was however won over to the view of Rev Butt, who proposed a simple inscription: The North Staffordshire Infirmary, Erected and Supported by Voluntary Contributions. This inscription was approved by the Governors, and appears to this day repeated in Minton tiles on the present (1869) Infirmary building.

A letter from Thomas Butt sets out his thinking. He was opposed to recording the Prince Regent's contribution, £500 from the local revenues of the Duchy of Lancaster, as it

By kind permission of the Rector

The memorial to John Tomlinson in Stoke Church. The inscription hints at the controversy and opposition he could arouse - his rigid enforcement of the Poor Law led to his being burned in effigy outside his house in Hanley.

was not significantly greater than those from men of lesser means. Furthermore, *the Prince Regent would not reflect credit on the Infirmary, rather the Infirmary would reflect credit on the Prince Regent.* At this early date Butt was not sure that the Establishment Scheme would flourish, and to record it on the Portico could be a source of future embarrassment: *'I have a great objection, independently of ye arguments from taste to introduce there the Establishment Subscriptions. It is not improbable that they will become small, or at least partial in their operation. It will then rather be felt as a stigma on the Supineness of the Working Classes rather than as a compliment to their zeal.'* In this opinion he was happily proved to be wrong.

John Tomlinson could not agree with the exclusion of the Royal donation, and in his letter to Josiah Wedgwood II, he let down the facade of detached professionalism, and bared his soul. He was very unhappy, everyone opposed him... *'I certainly experience much more difficulty than any other person in measures which I bring forward, however clear and beneficial they may be, and I am obliged to labour them with some in a way that is not called for from others...'* He had not minded slights, but now he was older he was more alive to them. In a postscript he gathers up his dignity: *'I know you will rejoice with me on my eldest son having a Rugby (School) exhibition (scholarship) adjudged (awarded) to him'.*

The Infirmary they built lasted until 1869, when it was abandoned due to undermining and atmospheric pollution from the encircling mines and ironworks. The Infirmary moved to a more salubrious site in Hartshill due in no small measure to the efforts of the son of Josiah Wedgwood II and the grandson of John Tomlinson, the Rev. Sir L.T. Stamer.

Had the question of moving the Infirmary from Etruria been settled quickly, the Hartshill site would have housed one of the very earliest of the Pavilion or Nightingale hospitals. Plans were received from Florence Nightingale in 1861 and at the time it is

A montage from the Hartshill inscription in Minton tiles

unthinkable that a hospital would have been built to any other pattern. Always called the Nightingale Ward in honour of Miss Nightingale, we must be clear she did not invent this style of ward, though she was a forceful advocate of the design. A pavilion ward was basically a long narrow ward, connected to the hospital by means of a long corridor running at right angles to the ward. The ward had windows on both sides allowing cross ventilation and was heated by open fires. The closets - the toilet accommodation - were usually placed at the far ends of the wards. The ward's virtues included ease of ventilation, with large opening windows assisted by the open fires or stoves, and the fact that it could readily be isolated from the rest of the hospital, by the simple means of locking the door to the corridor. However, having wasted five years in bickering, the North Staffordshire Infirmary fell well behind others.

The Infirmary in Hartshill, opened in 1869 was a hospital which was conventional. It embodied no great attempts at innovation. Unlike its predecessors it was built plainly and well, and the central core is still sound after more than 130 years. Forty years on, Sir Henry Burdett praised the quality of the construction on his visit in 1909. There were problems with the drainage, and the sanitary provision, especially for the staff, needed constant improvement. But it is fair to say that the major problems were an expression of steadily rising standards nationwide, and the twin requirements to accommodate medical advances and the increasing numbers of patients who sought treatment and the staff needed to care for them.

Mr Nicholls of West Bromwich and Charles Lynam of Stoke were jointly awarded the prize for the design, there being aspects of both designs which appealed to the Governors. Mr Nicholls soon disappeared from the scene but Lynam served as Honorary Architect for more than thirty years. He was part of the Infirmary *family*, having married the daughter of Robert Garner, Surgeon at the Infirmary, and his son was House Surgeon to the Infirmary for five years. He was one of those indefatigable Victorians, it is rare to find a minute of a monthly meeting during all those years which does not ask him to advise on some problem or improvement, usually finishing with a request to him to take the necessary action.

Sir Henry Burdett was not so happy about the Casualty and Outpatient provision at the Infirmary in 1909. Major reorganisation of the committee and fundraising allowed the buildings to be renovated. The major construction was the Outpatients Hall that still stands near Princes Road. Built in 1910 it still proclaims in faint letters that it was a memorial to Edward VII.

During the first World War new wooden buildings were erected to house the influx of wounded soldiers. Intended as a temporary solution, some of them remained in use for more than seventy years.

The work of extending the Infirmary in the 20th century is detailed in chapter 20. The coming of the National Health Service, it was hoped, would end all the anxious years of

- an exact repeat of the inscription on the Etruria Infirmary

fund-raising and hand the problems over to central government funding. The country had come through a desperate war, and much of the infra-structure of the country, the mines, the railways, industry, as well as the hospitals, were in need of major renewal.

Another problem for the new Health Service was the revelation of a hidden and unappreciated level of chronic health deprivation throughout the population. This led to an avalanche of requests for dentures, spectacles, corsets and hearing aids, and antibiotics were only one example of new treatments developed in the war years, which, while hugely beneficial, were increasingly expensive. Government may have briefly thought that the curing of the infectious diseases, which had previously been such an ever present cause of illness and death, would so improve health that there would be no great rise in total expenditure, but this hope was soon dashed.

Suffice it to say that anxieties about funding the Health Service had begun within months of the start of the service, and have never gone away. It is therefore no surprise that the hoped for major capital projects to renew the ageing stock of hospital buildings across the country were delayed until the 1960s and later. The only exception in North Staffordshire was when the occurrence of an outbreak of infection prompted the rebuilding of the Infirmary's operating theatres in 1958.

The Accident Unit, together with the new Thoracic and Orthopaedic wards and operating theatres constituted the first major development of this period. Next to be built were the Boardman Wards for Neurology and Neurosurgery. The name commemorates an entailed bequest from the Boardman family, originally given in 1917, and therefore the last major private benefaction to be received at the Infirmary. Specialised accommodation was added to provide a Renal Unit and for dialysis. Adaptation of wards provided an Intensive Care Unit and several wards changed their function to accommodate changes in patterns of treatment.

Future development was destined to be concentrated on the City General Hospital site. The City General Hospital had formerly been the Workhouse housing a working farm within its grounds that provided some occupation for the inmates and supplied food for the institution. This meant that a large site was available for new building when the farm was closed. The fortunate presence of so much land already belonging to the Health Service and lying within the boundary of the City has obviously had a positive influence on decisions regarding the choice of a site for future developments. The new buildings are growing on the City General site, most significantly the new Medical School.

The portico of the Etruria infirmary and its inscription: *The North Staffordshire Infirmary, Erected and Supported by Voluntary Contributions.*
The square plaque above the portico stands in front of the operating theatre window and bears the words North Staffordshire Infirmary.

CHAPTER 7
The Lost Physician: Dr Wilson Fox, M.D., F.R.S.

This chapter explains the process of appointing a member of the Honorary staff at a voluntary hospital, here the North Staffordshire Infirmary and how an exceptional candidate was attracted from London in the hope of advancing medical education in North Staffordshire. We see how local disputes interfered and Dr Wilson Fox returned to a distinguished career in London, and we reflect on the results for North Staffordshire.

As appointment committees go, that held on June 23rd 1858 must have presented quite a spectacle. No fewer than 160 Governors of the North Staffordshire Infirmary, bearing additionally 89 proxy votes, had come to cast their vote for a new Physician. Clad in their frock coats and carrying their tall hats, they overflowed the available room, and the meeting spilled out to be concluded on the steps in front of the Infirmary building in Etruria. The winner, with 210 against 49 votes, was Dr Wilson Fox. The name is, I am sure, totally forgotten in North Staffordshire, but I venture to claim that he was the most distinguished doctor, certainly of the 19th century, to have been on the staff of the Infirmary.

Who was he, and how did he come to North Staffordshire and gain so much support? He was born in 1831, of a prominent Quaker family. He attended University College, London 1847-1850, gaining his B.A. in 1850, and qualifying as a doctor in 1854, with gold and silver medals, and honours in Medicine. He became Resident House Physician at Edinburgh Royal Infirmary, and the following year he embarked for the Continent. Visiting the Paris hospitals, he moved on to Vienna before working in the laboratory of Dr Rudolph Virchow in Berlin.

Fox had received the best of British medical training and continued this in Europe. Virchow was a man of the highest reputation, a name alongside Lister or Pasteur. Advances in the quality of microscope lenses now allowed the understanding of organs at the cellular level and encouraged the use of post mortem and histological examinations, a key factor in the progress of scientific medicine.

From the introduction to his book on *Diseases of the Lung and Pleura*, a magnum opus of 1100 pages published posthumously, we learn that Fox took up practice in Newcastle-under-Lyme having been 'invited' to become a Physician at the Infirmary at the age of 27 years. The appointment was not in any one person's giving; the only way he could be certain of the post was to have the support of a majority of the Governors. The appointment to a medical post in a voluntary hospital such as the Infirmary depended on their votes. Subscribers to the Infirmary above a certain level, set fairly low, say one or two guineas a year, had the privilege of recommending patients to the Infirmary in proportion to the amount subscribed. They had another privilege in that they could vote in the election of a new member of staff. These privileges of course were aimed at keeping up the interest of subscribers in the affairs of the Infirmary, increasing the level of subscriptions and keeping the institution solvent. The system was not proof against abuse, but we must remember that in 1858 even Parliamentary elections were not yet conducted by secret ballots. It was quite in order for a candidate to appeal to Governors in person as well as by advertisements in the newspapers, indeed failure to canvass for support indicated a lack of seriousness in the application. It was also accepted that Governors would try to gain the support of their fellows to secure the success of 'their' candidate. The notices on pages 94-96, published in the *Staffordshire Advertiser* Sept 1839, and the comments , refer to the appointment of Joshua Seddon and illustrate the process.

For years there had been two Honorary (or as we would now say Consultant) Physicians at the North Staffordshire Infirmary. The duties of an Honorary Physician or Surgeon were unpaid, i.e. honorary. Nonetheless they could be quite onerous, thus the question was often asked, 'why only appoint two to share the work?' As the Honorary staff earned their income from private patients fees it was necessary that the district should contain enough people able and willing to pay to give Honorary staff an acceptable income. It was difficult for smaller or poorer towns to provide an income for honorary staff. This problem occurred in Stafford when the Infirmary lost its most famous son, Dr William Withering. He is remembered for having identified digitalis in the foxglove as a drug for the treatment of heart failure, but he had to leave Stafford for Birmingham when he found himself unable to maintain his new wife on £100 per annum.

Early in May 1858 it became clear that something was afoot in North Staffordshire: an advertisement appeared in the *Advertiser* calling Governors of the Infirmary to a General Meeting in order to consider changes to the Rules. It was proposed that there should now be a third Physician appointed, on the grounds that since the founding of the Infirmary the population and workload had doubled - or, alternatively, that a General Practitioner should be appointed as an Assistant Physician. This proposal was not carried. Robert Garner, Surgeon proposed that the increase in staff be delayed *until the hospital got its medical school.*

In the 1850s the whole profession of medicine was becoming regulated with the passing of the Medical Act and the formation of the General Medical Council. In Britain there was a plethora of institutions issuing medical degrees, some on a cash basis. Hospitals drew up lists of universities and colleges whose degrees would be acceptable in an applicant for a consultant post. The North Staffordshire Governors agreed approval should be granted to the University of London, whose reputation was rising rapidly.

What was going on? Why the urgency when considering an increase in the number of Physicians? And why was the approval of a London degree important? What was the hurry?

At the end of April there were two Physicians at the Infirmary: Dr Wilson who had been appointed in 1836, and Dr Wood, appointed in 1846; both well respected and liked but perhaps unlikely to set the world alight at this stage in their careers. Looking at the scientific innovations which had occurred in the last dozen years we see that this was one of those periods of exceptionally rapid progress in which it would be difficult for any doctor to keep up to date. Governors who were aware of this advancing tide of knowledge could not fail to observe that the Infirmary was in danger of falling behind the hospitals in London and the major towns. A new broom was needed, a man who had been exposed to a thoroughly modern medical education in Britain and in Europe. These Governors, using their contacts in London to gather information, had such a man in their sights - Dr Wilson Fox. His degrees being from London University necessitated the rule change, because as matters had stood he could not have been appointed in North Staffordshire.

As at this moment there was no vacancy for a Physician, an extra post still needed to be created to accommodate Dr Fox, regardless of the potential financial difficulties. On May 1st in the midst of these machinations the sudden and unexpected death of Dr Wilson was announced. This created a vacancy and removed the need to create the extra post.

Dr Wilson Fox's application and appeal to the Governors appeared promptly in the *Staffordshire Advertiser.* Another application came from Dr Bell of Chester. He withdrew his application, complaining that he did not fancy his chances as a large proportion of pledges (of votes) had been yielded to the activity of canvassers before the vacancy had even been declared! Not everyone was happy, as we can see from the letter from '*A Well-wisher of the*

Charity'. He was unhappy; he thought the institution was being damaged by this tampering with the rules. This tampering with the rules was being undertaken to promote the interests of individuals *'who seek by such means to become connected with the institution... for a personal object rather than to promote the interests of the poor.'* *Wellwisher* desired to preserve the status quo, and not have the medical boat rocked by a bright young chap who would only upset the even tenor of the ways of the older members of the profession in the district.

When the Governors met to make the appointment, it was necessary for each candidate to be proposed and seconded by a Governor. The Governors had already examined the diplomas of the candidates at a previous meeting and assured themselves that each candidate had the necessary qualifications. There were two candidates. One was Dr Gooday who had been in practice in Newcastle-under-Lyme for the past ten years, indeed since he had left Paris in the Revolution of 1848. He was Medical Officer for the Newcastle Board of Guardians. W.D. Spanton, later Consultant Surgeon to the Infirmary, who would in the future be Dr Gooday's House Surgeon, would later speak very disparagingly of him. Dr Gooday's nomination was proposed by Admiral Mainwaring. The Admiral had not actually been treated by Dr Gooday, thus he couldn't say much about his abilities as a Physician for he had never had the occasion to test them, nor could he tell them of his private history. The Admiral's performance as the proposer of Dr Gooday was hardly scintillating, the words 'damned by faint praise' come to mind.

The seconder of Dr Gooday was the Rev Charles Hebert, then the rector of St John's Church in Burslem. He had agreed to speak on behalf of his man but showed little stomach for the task. He said he had not made many enquiries with respect to Dr Gooday *...he saw no reason for refusing to accede to the request made to him by Dr Gooday that he would second his nomination.* In the Rev. Hebert's mind one fact settled the whole question of Dr Gooday's suitability for the post and this was his possession of a testimonial from Sir Astley Cooper (one of the most eminent surgeons of the 19th century). Sir Astley had treated Rev Hebert's mother, apparently a great day in the family's life. But the testimonial was dated 1840, some 18 years previously, and couched in rather general terms. There were testimonials from other stars of the medical firmament, among them Richard Bright and Thomas Addison, of Guys Hospital, but these were also dated February 1840. They smack of the notes distributed in times past to those who had completed their first house job in hospital, and were often little more than expressions of goodwill. The Rev. Mr Hebert was being very naive.

The other candidate was Dr Wilson Fox. His proposer, Francis Wedgwood, and his seconder, Edward Wood, constituted a highly professional team, and I am sure that they are the authors of the scheme to recruit a high flyer to advance medicine in North Staffordshire. These men were at the centre of charitable life in the Potteries, and were in touch, via friends and family contacts, with the scientific life of London. Through families such as the Darwins they could learn who were the up and coming professional men and make contact with them. There can be little doubt that Fox's supporters ran a highly organised campaign, and that these two men are the most likely suspects in this benign conspiracy.

Wilson Fox produced a set of distinguished testimonials, including those from the physician Thomas Hodgkin (Hodgkins Disease) and the surgeon Joseph Lister. Fox's scientific credentials were attested to by Dr James Spark, the Superintendent of Statistics for Scotland. An expression of goodwill sent by the students that he had taught in Edinburgh was an important testimony to his life long interest in the teaching of medical students. Frank Wedgwood turned to a remark of Rev. Hebert who had said it was important that an applicant should be capable and assiduous, saying that what was most important was that

THIS SEQUENCE OF NOTICES FROM THE *STAFFORDSHIRE ADVERTISER* SEPTEMBER 1839
ILLUSTRATES THE PROCESS OF AN APPOINTMENT AT THE INFIRMARY. *(Keele Library)*

The appointment of Joshua Seddon as Surgeon to the Infirmary in September 1839.
He had been House Surgeon to the Infirmary for 16 years.

TO THE GOVERNORS OF THE NORTH STAFFORD-SHIRE INFIRMARY.

My Lords, Ladies, and Gentlemen,

THE resignation of Mr. Wood having occasioned a vacancy in the Medical Establishment of your valuable Institution, I beg to announce myself a Candidate for the appointment thus placed at your disposal, and respectfully solicit the favour of your votes and interest in my behalf.

In addition to the testimonials required by the Statutes of the Infirmary, I take the liberty of bringing forward my past services to the Institution for sixteen years, in the capacity of House Surgeon, which, having been honoured on my retirement with the favourable notice of a General Meeting of Governors, as well as of the Medical Officers of the Infirmary, I feel to be the best pledge I can offer that, if I should be elected a Surgeon of the Institution, the duties of the office will be faithfully and efficiently performed.

I am, my Lords, Ladies, and Gentlemen,

Your's, very respectfully,

J. SEDDON,

Member of the Royal College of Surgeons, London, &c.

Albion Street, Shelton, Sept. 3rd, 1839.

NORTH STAFFORDSHIRE INFIRMARY.

A Special General Meeting of the Governors of this Institution will be held on Wednesday, the 9th day of October next, at 12 o'clock precisely, for the purpose of ELECTING a SURGEON, in the place of George Wood, Esq. who has resigned.

Gentlemen intending to offer themselves as candidates for the appointment, are respectfully requested to send their testimonials to the Secretary, on or before the 5th of October.

N. B.—No person is eligible to the office of Surgeon, who does not produce to the Committee a certificate of being a member of the College of Surgeons, of London, Dublin, Edinburgh, or Glasgow.

It will also be proposed to this Special General Meeting of the Governors to consider the expediency of restricting the privilege of medical practitioners being members of the Committee only to the Physicians and Surgeons of the Institution.

Annual Subscribers of two Guineas and upwards, and Benefactors of twenty guineas and upwards, are Governors, and entitled to vote at general meetings.

By order of the Committee,

HUGH DAVIES,

Secretary.

A Special Committee meeting is called. Hugh Davies was Secretary as well as House Surgeon.
The notice details the qualifications needed by an applicant and says who is entitled to vote.

Robert Garner, another candidate, here protests that a rival candidate, presumably Joshua Seddon, has been unfairly favoured in the election. Garner was naive to think he could topple such a well-respected local candidate, but he did succeed later in becoming a surgeon to the Infirmary - although he had to wait until 1850.

TO THE GOVERNORS OF THE NORTH STAFFORD-SHIRE INFIRMARY.

My Lords, Ladies, and Gentlemen,

I Beg leave most respectfully to solicit your support, a vacancy having occurred in the Office of Surgeon to your benevolent Institution.

I refer you with confidence to the copy of testimonials, which I have distributed amongst you, and I beg you to observe that those testimonials are from Medical Gentlemen connected with very different institutions. I may also mention, that besides having held the situation of House Surgeon to a public institution, I have been engaged for seven years in the more responsible duties of private practice.

I am in justice to myself bound to add,—should I now for the second time be unsuccessful, it will solely occur from the unusual circumstance, which, to my surprise, I very soon ascertained, when I commenced waiting upon you,—I found that by the premature canvass of one party, either directly, or through the medium of friends, most of you had been solicited long before any vacancy had occurred, and before any other candidate had considered that he could with propriety take the field.

I remain,

My Lords, Ladies, and Gentlemen,

Your obedient faithful servant,

ROBERT GARNER, F.L.S.

Member of the Royal College of Surgeons.

Stoke-upon-Trent, Sep. 6, 1839.

The next announcement (opposite page) is the report of the Special Committee which made the appointment of Joshua Seddon as Surgeon to the Infirmary. It reports the votes cast for each candidate and is signed by George Tollett of Betley Hall as chairman.

These reports demonstrate the etiquette that pertained to the process of applying for a post in a Voluntary Hospital at the time. The actual voting was in the hands of the committee. It was quite usual for friends and family to openly solicit support from the Governors who were eligible to vote. We know that Josiah Wedgwood II, in his capacity as a Governor of Westminster Hospital, received letters from Lady Caroline Lamb seeking his vote for family members. Medical staff were also represented on the committee although in a minority, and they were responsible for examining the qualifications and testimonials of the candidates.

In the *Advertiser* report, immediately following the report of the 'Appointment Committee' appears a letter of thanks from the successful candidate, and a gracious acknowledgement of support received from an unsuccessful candidate.

It is difficult to imagine that Robert Garner's protest would have endeared him to the Governors!

AT a Special General Meeting of the GOVERNORS of the NORTH STAFFORDSHIRE INFIRMARY, held on Wednesday, the 9th day of October, duly convened by advertisement, for the purpose of electing a Surgeon, in the room of George Wood, Esq. who has resigned, and of considering the expediency of restricting the privilege of medical practitioners being members of the committee only to the Physicians and Surgeons of the Institution;

GEORGE TOLLET, Esq. in the chair;

Resolved,

That after the expiration of the current year no medical practitioner, except the medical officers of the Institution, be elected members of the committee.

It was proposed, and unanimously resolved,

That the thanks of this meeting be presented to George Wood, Esq. for the very efficient manner in which he has discharged the duties of Surgeon to this Institution for thirty-six years.

Mr. Garner, Mr. Seddon, and Mr. Blunt having been respectively nominated as candidates for the vacant office of surgeon to the North Staffordshire Infirmary, and a ballot having been demanded, Mr. Seddon was declared duly elected; there appearing for

Mr. Seddon,	120
Mr. Blunt,	50
Mr. Garner,	47
Majority,	70

GEORGE TOLLET, Chairman.

The thanks of the meeting were unanimously voted to the Chairman, for his patient and impartial conduct in the chair.

The Annual General Meeting of the GOVERNORS will be held at the INFIRMARY, on Thursday, the 31st of October, at twelve o'clock.

HUGH DAVIES, Secretary.

TO THE GOVERNORS OF THE NORTH STAFFORD-SHIRE INFIRMARY.

My Lords, Ladies, and Gentlemen,

HAVING been elected a Surgeon of your Institution, I hasten to offer my sincere thanks to those kind friends by whose assistance I have been placed at the head of the poll; and beg to assure them, and the Governors generally, that I shall use my best exertions to fulfil the important trust which has been committed to me.

I am,
My Lords, Ladies, and Gentlemen,
Your's very respectfully,
J. SEDDON.

Albion-street, Shelton,
Oct. 9th, 1839.

TO THE GOVERNORS OF THE NORTH STAFFORD-SHIRE INFIRMARY.

My Lords, Ladies, and Gentlemen,

UNSUCCESSFUL as I have been in the late contest for the office of Surgeon to your Institution, I am much gratified at the thought that I have been supported to an extent highly flattering to my feelings, in a competition of such a kind, with an individual of long-tried zeal and ability in your service. I, therefore, take the opportunity thus publicly of tendering my warmest acknowledgments to the friends from whom I have received support, and especially to the many gentlemen who travelled long distances to vote for me. In conclusion, I trust you will pardon me for expression of the hope that on some future occasion I may receive your more effectual assistance towards obtaining the honourable post which I have recently sought at your hands.

I have the honor to be,
My Lords, Ladies, and Gentlemen,

THE VOTES CAST AT THE MEETING

MR SEDDON THANKS HIS SUPPORTERS

MR BLUNT GRACEFUL IN DEFEAT

the successful candidate should be *'the most capable and assiduous'*; he felt Dr Fox was the man.

Edward Wood seconded the appointment of Dr Fox. He said he placed little faith in testimonials, they were not evidence and it was very easy to get them. Cleverness was not enough, energy and zeal were required for success. But in his absence from home he had made enquiries among Dr Fox's friends and discovered from them that he was a man of the most determined zeal and perseverance. He said that if he was ill himself he would want the best physician, and that the poor man should have the same advantages. Dr Fox was the best man, and he therefore seconded his nomination. A show of hands was in favour of Dr Fox, even so Captain Steele demanded a poll on behalf of Dr Gooday.

Dr Wilson Fox was a member of the Consultant staff of the Infirmary for only four years until 1862. He returned to his own teaching hospital, University College Hospital in London as Professor of Pathological Anatomy, recommended to this appointment by Professor Virchow, his old teacher, there being no referee who would count more highly in the world of pathology at the time. Wilson Fox wrote to the Governors tendering his resignation. It was accepted with regret, the Governors congratulating Dr Fox on the high honour accorded him.

Yet again the death of a Physician was to affect the plans of the Governors to make an appointment. Dr Fox's resignation followed upon the very recent death of Dr Wood, the other Physician, leaving vacant both posts. Dr Wood's death had opened the way for an older physician from Chester, Robert Hutchinson Powell to apply, together with the indefatigable Dr Gooday. Recognising that Dr Gooday's sheer persistence would probably be unstoppable, the committee which might have stomached his presence on the staff if Wilson Fox had been still there, were unwilling to replace Wilson Fox and Dr Wood without attempting to make one distinguished appointment. It was therefore proposed that, *'without any disregard for the present candidates'*, the appointment should be delayed for five weeks in the hope *'that men of eminence might be induced to apply'*. The Governors approved this measure by 20 votes to 19.

It has always been a mystery why Dr J.T. Arlidge came to North Staffordshire from London, when he had no previous connection with the area - and having already declined the Chair of Medicine at the University of Melbourne in Australia. It seems plausible that networking in London had led to his nomination as a man of eminence to replace Wilson Fox, and incidentally act as a consolation prize for the loss North Staffordshire had sustained.

The meeting to appoint the new consultants was again in the open air on account of the numbers. It was agreed that the person gaining most votes would be the senior consultant.

J.T. Arlidge founded his application on his experience, his testimonials and his published work. He had studied in France, Germany and Italy, had experience in London, in psychiatry and as senior physician at the West of London Infirmary. Dr Gooday produced a new testimonial relating to his work in the cholera epidemic in 1849, and this time we learn that prior to his time in Paris he had been in India with the East India Company. The voting was: Dr Arlidge 177, Dr Gooday 130, Dr Powell 48. Dr Arlidge and Dr Gooday were appointed, Dr Arlidge as Senior Physician. An interesting footnote to this election was that due to a recent change in the law, proxies had to bear a sixpenny stamp in order to be valid - and stamps were minuted as available for the convenience of the Governors. Dr Arlidge stayed at the Infirmary for the rest of his long career, becoming a nationally respected pioneer in the field of occupational medicine. Dr Gooday left after 4 years.

Dr Wilson Fox, in London, succeeded his friend and mentor Sir William Jenner as Professor of Pathological Anatomy, then followed him as Holme Professor of Clinical Medicine and as Physician at University College Hospital. Jenner is best remembered for making clear the distinction between typhoid and typhus fever. He was in attendance during

Prince Albert's final illness, typhoid fever, and he became Physician to the Queen. Wilson Fox followed him as Physician Extraordinary to the Queen.

Wilson Fox became a noted teacher and was deeply involved at the Royal College of Physicians in the development of medical education. His early work in pathology was on the diseases of the stomach. He did many of the pathological examinations of Spencer Wells' massive series of resections of ovarian tumours. Originally unconvinced of the infective nature of tuberculosis, he was open minded enough to immediately recognise the importance of Koch's discovery of the tubercle bacillus, and much of his later work was on diseases of the chest. Sadly during his stay in North Staffordshire, the prevailing hostility in the district to post-mortem examinations meant he only did two examinations on potters and none on miners. One must consider that this was North Staffordshire's loss, for to have one of the country's leading pathologists in their midst and not to have used him was a tragedy. Properly employed, he could have advanced the knowledge of industrial disease in the Potteries to the great advantage of the working population.

J.T.Arlidge was indeed an acquisition, but when Dr Gooday resigned no applicants came forward to replace him, so no appointment of a Physician could be made. So ended a positive attempt to recruit men of talent and experience to the Potteries. Recourse was to the appointment of duly registered practitioners as Medical Officers to the Outpatients Department. They would be full members of the staff and eligible in time to be appointed to vacant consultant posts. Dr Barnes and Dr Orton were duly appointed, the latter eventually becoming a consultant physician.

While Arlidge was a very worthy replacement, Dr Wilson Fox was far and away the most eminent of the staff of the Infirmary in the 19th century.

I posed the question - what was going on? Why did such a rising star appear in North Staffordshire, and why were such efforts made to secure his appointment? And when he was invited to return to London why was no attempt made to retain his services? I believe the answer is nothing less than the ambition to add a medical school to the Infirmary. It is mentioned in newspaper reports of Governors meetings as an accepted intention, especially between 1858 and 1862, the years when the prospect of a new building for the Infirmary on a new site was fresh. By 1862, when Fox left there was still no prospect of a decision being reached. These were the years of the battle over moving the Infirmary. Years would pass before the fratricidal struggles of the Pottery towns would cease. With a glittering prize in prospect in London he had no choice but to move. Could it be that by 1866, when there were no applications for the post of a consultant physician to replace Dr Gooday, the heart had gone out of the drive for the medical school even though the new Infirmary was at last to be built in Hartshill? The internal strife was certainly known of in national medical circles and could well have discouraged men of distinction from applying to North Staffordshire.

Although the wish to have a medical school occasionally sputtered into life later, I believe the battle over the new site spelt the end of plans for a medical school in North Staffordshire for a hundred years and more.

Many of the provincial medical schools were founded in the 19th century. Some were associated with a hospital, some were descended from private anatomy and medical schools. They prepared students to sit the examinations for the diplomas of the College of Surgeons and the Society of Apothecaries in London. An accepted route to these examinations was to become a pupil of a surgeon, a process directly analogous to an apprenticeship, requiring a premium and fees, allowing the pupil access to the Surgeon's patients and the opportunity of gaining practical experience by looking after patients under supervision. This commonly lasted five years and was followed by a prescribed period of time on the wards of a teaching hospital and attending an approved course of lectures. The Infirmary had pupils throughout most of the 19th century, who then moved on to medical school, often to London.

As a result of the enquiry into medical education by the House of Commons in 1834, the Royal College of Surgeons began to accept certificates of training from provincial medical schools; attendance at a London hospital was no longer a condition of being allowed to sit the Colleges examination. In October, 1840 the committee of the Infirmary instructed the House Surgeon, *'That Mr Davies write to the Secretary of the College of Surgeons to enquire the rules and regulations to be conformed to in order to get this Infirmary recognised by that body'*. No reply was recorded, which in the minutes usually implies a negative response.

By 1858, the year of Wilson Fox's appointment, many of our provincial medical schools had come into existence, for example Birmingham and Manchester. It was recognised that the association with a new medical school had a powerfully stimulating effect on a newly founded university or university college. Equally a new university or college was an important acquisition for a city or town that had ambitions to be one of the great centres of the kingdom. Clearly, North Staffordshire still had aspirations to have a medical school even after the departure of Dr Wilson Fox. During one of the debates about the new Infirmary in 1864 Godfrey Wedgwood said the average cubic capacity of air in the Etruria Infirmary building was only 600 to 700 cubic feet per bed. He said that the Royal College of Surgeons would not recognise a hospital with less than 1000 cubic feet of air per bed, *'therefore the Committee could not have such a school of medicine as they desire'*.

We may pretend that failure didn't really matter, but had the medical school succeeded and led to a university in the latter half of the 19th century, the benefits for the development of North Staffordshire as a whole could have been incalculable.

Eventually, in May 1870 when the new Infirmary was built in Hartshill, the Royal College of Surgeons were pleased to add the North Staffordshire Infirmary to the list of recognised provincial hospitals. The way was open to found a medical school, but by then the protracted effort to move the Infirmary had exhausted the Governors. The ambition had departed, as had Wilson Fox, and it would be more than a century before a successful bid would be made for such a foundation.

Dr Wilson Fox, M.D., F.R.S.

J.T. Arlidge

Charles Parsons MD, 1833-1922, House Surgeon in 1852. He and Dr Arlidge were quoted by Karl Marx in *Das Kapital*, on health in the Potteries.

Chimneys of 'Shelton Bar' - the Iron and Steel works - pre 1870. Shelton Iron and Steel was gradually filling the valley. The view is looking west towards Basford. The 'Infirmary' gables can be seen between the factory buildings extreme left (circled). The insert is an enlargement of this edge of the photo.

CHAPTER 8
Location: A Move from Etruria

The location of the Infirmary had a profound effect on its history. The Dispensary and House of Recovery was on a central but fatally small and threatened site. The second site seemed a perfect solution, central and attractive, but it soon became threatened by the pollution of the air about it and destroyed by the mines underneath it. It soon became clear that there would be no satisfactory central situation for a hospital, and it took years of dispute before a new home was found for the infirmary in Hartshill. The battle between the Committee who favoured Hartshill and the supporters of the Northern Pottery towns, Tunstall, Hanley, and especially Burslem, is a paradigm for the internecine struggles which shaped, or rather failed to shape the Potteries into a great Victorian city. This battle eclipses the much quoted account of Hospital feuds in George Eliot's novel Middlemarch.

Nothing in the history of our hospital compares with the saga of deciding the proper site for the second Infirmary. It occupied the minds of the Governors and the leaders of the Pottery towns for the middle years of the 19th century. The site of the original Dispensary and House of Recovery of one acre was part of the Wedgwood estate in Etruria and lay at the confluence of the Caldon and Trent and Mersey canals, near the main roads crossing the Potteries. It at first seemed ideal. It was at a point half way along the valley which contains the Pottery towns, and on the side of the valley nearest to Newcastle where there was a large concentration of doctors willing to serve it. They treated outpatients, offered free vaccination and cared for some fever cases.

But although this small institution did good work, a busy concentration of mines, ironworks and potteries was bound to produce a substantial toll of accident victims who needed hospital accommodation and it was increasingly seen as unacceptable that these patients should travel to the Infirmary in Stafford in a cart. A proper hospital capable of dealing with such patients was needed. A building committee was formed in 1814 to examine the possibility of extending the existing building. They found that it had not been sufficiently strongly built to allow it to be expanded economically and the site, between two principal canals, was bound to attract future industrial activity. There was no room for expansion and it was not well served by road. Moreover, it was not prominent - which meant that it could not be seen from the main roads by all who passed by, an important consideration when the whole means of support came from charitable donations from the public.

Thus ten years after the opening of the Dispensary in 1804, the decision was taken to relocate the whole institution as an Infirmary to a new site in Etruria, larger, at the junction of two main roads and on an eminence, visible to all. By acquiring nine acres of land on a low hill in a pastoral setting, well set back from any existing industry, the Governors thought that they had secured the Infirmary's future against any possible encroachments. On March 13th, 1816, having completed the purchase of the land, again from the Wedgwood estate, they recorded in the minutes: *Your Committee conceive that they have thereby secured to the Infirmary, for ever, the advantage of an open situation, free from all nuisances.* Oh dear!

It is easy now to see how comprehensively they underestimated the rate of change that was accompanying the Industrial Revolution. But if these men could fail to appreciate the rate of change, who at the time would appreciate it? Consider Josiah Wedgwood II. He was in personal contact with the leading industrialists and scientists of the day, with both Boulton and Watt, and with Humphrey Davy. He was familiar with the leaders of London medicine. He, if anyone was, was in a position to assess the changes taking place. His lifetime from1769 to 1843 spans the age when the rate of travel changed from the pace of a good horse to an express train. He was not alone, the other members of the optimistic Committee were the cream of the manufacturers and professional men of North Staffordshire. We must recognise that the rate of change of their lives was as rapid and confusing as that which we experience today in the computer revolution.

The first threat to the peace of the Infirmary was the projected Cheshire Joint Railway, planned to pass through the Potteries from Manchester. In January, 1837 the Governors agreed to meet the railway promoters to discuss their desire to purchase some of the Infirmary's land. The Governors felt that the railway would be a nuisance, but they did not wish to hinder public works. They were concerned that a cutting might take water away from the well, that the railway would bring spoil tips or brickworks. They would have very much preferred it to be in a tunnel out of sight, but were told that it was too expensive. Land was eventually offered at £500 per acre, but the new line was not developed and the matter dropped.

In 1839 it was agreed to make representations to Earl Granville, who was at that time President of the Infirmary, expressing concern about the effect of four blast furnaces that he was building only 350 yards from the Infirmary. They could not fail to disturb and harm the inmates of the house.

A reply came via the Earl Granville's Agent, Mr Lowndes *'who has the management of my affairs in England'. He would be most careful to consider the site, the site was not the most eligible for the advantage of the works... hoped the least inconvenience would be occasioned to the neighbourhood, particularly to the Infirmary... had I known before... too expensive to move them now...*

The Governors set up a sub-committee to seek the advice of practical men, to advise on the effects likely to be produced by this encroaching industry. Remarkably, in 1839, they set out to achieve a prospective environmental study. The sub committee visited the blast furnaces at Apedale, Silverdale and Lane End. They were told the worst effects were noticed down wind, and a great nuisance was to be expected more than 400 yards away. Samuel Peake, supervisor of Ralph Sneyd's furnaces at Silverdale, said there would be a great deal of smoke and noise, especially down wind, though it was less with the introduction of the hot air blast. He thought the conditions would be injurious to those with pulmonary and cerebral complaints; there would be a serious amount of noise if bar iron were made. The manager at Lane End lived 300 yards from the furnaces, the vegetation there was much affected and injured from smoke and sulphur. The cold air blast was heard all over Lane End, though the hot air blast was quieter. He agreed with Mr Peake that the production of malleable iron caused incessant noise.

In view of Earl Granville's intention of distancing himself from the concerns of the Governors, and the continued economies forced on them at this time by the depressed state of the finances, the Committee could do little but await events. In July 1843 there was a deficiency of water in the well, thought to be due to the mining operations of Earl Granville's agents. An engineer's report was commissioned, which advised that the best, though most expensive, action would be to take a supply from the waterworks in Hanley. The cheapest would be to deepen the well, and as it was thought there would be no deeper mining to interfere with the flow of water in the foreseeable future, that course was adopted.

In March 1844, the attention of the Committee was drawn to the state of the sewers, the smells in the men's ward and the surgery being at times exceedingly offensive. Subsidence was damaging the sewer that ran beneath the building. Throughout the year the smell continued to be offensive, and a sub-committee was appointed to review the accommodation offered by the Infirmary to patients and staff, and remedy the inconveniences felt in every department of the Infirmary. It was recommended that no further building should be commenced until the foundations could be secured from mining operations.

A meeting of the Committee held on December 19th, 1844 and chaired by the President, the Duke of Sutherland, debated whether in order to provide much needed accommodation they should lay out money on proposed Fever Wards, or whether it would be advisable to look for a site free from mining operations and other disadvantages. The cat was now out of the bag, the idea of a move had been aired at a high profile and widely reported meeting chaired by the Duke of Sutherland. The issue would never be settled until the Infirmary did move, almost 25 years to the day after this initial suggestion.

The problem lay with the Lord of the Manor of Newcastle, the Duchy of Lancaster, that is the Crown. The mining rights were owned and jealously guarded by the Duchy, and leased out to entrepreneurs like Earl Granville to be exploited. He in turn was anxious to get a return on the money he had laid out for the lease. The sub-committee had approached the Duchy which was unwilling to give a guarantee to secure the Infirmary from mining operations, nor were they prepared to give a sum of money to pay for the Infirmary to move to another site. The sub-committee reported that as the question of compensation for damage done to the buildings was not settled, no major new work should be undertaken. Any improvements to the accommodation should be undertaken at the least cost.

In April 1845 , a special meeting was told that satisfactory arrangements could not be made with the Duchy, though that may be possible in the future. The medical staff put their requests for accommodation in better consulting rooms in abeyance, and the servants who had been to due to be rehoused were accommodated in wards appropriated for the purpose.

In November another sub-committee was requested to look into the ventilation, crowded state and general faulty condition of the wards. They reported in December that for general patients there were 82 beds, these had 568cu/ft of air for each patient - the usual provision at this time was 1000 cu ft. The Fever wards were slightly better ventilated, 18 beds each having 743 cu/ft of air. The ventilation of the general wards was very deficient, the only recourse being to open doors and windows. The mens' venereal ward and burnt ward were the worst, the atmosphere was very bad. The water closets were dirty and appeared to have no traps, allowing smells from the common sewer to enter the building. The general management of the wards was poor, improvement in cleanliness and order might not aid recovery but would add to the comfort of the patient.

At this time no one had worked out the actual relationship between dirt and disease, the smells which commonly accompanied them were thought to be themselves the cause of disease, a miasma, a noxious something which existed in bad air and generated disease, hence the emphasis on proper ventilation.

In December 1847, yet another sub-committee made yet another list of suggestions for improvements, including whether or not it would be convenient and useful to establish a Dispensary in each principal Town, at the cost of and under the management of the Infirmary. *They concluded by posing the question whether or not the erection of another Infirmary in a more safe and healthy situation should not be undertaken at the earliest possible opportunity?* This was a formidable sub-committee, consisting of John Ridgway, Edward Kinnersley, Rev

R.E. Aitkin of Hanley, Michael Daintry Hollins and Frank Wedgwood.

The efforts to keep the ailing building in repair continued, competing with the constant search for economy in the wards and at Matron's table. In February 1850 there was some financial relief when the Staffordshire Potteries Water Works offered a free supply of water to the Infirmary, subject to the Governors providing a pipe, fittings and a ball-cock to the cistern at the cost price of £30, an offer gratefully accepted.

Despite the embargo on new building, in 1851 it was agreed to build a new ward for burnt patients, at a cost of £580 of which £450 was raised by the Surgeon, Daniel Ball. The old burnt wards were recorded in 1853 as being in a disgraceful condition, the area being very dirty, remedied by whitewashing. Even the new wards did not eliminate the problems: 'Recommend a pair of baise-lined doors between the burnt ward and the House (the rest of the Infirmary) to keep the smell from the interior. Presumably the infected burns and the dressings that covered them soon began to smell, and this smell permeated the building.

The finances continued to be in a parlous condition, and in December of this year it was decided only to allow fires in staff bedrooms on Tuesday and Fridays, a decision mercifully soon rescinded after protests from the Medical Board. Candles were rationed and some wards had to make do with rush-lights at best. In January 1854 an appeal was circulated to the wealthy and benevolent of the area for contributions to overcome the deficit of £311, caused by the great advance (rise) in the price of provisions and fuel. The state of the building was a constant drain.

August 1854 saw a discussion of the likely effects of the Calcination of Ironstone at Earl Granville's works, thought to be seriously injurious to the Infirmary. Changes were made by moving the Dead House and improving the washing facilities and water closets, the new building work costing £870. Less cheering was the minute of June 1855 that a grate (grating) be supplied for the main sewer or drain to keep rats out of the Infirmary; this was later changed to a stench trap as a grating could get blocked.

There are many references to the necessity of ridding the Infirmary of offensive smells. The nurses sleeping accommodation was seen as unacceptably foul, even positively harmful to their health. Despite concerns about the site, when Charles Keeling, a Governor of the Infirmary raised £1300 to build a new wing to overcome the shortage of beds, the offer was accepted and the new wards built in 1855.

The long struggle to keep the building viable continued. In 1858, gas pipes were installed, but not to the wards themselves. The main sewer was ordered to be enlarged to a diameter of two feet, and extended to the water course, i.e. the stream nearby. The outflow would pass on into the Fowlea Brook and then into the River Trent, which was by now the open sewer that drained the entire area. The buildings themselves were examined, the general settlement, especially in the East was considered not to be dangerous, yet, and the stone landing which was becoming detached from the walls was to be secured with iron cramps, and the cracks in the walls stopped up. A little later the Shelton Bar Company were asked what they were doing to the outlet to the Infirmary sewerage, which passed through their land on its way to the sea!

In 1860 the North Staffordshire Railway desired to purchase 1 acre and 20 perches of Infirmary land in order to build the Potteries Loop Line. It was offered for sale at £1300, but the valuation was referred to a Jury to adjudicate on the price.

On December 6th, 1860, the Medical Committee reported on the state of the Infirmary. For a considerable time the suitability of the Infirmary as a place for the reception of invalids had been deteriorating, due to circumstances over which the Governors had no control.

Surrounding the Infirmary there had been an increasing number of chimneys, factories and forges, iron works and collieries. They produced smoke and noise, while waste from the forges to the East came within 100 yards of the building. This waste produced sulphureous fumes - recently children at play had been overpowered by the fumes and *only with difficulty restored to animation*. The air was injurious even to healthy persons. There was a want of air in the wards, which the demands of the neighbourhood had compelled the Committee to cram with patients, further diminishing the cubic space allotted to each patient. They felt that a Special Fund that had been inaugurated to provide comforts to patients would be better served by the erection of a more suitable building on a healthier site.

The main Committee received this report on January 3rd, 1861, and decided to proceed with the Special Fund but also set up a sub-committee to see if any site in the district was suitable for a new Infirmary, in case circumstances led to removal from the present site. Sites were examined in Basford, Fenton, Hanley, Oakhill and the Mount at Hartshill.

In April 1861, Mr Massey the surveyor reported on the state of the buildings. Numerous cracks and settlements were found in the inside and outside walls, few rooms were entirely free of them. He had examined the timber bearings of the floors and the roof; *'they were not at present dangerous; some cracks were recent, and should be observed before painting was done'*. He agreed that the worst patches should be repaired, and he would return from time to time.

Daniel Ball, 1800-1894, Surgeon to the Infirmary. Starting as a pupil until his death when he was 'Extraordinary Hon. Surgeon', he was connected with the Infirmary for nearly 80 years.

In May, architects Messrs Ward of Hanley were commissioned to survey the buildings, and more importantly to determine the present and probable future mining damage, estimate the annual cost of repairs, and the length of time that the building was likely to stand at the present rate of settlement. *Their report confirmed that early removal of the Infirmary was inevitable.* They reported that there were existing mines under the Infirmary, of coal and ironstone, and more were planned. The total thickness of the coal seams was 45 feet, which extended in all direction. The broken sewer allowed fluid and smells into the basement. The walls to the East were out of the perpendicular, the new ward to the East had already sunk five inches, and the roof timbers were already drawn out of place.

The battle lines were now drawn by the relationship of the Infirmary to the Pottery towns. There was undoubtedly a large element of civic pride involved. The catch was that any potential alternative sites close to the manufacturing centres of the Potteries were already crowded, polluted and undermined. The last consideration was to be decisive. The Duchy would not give up their mining rights on any new site. They could be bought at great expense, or paid for in the form of a lease, forming a constant drain on the Infirmary finances. If mining was carried out under the new site, it was likely that the present problems would be repeated. A delicate situation now arose in the Committee's relations with Earl Granville, then President of the Infirmary. His miners were literally undermining the Infirmary. The Committee wrote to him, being very careful to disclaim any suggestion that he wished any harm to befall the Infirmary, but asking him again to desist from mining underneath it!

In an attempt to reconcile the various factions, and the undoubted difficulty of providing medical cover for the scattered centres of population of North Staffordshire, the Medical Committee proposed that satellite dispensaries should be established. There were offers of land for such dispensaries from the Pottery Towns. It would not be possible to please everyone; the aim had to be the most effective use of resources offering the greatest good to the greatest number.

In August 1861, Mr William Yates of Hanley offered to the Governors the sum of £5000 conditional on him receiving an annuity of £250 per annum. The gift was further conditional on the Infirmary erecting a new building, or at least a new wing within a specified time. As intended it gave a new urgency to the proceedings.

In October 1861, the Committee of the Infirmary recorded with apparent surprise the receipt of a letter from Florence Nightingale, with advice and plans. An approach had been made to Miss Nightingale by the House Surgeon via a Miss Jones. The House Surgeon was Charles Parsons, who, before he came to North Staffordshire, had been a House Surgeon at Kings College Hospital in London. The Miss Jones referred to is most likely Miss Mary Jones, head of the Nurses at St John's House. She became Matron of Kings College Hospital; St John's House provided it with the nursing staff and a Nurses' Training School which rivalled the Nightingale School at St Thomas's. A friend and supporter of Florence Nightingale, she would have known and worked with Dr Parsons. I have found no support for the story that the Duchess of Sutherland was in any material way associated with the purchase of the land in Hartshill and no supporting evidence for the romantic story of the plan for the Infirmary being drawn on the tablecloth when Florence Nightingale dined with the Duchess. The Committee thanked Miss Nightingale for her trouble in sending plans and for the valuable suggestions contained in her letter.

At the Annual General Meeting on November 7th, 1861, the discussion continued. If conditions were so bad, the Committee was asked, why had new buildings been erected? Mr Folker, Surgeon, replied that the decision was taken before it was known that Earl Granville had determined to fill the valley with refuse. He pointed out that Earl Granville could mine where he liked, and his agents denied all responsibility for the state of the Infirmary, and gave no undertakings for the future. It was resolved that immediate steps should be taken to move to a better site, and that the committee be requested to advertise for a site.

The committee was asked, on December 5th, to assemble at Longport station to inspect the proposed sites; those unable to attend being asked to visit at their convenience. Of the sites offered, the two that attracted the most attention were the Mount site in Hartshill and Kingsfield in Basford, on the opposite side of the main road to the present New Victoria Theatre. The Basford site was offered for development by the Newcastle and Potteries Villa Residences Society. They were deeply offended when Mr Garner opposed the site on the grounds that Building Societies build the worst class of houses!

Letters to the papers are an important barometer of public opinion. In the *Advertiser*, writers protested that the Mount was at the top of a hill, others felt that the decision should be delayed until trade improved. In January 1862 a most significant letter appeared from '*A Coal Owner*'. He urged the Governors *DO NOT build without the ownership of the coal rights.* He continued that nothing was more uncertain as where mines do or do not exist.

January 1862 saw yet another meeting at which a decision seemed imminent, and the sites in Basford and Hartshill were discussed. The Mount site was favoured by the committee, but yet again the decision to defer a choice was taken.

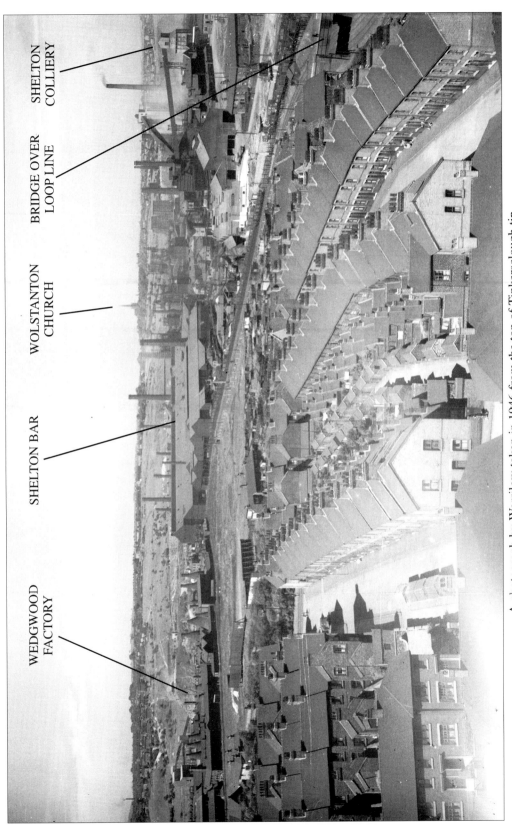

WEDGWOOD FACTORY

SHELTON BAR

WOLSTANTON CHURCH

BRIDGE OVER LOOP LINE

SHELTON COLLIERY

A photograph by Warrilow taken in 1946 from the top of Tinkersclough tip. The houses below are built on the site of the Etruria Infirmary. The photo shows well the encircling industry.

At a March meeting another Architect's report was received. In the eight months since the last survey the building continued to crack, the new wing had sunk a further two inches, and the sewer was becoming blocked by loose brickwork. Foul water and smells were spreading in the cellar and onward via cracks into the building. The sewer could be temporarily repaired with an iron pipe, but the building was becoming untenable. Nevertheless, a motion to purchase the Mount site was deferred, and the matter again referred to a committee. *On the positive side, it was confirmed that the Duchy of Lancaster was prepared to sell the mining rights under the Mount site for £1 per acre.* M.D. Hollins advised that they should support the Mount site, and that they should not suppose that the Duchy of Lancaster would be so generous elsewhere.

The battle rolled on. Mr Twemlow was concerned about the increased distance patients would have to travel to reach the Mount. He worried about how the move was to be financed. The view was expressed that increased distance from the industrial areas was more important than smoke. A site near Shelton Old Hall, near Hanley Park today, was offered. It was thought that as it abutted on to the new Hanley Cemetery it could not be approached by industry, and surely the Duchy of Lancaster wouldn't mine under the cemetery! Earl Granville however did not feel called upon to give up any of his rights. It was pointed out that the mines already extended to Shelton Church, and the constant stream of funerals would not be a cheering prospect for the patients. Mr Mayer now appeared to have changed his mind; he had not wished to move the Infirmary, but seeing was believing. He still favoured a central site, *but he felt it was most important that provision should be made for a Medical School and a first rate Infirmary.* Mr Keary added sagely that the only reason for the offer made by the Duchy of £1 an acre for the mining rights at the Mount was that there was no coal there.

On the 19th of June, the architects delivered a further report of the worsening state of the building to a Special meeting of Governors. They had been shown plans, and confirmed that the worst damage to the Infirmary corresponded to the greatest concentration of mines. It was at this meeting that surely the most remarkable exchange of this whole debate took place. Mr Peake, who was obsessively opposed to any move to build the Infirmary on a different site made his radical intervention. *If the mines had been worked prejudicially to the Infirmary on one side, the working of them on the opposite side would surely bring it back to its original perpendicular.* If his Lordship took only fifty inches on the West side, that would draw the building right again! He hinted darkly that the doctors were behind the move towards Newcastle, presumably because it brought the Infirmary nearer to the homes of many of them, and he repeated that he still thought the existing site salubrious.

There was a condition attached to the large bequest of Mr Yates, that a decision be made by June 25th, and the approach of that date gave some much needed urgency to the discussion. Eventually the matter was put to the vote, and the decision was taken to adopt the Mount as the future home for the Infirmary.

On July 22nd a meeting was held to consider the methods available to guarantee the payment of the annuity to Mr Yates. A purchased annuity would cost £2200, which would be subtracted from the original donation of £5000. If the Governors guaranteed the annuity by using the Infirmary property as security, it could lead to the bizarre possibility that Mr Yates could seize the Infirmary building in the event of his annuity not being paid! It was decided that fifty Governors would personally guarantee the payment in the sum of £10 each, a solution acceptable to Mr Yates. Very soon after completing the transfer of the money to the Infirmary, Mr Yates died. His relatives accepted a settlement of £500 and £4500 came to the Infirmary.

In August of that year an advertisement was placed in *The Builder* and other newspapers for designs to be submitted for a new infirmary of 150 beds together with all the necessary offices, and accommodation for 300 outpatients. The land at the Mount was marked out, and the solicitors Messrs Keary and Shepherd negotiated the diversion of a footpath that crossed the site. At the Annual General Meeting, December 4th, 1862, it was agreed that one and not more than three Branch Surgeries be established in connection with the Infirmary, but the decision to use £2000 from the Accumulating Fund was deferred for further discussion. A letter was received from the Guardians of the Burslem and Wolstanton Union: they could not recommend any such dispensaries and earnestly objected to the removal of the North Staffordshire Infirmary from its present central position, there being in the opinion of the Guardians no bona fide reason or cause for such removal.

A meeting of the Governors from Hanley also objected in similar terms, adding that the Mount site had been rejected at a meeting in March 1862, which had attracted the largest number of Infirmary Governors. The Mount site had been favoured by the Committee looking at new sites, but relying on procedural rules, the dissenting Governors persuaded the general meeting that decisions favouring the Mount and dispensaries were *'inexpedient, informal and irregular'* and should be reconsidered.

It was agreed on a motion of Godfrey Wedgwood and Colin Minton Campbell that statements to allay the misapprehensions regarding the decisions of the Committee should be published and paid for by private subscription. The objections turned on whether or not the Committee seeking a new site could act on the behalf of the Governors who held final responsibility for the Infirmary, and whether the calling notices for meetings had fully spelled out the decisions which were to be taken.

The turn of the year, 1862-3, marks the halfway point in the battle to decide the future location of the Infirmary. The next meeting of the Governors would be called ostensibly to decide on procedural matters, but it would end dramatically.

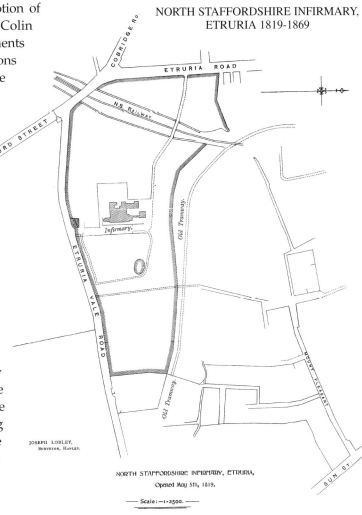

NORTH STAFFORDSHIRE INFIRMARY, ETRURIA 1819-1869

JOSEPH LOBLEY,
Surveyor, Hanley.

NORTH STAFFORDSHIRE INFIRMARY, ETRURIA,
Opened May 5th, 1819.

Scale:—1-2500.

THE HARTSHILL INFIRMARY FRONTAGE 1869.

To the left of the window next to the front door is the Foundation Stone laid by the Prince of
Wales in 1866. Notable absentees at the ceremony were Frank Wedgwood and his son. Frank
could not abide the hypocrisy of those who had raised every obstacle to the move and now came to
bask in the presence of royalty.   He wrote to his son: '*As to HRH he will be mortified* (by FW's
absence) *but he must do without me. The Bishop* (of Lichfield) *is to bring in a bit of Pharisaism,
and if I could face HRH I couldn't face that.*'

CHAPTER 9
Location: The Move to Hartshill

On one side was ranged the Building Committee, including the men who had been the most active in keeping the Infirmary afloat through many difficult years, and who had gone to great trouble to find the most advantageous site for a new building. On the other side was a dissident coalition, mostly from the Northern Pottery towns of Hanley, Burslem and Tunstall. The members of the coalition were united by two desiderata, firstly that the Infirmary should not be removed at all, and secondly, if it had to move it should be as near as possible to their own town.

The Committee charged with finding a new site for the Infirmary on behalf the Governors had undertaken all the work of exploring the various options. They were accused by the dissident Governors of exceeding their remit, of having *'assumed the right'* to act for the Governors as a whole. The Committee replied that they were only following the instructions of Governors meetings, and complained that the dissidents left others to do the work and only came to meetings when they found something to dislike, using procedural quibbles to delay decisions.

The first issue of the *Advertiser* for 1863 carried a Calling Notice for yet another meeting of the Governors. The Agenda was outlined in the notice:

(1) To review the proceedings of the Committee, had it assumed the right to enter into a contract for the purchase of land for the site of the new Infirmary, and to advertise for plans

(2) To consider the expediency of spending £2000 from the Accumulating Fund.

(3) To consider Dispensaries in various parts of the Potteries.

(4) To consider the £5000 received from Mr Yates, and the terms and conditions attached to it.

(5) To consider the legality of the sale of the (old) Infirmary.

(6) To review the proceedings back to January 1861.

This series of motions was signed by representatives of the Northern pottery towns: Messrs Twemlow, the Haywood brothers, Ayshford Wise, Thomas Peake, and George Baker, Chairman of the Burslem Board of Guardians.

The note which the President, J.E. Heathcote caused to be appended to this notice in the *Advertiser* expressed his anger at the tactics. He called the meeting as he was duty bound to do, *but regretted the time that had passed since the events complained of.* He objected to the phrase *'assume the right to'*. The Committee had assumed nothing, *they had acted as agents for the Governors. On November 7th, 1861 the Governors had decided that the Infirmary should be moved. On the 19th of June 1862 the governors had ordered the (Building) Committee to purchase the site for which a contract had been entered into. And now they* (the Governors) *are asked to get rid of this contract, and rescind resolutions that they either voted for, or have consented to by their long silence, and upon which the Committee have acted.*

At a public meeting in Burslem, Mr Mayer had produced figures to demonstrate the value of Establishment Contributions from that town and said that it would be useless to ask the people of Burslem to subscribe to an Infirmary at the Mount

At a Special General Meeting on 16th January 1863, at the North Stafford Hotel the Medical Committee has reported on the present state of the building. It is difficult to see how the dissenters could disregard such a report if they were serious supporters of the Infirmary. The Medical Staff repeated their opinion of the insalubrity and unfitness of the present building for the treatment of patients.

The present structure was built half a century ago and did not meet the requirements of a hospital as understood and insisted upon at the present day. The capacity of air per patient was less than half that recommended for the health and recovery of patients. The wards were badly ventilated and lighted, accommodation was inadequate for the demands of the district, increasing every day in population. The accident ward was most unfit, and operated prejudicially on its inmates. Even for those suffering from general disease the locality of the Infirmary was objectionable. Blast furnaces, iron works and mine shafts produced an air which was insalubrious for patients, especially those from more rural areas. An additional objection to the present site was the constant glare and noise from the furnaces. A new building was required that the sick poor could experience modern treatment essential to their well-being.

Not a whit abashed, the Inhabitants of Burslem presented to the Governors a Memorial, extolling the benefits *'over a long series of years brought by that excellent institution* (the Infirmary). *Its usefulness in this part of the district* (the North) *would be greatly impaired'*, and they wished the Governors would reconsider and preserve it on its present site.

The President, John Heathcote opened the debate from the Chair, reminding the meeting of the necessity of meeting the needs of the remoter part of the district, be it by the provision of Dispensaries or other facilities. *'The town of Longton is not a very insignificant one, whatever the people of Burslem might think on the subject'.*

Mr Ayshford Wise urged delay. He recalled that *the good old Governors of the Pottery district travelled by Parliamentary* (very slow) *train, not an express, but they did not get off the line and down an embankment.* He commended *the frugal and industrious men who contributed so largely to its funds through the Establishment subscriptions.* He referred to the Medical report: in London he was told that *medical authorities were not allowed to interfere at all in the management of a hospital.* (Only true of some London hospitals - and those the most reactionary). He opposed the use of money from the Accumulating Fund, *it was not to be touched until the interest produced £1000 a year i.e. £20,000 at 5% interest.* Chiefly he opposed the decisions taken by the Committee on the grounds that their intentions were not clearly expressed before the meetings were held. He called upon the Governors to rescind these decisions on the grounds that they were *informal and inexpedient, and that such a move could seriously affect the interests and prosperity of the Institution,* i.e. the offended towns would withdraw their subscriptions. He was supported by Mr J. Edwards, who *'represented the interests of the working classes'.*

Back-tracking somewhat, these gentlemen acknowledged the anxious labours and benevolent motives of the (building) committee but they wished to promote the welfare of the Infirmary. They proposed to seek amicable arrangements with Mr Bishop, the owner of the Mount estate, with whom an agreement had been reached to purchase the land, for the purpose of cancelling that contract. Further, these dissenting Governors wished to record that removal (from Etruria) would bring inconvenience and inaccessibility to patients, especially in cases of urgent sickness.

The Rev Stamer spoke for the Committee and said that the decision taken had not been arrived at precipitately. He found that the opposition came from Hanley. The Chairman added *'Burslem and Hanley'.* The Rev Stamer continued that *the late Mr Ridgway who had been the leading citizen of Hanley had left £500 to assist the removal of the Infirmary to a cleaner site. Mr Ridgway had recognised the importance of that which Hanley now opposed.* The report of a Mining Engineer, Mr Samuel Bailley confirmed that the present site of the Infirmary was untenable. He, Rev. Stamer, did not wish to break the contract with Mr Bishop, he did not think it could be done amicably. It was well known that opinion was in favour of the Mount site. He returned to the report of the Medical Committee: *In all respects this (Medical) Committee maintains that a new building is required considering that the sick poor should obtain all the advantages which modern experience suggests and proves to be essential for their well being.* The present Infirmary was *a disgrace*.

Mr Twemlow supported Mr Wise, while Mr W.H. Mayer produced a memorial signed by 2449 inhabitants of Hanley opposing the move. Mr M.D. Hollins supported the Committee, and produced figures to show that the bulk of the income of the Infirmary did not come from the disaffected (Northern) districts. The egregious Mr Peake said he had very recently visited the Infirmary and his personal observation was of its cleanliness, it being commodious and substantial. He was convinced that there was no mining under the building.

The surgeon Robert Garner reported on the dilapidated state of the walls in the consulting room used by Mr Folker. Mr Spark, who had designed the new wing had told Mr Garner that he was ashamed of it, especially when compared with other hospitals here and abroad. Mr Garner continued that *any man with a nose could not go over the building without concluding that the sewer was a very great nuisance.* He added that Mr Peake had said that *the inhabitants of Tunstall would be happy with the Mount site if an ambulance was provided.* He attacked the arguments put forward by the Northern towns, *the Mount site would still be nearer to the nearest extremity of Burslem than it was to Longton, it would be in a denser area of population in Hartshill than now in Etruria.* Mr Garner refuted the argument that the population of the district was growing most rapidly to the North by comparing the populations of the Pottery towns in the censuses of 1851 and 1861, showing that the more rapid growth was in fact towards the South.

Mr Wise rose to challenge the view that he wanted to throw blame on the Committee. The Chairman said that the memorial from Burslem showed that *they thought that Burslem was North Staffordshire, and North Staffordshire was Burslem.* (Cries of No! No! order! order! Hisses)

The Chairman continued, *why was it right for that the rest of North Staffordshire should give way to Hanley, Burslem and Tunstall, ignoring the claims of that insignificant place called Longton with 22,000 inhabitants, and other parts of the district?* He quoted a letter from Mr James Bateman of Biddulph approving the choice of the Mount. He recalled Florence Nightingale's opinion that Infirmaries should have salubrious surroundings. *If anyone asked Mr Bishop to rescind the contract he would advise Mr Bishop to kick him out.*

Messrs Twemlow and Haywood put forward an amendment; they recognised the Committee's sincere desire to promote the Infirmary, but in the divided state of opinion it was expedient to postpone matters to a special Meeting in the future, and to approve a deputation to Mr Bishop to see on what terms he would cancel.

Michael Daintry Hollins proposed an amendment that they support the resolution of November 7th, 1861 that it was desirable to move to a more eligible site. This amendment was defeated, and that of Messrs Twemlow and Haywood (of the Northern party) was approved. The original motion was withdrawn, thus the outcome after seven hours of debate was yet another postponement, and referral to yet another Special Meeting of Governors.

The President, Mr Heathcote now said their next business would be to elect a new President for the Infirmary. With *'scarcely concealed emotion'* Mr Heathcote defended the course he had taken since his election to the Office of President. He observed that *to ask Mr Bishop to cancel the agreement that had been entered into would be un-gentlemanly and un-Christian, and that being the case he would not degrade himself by being a party to any such proceeding.* He therefore wished the meeting goodnight. His resignation was joined by M.D. Hollins, a Vice-President, Colin Minton Campbell, the Rev Sir L.T. Stamer Bart. Vicar of Stoke, Rev E.J. Edwards Vicar of Trentham and Mr Blakiston. The meeting then dispersed.

Letters soon appeared in the *Advertiser* suggesting as a compromise the building of a Convalescent Hospital away from the pollution of the central site, but leaving the original building to be an Accident Hospital. A letter from *'One who had voted against the removal of the Infirmary'* concurred with this proposal. He added: *I do hope that as the district is suffering so seriously by the Northern and Southern contests* (Civil War) *in North America, we may not have an analogous suicidal conflict on a smaller scale in North Staffordshire, producing the same results, viz. the infliction of misery on innocent and dependant persons by depriving or withholding from them that which is necessary for their well being.* The writer was painfully near the truth. Both conflicts began in 1861, and by the time the last shots were fired in North Staffordshire in 1865, the quarrel had outlasted the American Civil War, which had severely damaged the export trade of the Potteries.

Meanwhile, advertisements had already been inserted in the papers inviting architects to submit plans for a new Infirmary, and it became necessary to examine and adjudicate on these plans in fairness to the architects, despite the lack of a positive decision. It was agreed that as the plans submitted by Mr Lynam and Mr Nicholson both had particular merits that the prize should be shared, to which proposal both gentlemen assented.

While the Governors were debating the wisdom of a delegation to Mr Bishop, they received a letter from him on April 22nd, 1863. *The contract for purchase of 10 acres of my land made last Christmas... circumstances have made it necessary to ask it be carried out without delay.* He had in fact a large mortgage on the property. He continued that he needed to know whether *the Committee will complete the sale, or whether he must ask those gentlemen who entered into the contract with him to carry it out.* In other words, if the Committee would not complete the contract, he would call on those Governors who made the contract to carry it out as private citizens who were personally responsible for the contract. It was decided to acknowledge the letter, and consider their course of action.

At an adjourned meeting, Frank Wedgwood being in the Chair, Mr Bishop proposed that *the committee either complete the contract, or pay him £200 plus £300 as a forfeited deposit, additionally lending him £2000 as a second mortgage at 4%,* the usual interest in the 19th century being 5%. The meeting adjourned. At the resumed meeting in June, it was reported that Mr Bishop would not accept the decision of two referees and an umpire. The only decision possible was to recommend that the sale go ahead, as there seemed no possibility of agreeing terms to rescind the contract. It was pointed out that it could take Mr Bishop ten years to sell the land, in that time £1000 in interest would have to be paid to Mr Bishop, in addition to the £500 for cancelling the contract. It would be better to keep the land than risk losing this money. It was agreed to put the decision to complete the sale to the Annual General Meeting.

This Annual General Meeting on November 19th, 1863 was faced with the resignation of Frank Wedgwood from his post of Auditor to the Infirmary, a task he had undertaken for the past 38 years. It was his protest at the prevarication about the future of the Infirmary: *I have not the courage to undertake the responsibility of managing the Infirmary where it stands, nor energy for the labor and trouble of getting it moved.* He received the thanks of the meeting for his services, and was succeeded by his son Godfrey.

Frank Wedgwood was head of the family in Staffordshire and a tireless worker for the Infirmary and when he spoke of managing the Infirmary he meant precisely that. His force of personality and his minute and continuous attention to detail had kept the ramshackle institution and its equally shaky finances afloat. His protest seems to have galvanised the meeting into making a decision. He did not intend to abandon the Infirmary. He was elected a Vice President and a Trustee of the Funded Property, his fellow Trustees being Mr Twemlow and Mr James Bateman. Their first action was to authorise the Committee to pay Mr Bishop, using some money from the Funded Property and some from the money paid by the North Staffordshire Railway for land.

We come to the critical year, 1864. It might be thought that having paid Mr Bishop for the land, the decision was made. To do so underestimates the tenacity of the representatives of the Northern towns.

Those members who had resigned from the Committee in January had been re-elected at the Annual General Meeting of 1863, *'even though their views were entirely unaltered, they would continue to take the necessary action to keep the existing building in operation'*. Yet another Special meeting was called to affirm that *'The present Infirmary is totally inadequate for the requirements of the important district of North Staffordshire'*, and to decide to build a new Infirmary on this or another site. On March 3rd, 1864, at a monthly committee meeting, it was agreed unanimously that *the present Infirmary was totally inadequate*. Further it was proposed that *the Treasurer should open a Building Fund, and a sub-committee be formed to lay out the deficiencies in the old Hospital, and the desiderata in a new one*. A committee was set up under the Chairmanship of Godfrey Wedgwood to determine the requirements of a hospital as understood in the present day. At last sufficient momentum was building to guarantee action.

Rev E.J. Edwards and Godfrey Wedgwood were asked to personally urge the attendance of the Patron, President and Vice presidents of the Infirmary, the Trustees, Members of Parliament for the Northern Division of the County and for Newcastle and Stoke-on-Trent at a Special meeting of the Governors.

On April 9th a typically blunt letter from Frank Wedgwood appeared in the *Advertiser*. It was short and to the point. The decision was not should the Infirmary be moved, or between this site or that, but embodied in the answers to two questions. *Is the Infirmary all it should be, and if not how can matters be mended?*

On April 14th, the Special meeting took place, attended by 80 governors and with Frank Wedgwood in the Chair.

The first resolution, that the present Infirmary is totally inadequate was carried unanimously.

The next resolution, that the present situation ceased to be suitable for the sole Infirmary of the district, and that it was inexpedient to spend any money on enlarging it, or on a new Infirmary were it to be built on the present site, was carried; 2 votes were cast against.

An amendment to the second motion, that the present Infirmary, with such alterations as may be necessary was quite adequate for the wants of the district was defeated, with 4 votes in favour.

The third resolution, that a new Infirmary should be built was passed unanimously.

The fourth resolution, that a committee (to be composed of a huge number of Governors plus the Medical Staff) should be appointed to consider the whole question of accommodation for the sick poor, was passed unanimously.

Thus the minutes reported the meeting, but the newspaper report is much fuller and more interesting. Godfrey Wedgwood addressed the meeting, and showed a remarkable grasp of hospital planning. He referred to the deficiencies of the Infirmary dating back to 1844, and the dangers, not so much of the imminent collapse of the building but of spreading disease among those crowded within its walls. He accurately summed up Florence Nightingale as the authority who had brought together and condensed the opinions of the best authorities on hospital construction. He referred to the plans made by the French Academy of Sciences in 1788 for the replacement of the principal hospital in Paris, the Hotel-Dieu. Built on the pavilion principle, it had a width to the wards of 25ft, with 12ft between beds, exactly as Florence Nightingale would later propose. Godfrey Wedgwood had read and appreciated the writings of Dr Roberton of Manchester, whose articles Miss Nightingale had appropriated as her own without acknowledgement. He praised the design of the best hospital in France, the Lariboissiere (to the plan of which the new Infirmary would most nearly correspond), and the hospital being built at Leeds on the same plan. He spoke of the Herbert Hospital then being built which he believed would surpass them all in hygienic matters

He said anyone who doubted the deficiencies of the Infirmary had only to walk round it. Part of the cause was that it now catered for a different class (type) of patient than it had when first built. The increased use of machinery had led to a great increase in surgical cases, for whom ample room was required. He quoted Roberton who had asked how many people in England died of accidents, and how many died of the house (a hospital.) The Infirmary had only 600-700 cu ft of air per bed, and the Royal College of Surgeons would not recognise a hospital for training that had less than 1000 cu ft per bed. This meant that the Infirmary could not have the Medical School as was desired. This caused a real difficulty, as in many hospitals the pupils did the dressings, and this potential loss of pupils limited the usefulness of the Infirmary.

There now followed a volley of opinions embodying many of the undercurrents that had plagued this whole discussion.

The Rev Stamer had written to the local clergy urging that they should promote individual or private subscriptions from members of their congregations. He appeared to regret the preponderance of the Establishment subscribers over the independent charitable donors who did not gain personally from their contributions, saying the Infirmary was more a sick club than a charity.

Mr Ayshford Wise rebuked the Revd Baronet (Stamer), warning him against offending the Establishment subscribers on whom the Infirmary depended.

The Rev Stamer said he believed that the Infirmary being a Charity it should be paid for by the better off rather than depending on a tax on the lower orders, an interesting slant on the dual funding of the Infirmary.

Mr Baker said there were two opinions on smoke, some thought it beneficial as it kept fevers at bay. He raised the possibility of keeping part of the existing building as an accident ward or a dispensary.

Dr Arlidge said no one would place a hospital in the centre of a town if it could be avoided. With a long straggling district such as the Potteries, if it had to be an equal distance from all the towns, and equally accessible to all parties, the new Infirmary should be built beyond Wetley Rocks (ie seven miles away, where it then would be equally inconvenient to all parts of the Potteries!) The Outpatients department of the Infirmary had acted as a Dispensary for Hanley, and the inhabitants would no doubt miss it, but it was important to remember the country people. He was not keen on Dispensaries or Outpatient Clinics, as the numbers attending were so great that it was difficult to offer them more than small benefits. He spoke against the smoke and other nuisances in Etruria. Would the governors like their friend to be treated there? He said that distance from the Infirmary was rarely the most important factor in an emergency, only important in the case of laceration of a major blood vessel.

Mr Walker of Burslem agreed with Dr Arlidge, vegetation was dying in the atmosphere surrounding the Infirmary. He hoped that the unanimous opinion of the Medical Board would have due weight with the Governors, indeed if they thought the present Medical staff was not competent to form an opinion on the subject, they had better get a new one.

The Rev Stamer said he would not spend sixpence on the old buildings. A new building was needed which was appropriate to the needs of the district. The Workhouse hospital had as many beds as the Infirmary. Recently three patients had transferred from the Infirmary to the Workhouse hospital and found the latter was more comfortable! He concluded with the encouraging thought that in a better hospital patients would get better more quickly and therefore at less cost.

At this moment a distinguished visitor was making his way through Staffordshire. Dr, later Sir, Benjamin Ward Richardson, Senior Physician to the Royal Hospital for Diseases of the Chest, was visiting hospitals throughout the country, and reporting his findings in the national medical journal *The Medical Gazette and Times*, extracts from which were reprinted in the *Advertiser*. Here we have an independent view of medicine in North Staffordshire.

He described the area and its industries. He was very unhappy about the way that the cattle made Newcastle into a midden on market day. He observed the preponderance of chest diseases, and confirmed the observation of others of the unhealthy appearance of the inhabitants. He was impressed by the dual method of funding, the combination of Individual and Establishment subscriptions which he regarded as so unusual and successful as to require him to set out the details. He was complimentary about the quality of the medical staff he met at the Infirmary, as good as any in the country he said. He commended their efforts to maintain standards in the very unsatisfactory conditions that prevailed in the Infirmary. Most usefully he took a walk through the Infirmary describing it ward by ward, the only such account that has survived.

He commended the original choice of the site, he quoted Hugh Davis, formerly a House Surgeon to the Infirmary who said that in his time Etruria Vale was most beautiful. Then the air was pure and clear, the scenery open and varied, and all around was like a garden.

Now, he said the Infirmary must be moved. The foundations were shaken by mining, the walls had deep clefts, supported by strong girders, and ill fitting doors and windows. Now the view was usually obscured by sulphureous smoke. Within 400 yards he found four blast furnaces, while around were mine shafts, bone works: the constant thunderstorms of steam hammers playing day and night within 200 yards of the house, or the lightning glare of the furnaces flickering through the windows in the dead of night. Rest was impossible for the patients.

He said the Infirmary was not built on what were now accepted as scientific principles, and was grossly inadequate for the demands of the district. Several times wards had had to be closed and operations suspended, due to infection. His criticisms featured the lack of air per bed, the narrow corridors, the poor ventilation and heating, and the lack of light. He observed that flowers placed on the window sills invariably dwindled and died. He commented that the staircase in the middle of the building was so situated as to act as a chimney bringing smells from drains and kitchen through the building. He found only two baths, and the water closets were unventilated in the wards. The smell from one water closet diffused itself so steadily through the ward to which it was annexed, that the following placard had to be placed in a prominent position: *Put down the closet lid, and shut the door, when you come out of the closet.* The catalogue of faults continued, he described the whole building as a blot on the map of Sanitary Science.

Richardson reported that *The nurses one and all, appear to be obliging, kind women, but overworked and depressed.* He was very concerned at their low numbers, as we have seen, their accommodation was poor, and wards had been taken over to provided them with somewhere to sleep. *But is it possible to imagine the attention that can be paid to the patients, on thirty seven of whom one nurse must attend? The reason of this deficiency is want of accommodation* (for nurses). *In a Hospital where, as it sometimes happens, two patients have to be put in one bed, where is there room for nurses and attendants?*

Richardson concluded the accounts of his visit by saying that the Infirmary had to move, and he hoped that they will allow no tradition, no idea of expense, no temporary agitation to prevent them razing the old building to the ground, and erecting a pavilion hospital in some new and more favoured spot, where the air is unpolluted, where there is rest for the sick, and where a surrounding healthy vegetation tells the story that life is there respected and held at its prime worth.

On July 7th 1864, another Special General Meeting was held, Frank Wedgwood again in the Chair. The first resolution proposed that the matter should be referred back to a Committee who would report on the different sites which were available, the distances of each of the sites from all the Town Halls and the distances from the principal Collieries and Iron works, and the advantages and disadvantages of each site. The Committee should also look at the soil, the water supply, expences of fencing and draining and the problems of diverting footpaths. They should enquire into the possibility of gaining exemption from present nuisances, and the possibility of continued exemption locally, and if the land was copyhold, to check with the Duchy of Lancaster about the likelihood of mining. This was carried by 45 votes to 12. An amendment to accept the Mount site, on the grounds that the site was purchased and the mining rights had been granted, was withdrawn.

The second resolution, to refer the matter to the Committee who were to report in three months, was carried unanimously.

The next meeting called after the appointed three months heard that no decision regarding mineral rights had been taken, as Lord Clarendon, the Chancellor of the Duchy of Lancaster was out of the country. This led to another month's postponement of any decision.

On November 17th the report on the sites was ready. Of those originally submitted, the following were discussed.

(1) Hartshill on the North side of the road between Stoke and Newcastle, near Hartshill Church: the advantages were a sloping site, well drained, a spring, and near the main road. Disadvantages: Near the railway, Iron, Gas and Copperas (Ferrous Sulphate) Works. No sewer, it drained to the Fowlea Brook.

(2) Basford site near the railway tunnel (on the line through Newcastle to Market Drayton): advantages an even site well fenced and planted, pleasant aspect. Disadvantages: Mines, the rights held by the Duchy of Lancaster, wet clay, Building approaching nearby.

(3) Basford, Kings Field. Advantages: Central, a spring, a good fall to a nearby sewer. Disadvantages Mines under and around the site, brickworks and railway nearby, approaching buildings.

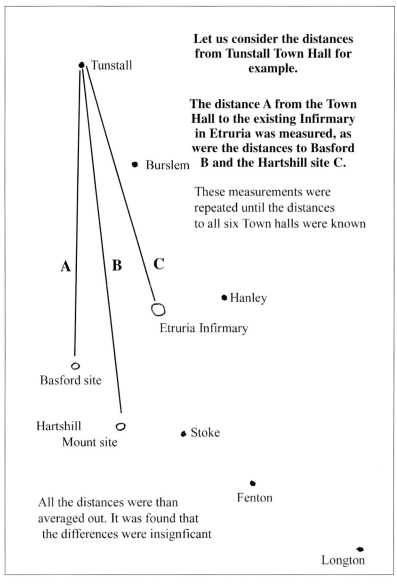

Let us consider the distances from Tunstall Town Hall for example.

The distance A from the Town Hall to the existing Infirmary in Etruria was measured, as were the distances to Basford B and the Hartshill site C.

These measurements were repeated until the distances to all six Town halls were known

All the distances were than averaged out. It was found that the differences were insignficant

In an attempt to achieve a satisfactory solution to the question 'Where shall we build the new Infirmary?' it was decided to apply mathematical procedures to solve the matter. The distance from the existing Infirmary in Etruria to the Town Halls of the six Pottery towns was measured. The distances from the Town Halls to the most favoured alternative sites, Basford and Hartshill were also measured, and the distances were compared (Newcastle under Lyme does not seem to have been considered).

When all the measurements were compared it was found that the differences in the distances were insignificant in relation to the whole Potteries conurbation. Some towns were nearer to the new sites, some further away but the crude measurement of distances took no account of the numbers living in each town. Despite the claims of the Northern towns, a comparison of the 1851 and 1861 censuses showed the population was increasing most rapidly in the Southern towns. As an example the sketch map shows the measurements to be taken from Tunstall Town Hall to the existing Infirmary and the two potential sites for a new building.

(4) Hartshill, The Mount. Advantages: the aspect, a sewer laid in the road, no mines underneath or within 650 yards, quietness, little noise from the railway or the Ironworks. Disadvantages: the distance from Tunstall, and Burslem, the cost of diverting the footpath.

Name	Situation of Property	Whether Freehold or Copyhold	Quantity in Acres	Price per Acre £
Mr. R. D. Vivian	Land near the Kennels, Wolstanton	Copyhold	13	300
Newcastle and Potteries Freehold Villa Residence Society	Land in King's Field, Basford Bank, (if smaller quantity taken, the price to be increased)*	Freehold	22	350
Wm. Davenport. Esq.	Land near Cliff Bank, Stoke	Copyhold	14	300
Mr. James Dimmock ..	Land above the Public Baths, Stoke	Copyhold	10	400
Mrs. Lowe	Land near Burntwood, Lichfield. (quantity and price not stated)			
The Rev. M. W. McHutchin	Land at Basford, near the Tunnel of the Newcastle Branch Railway	Freehold	9½	250
Sir George Chetwynd, and Miss Sparrow	Land near Watlands, Wolstanton. (If less quantity taken £350 per acre)	Copyhold	27	300
F. Bishop. Esq.	Land near the Mount, Stoke, on East side of New Road from Hartshill to Penkhull	Freehold With Mines reserved to the Duchy of Lancaster.	10 to 15	300
F. Bishop, Esq.	Land near the Mount, Stoke, on West side of New Road. looking towards Newcastle (Mr. Bishop offering to give £500 out of the purchase money as a donation).			300
Mr. Thomas Heath	Land between Dimsdale and Chesterton. (House to be taken at a valuation)	Freehold	10	17
Mrs. Barlow	Land adjacent to No. 10	Freehold	8	26

*N.B.—A subsequent offer has been made to sell any portion of this land (if taken from the Etruria side of the Property), at £350 per acre.

Offers of land made to the Infirmary for the site of the new Infirmary.

On December 8th at the Railway (North Stafford) Hotel, again with Frank Wedgwood in the Chair, the Special General Meeting took place. The Duchy of Lancaster would not release the mining rights, other than those under the Mount. The proposal to delay yet again was dropped when it was pointed out that with all the delays the Governors were beginning to look ridiculous in the eyes of the County. The sniping continued: the district would be divided into two halves, the Mount would be useless to the Northern half and another Infirmary would have to be built. Another suggested that this move to would do the Infirmary more harm than good had been done in the past fifty years. Sir Smith Child had made available £500 to start a fund to build a hospital in Tunstall.

In order to evaluate the different sites proposed for the new infirmary, the average distance from the site to the six town halls was employed. The average was 2½ miles in the case of the existing infirmary at Etruria, the same distance as the King's Field site in Basford. The Mount was a quarter of a mile on average further from the town halls. The average distance from 17 major collieries and ironworks, when Basford and the Mount were compared, was only 47 yards different - an insignificant amount.

Major Coyney addressed the meeting. Everyone wanted the Infirmary as near as possible to their own District but what was needed was a healthy situation especially with respect to the prevailing winds. He reminded the meeting that collieries were spreading throughout North Staffordshire and were not confined to the Pottery District. He also referred to the handsome donations from Cheadle and Tean.

The resolution that no better site having been found within 3 miles of the present Infirmary the meeting should adopt the Mount site, and give consideration to the setting up of outlying dispensaries was put to the meeting and passed unanimously.

Motions to proceed and to enlarge the Committee and set up a Building Fund all passed with no dissenting vote.

The decision had taken twenty years since the first proposal to move from Etruria had been put forward, and it would be another five years before the new Infirmary was opened in Hartshill.

It must not be thought that Mr Peake was silenced. He was still expressing the view that to move the Infirmary was a crime. Unedifying comparisons were made between the towns, comparing the amount subscribed with the number of patients each had had admitted. There was no evidence of the wider vision that would be needed for successful federation into a united City.

One man had a clear and modern view of the situation. He was the Rev. Hawes, Vicar of Tunstall. Having discussed the concepts of Dispensaries and/or ambulances, he said local hospitals must not try to be rivals of the Infirmary. He said it was essential to have one superior institution in the area securing the best possible attendance in serious cases, and that he thought it dangerous to interfere with the funds of the Infirmary.

In order to untangle the Byzantine knots of this long and at times almost farcical process, it will be useful to ask several questions:

One: Was the site of the existing Infirmary really untenable?

I believe that we must trust all those who reported on its condition. The Medical Staff were practically united in condemning the building, not only those of the consulting staff who would derive long term benefit from improved working conditions, but a departing House Surgeon on leaving the district had felt moved to complain of the difficulties of treating patients there. The reports from surveyors and architects are consistent in their record of a building needing more and more attention, and moving towards ultimate collapse.

The effects of undermining and subsidence could be seen in the old Wedgwood factory at Etruria as it sank in comparison to the level of the canal. Well within today's living memory the furnaces of the Shelton Bar Iron Company still surrounded the site of the Infirmary, and the prophecies of the 1839 survey became all too true. Nor should we forget the huge tip of slag from the furnaces dumped on a huge mound on Tinkersclough, near the lower end of Clough Street.

Whatever else was in doubt, the noses of most visitors noticed the fractured sewer and pervasive smell from the foul effluvium in the cellar.

Two.: If not already undermined, as Earl Granville's agents insisted, what were the prospects for the future?

Land in the Potteries was largely copyhold, the mining of minerals under that land was reserved to the principal landlord. Even if land was purchased which was freehold on the surface, the mineral rights below the surface would not be owned by the purchaser, and he could not easily guarantee himself against undermining. The only guarantee would be to find a site with absolutely no minerals underneath it, a rarity in the Valley of the Trent in the Potteries, to lease the mineral rights, or to buy them out.

Virtually all the sites offered for sale were either already undermined, or had minerals

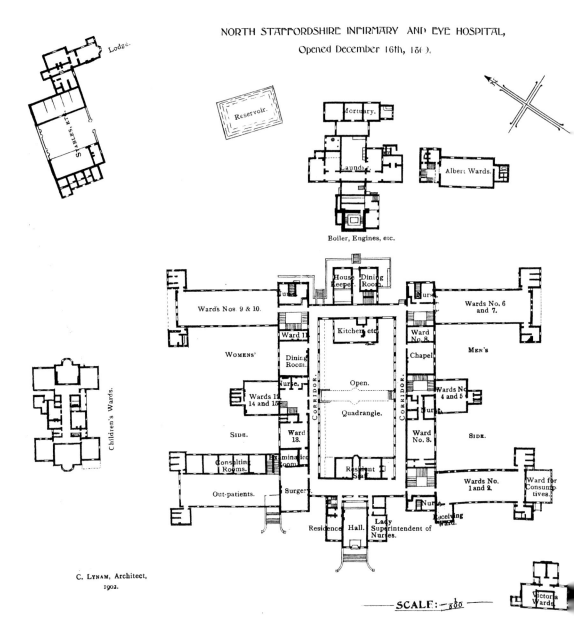

NORTH STAFFORDSHIRE INFIRMARY AND EYE HOSPITAL,

Opened December 16th, 186().

C. Lynam, Architect,
1902.

SCALE: $\frac{1}{500}$

Plan drawn by C. Lynam, the architect of the Hartshill Infirmary for Hordley's centenary book.

The North Staffordshire Royal Infirmary stiil looked much the same in 1930. The Pavilion design, with long narrow wards stretching out from the central square, is very obvious in this drawing.

The detached building at the top left. replaced now by the Administrative Offices, was the lodge, with stables for doctors' and governors' horses, and along the lower wall were pigstyes.

At the lower left of the plan is the former Smith Child Ward, at this time the Children's Ward, and replaced by a new Pathology Department in 1940.

Upper right are the Albert Wards, being detached they were used as fever wards and later for radiotherapy patients.

Lower right is the Victoria Ward, used to provide clean isolated accommodation for gynaecological operations and later extended to form the Children's Ward.

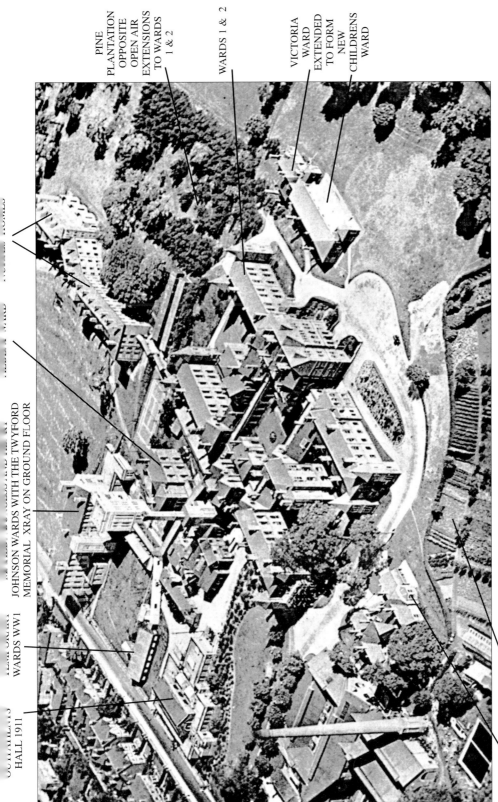

PINE PLANTATION OPPOSITE OPEN AIR EXTENSIONS TO WARDS 1 & 2

WARDS 1 & 2

VICTORIA WARD EXTENDED TO FORM NEW CHILDRENS WARD

JOHNSON WARDS WITH THE TWYFORD MEMORIAL XRAY ON GROUND FLOOR

WARDS WW1

HALL 1911

SMITH CHILD'S WARD - REPLACED 1940 BY THE PATH LAB

KITCHEN GARDEN

NORTH STAFFORDSHIRE INFIRMARY.

Hospital Sunday and Hospital Saturday Collections

IN AID OF THE ABOVE INSTITUTION.

HOSPITAL SATURDAY, FEBRUARY 7th, 1880.
HOSPITAL SUNDAY, FEBRUARY 8th, 1880.

The Hospital Sunday and Saturday Committee are called upon to make their 10th Annual Appeal to the inhabitants of North Staffordshire in aid of the funds of the Infirmary. Happily the beneficent work of this Institution is too well known to need that a long detailed statement should be embodied in this appeal. But the ever increasing claims which are being made upon its resources, necessitate the urgent call which the Committee this year feel bound to make upon all Congregations, and places of Business, for a larger and more generous response on the days fixed for the Collections. They trust also that these Collections may, as far as practicable, be made simultaneously. The benefits which such an Institution as this confers upon this whole neighbourhood— physically and morally—must be very great indeed, and the liberality of every man and woman can never be directed through a nobler channel than this.

Appended is a brief abstract of the work done during the past year—

Total No. of Patients 1878-79.			Total.
	In-Patients	1,500	
	Out-Patients ..	9,618	11,205
	Children's Wards	87	

Balance due to the Treasurer, October 25th, 1879, £500 5s. 0d.

The following were the Collections last year—

		£	s.	d.
Hospital Sunday, 210 Collections	..	788	11	3
Hospital Saturday, 61 Collections	..	222	12	5

EXTRACTS FROM THE MEDICAL REPORT.

"The surgical work during the year has been remarkable for the number of operations performed, and for the eminently satisfactory results which have been obtained. As will be seen by the table, no less than 311 operations have been performed, not including the application of Sayre's spinal support, which has been adopted in 21 instances."

"Of these operations, no less than 30 have been amputations of the large limbs, including one at the hip joint for an enormous tumour of the thigh ; and 8 were excisions of the hips and elbow joints."

"The most satisfactory feature however remains to be noticed, that is, that among the whole number of 311 operations, only 7 deaths from every cause occurred, giving a rate of mortality of 2.22%. Of these deaths, only one can be clearly traced to blood poisoning, and that gives a mortality from that cause alone of only 0.58%. Such results as these your Medical Board believe will surpass the statistics of any hospital as yet published, and far exceed those which, during this year, have been considered to approach perfection in surgery."

"The extent to which the Children's Wards are resorted to for surgical aid is remarkably evidenced by the fact that, of the little ones treated, as many as 42 of their number underwent operations of greater or less severity :—including amputation of the thigh, excision of joints, cutting for stone, and the radical cure for hernia. This record of work done is sufficient of itself to demonstrate the value of this new department of the Infirmary, and should, at the same time, stimulate the generosity of the public to further develope it."

THE HOSPITAL SUNDAY & SATURDAY COMMITTEE.

January 2nd, 1880.

C. Hickson, Printer, Newcastle.

An advertisement for support for the Sunday and Saturday Collections in 1880. Note that the operations are still mainly amputations, abdominal surgery was still very uncommon until the building of the Victoria Wards in 1882 waiting to be exploited. The Mount had the supreme advantage that there were no accessible minerals under it, and therefore the Landlords, the Duchy of Lancaster were prepared to confirm this by selling those rights at the nominal sum of £1 an acre, with a cost of conveyance not to exceed £7-10-0. We may note in parentheses that, when the Governors sought in later years to buy additional land from the Mount Estate, the mineral rights were no longer available, mining techniques having advanced, making more coal available.

The mining rights would always be central to the decision in favour of Hartshill, in view of the geology of the area, and particularly in view of the severe effects of subsidence on the Infirmary in Etruria. We can see a group of what we may call senior Governors, industrialists who were entirely convinced that the Infirmary had to move and the only sane place to receive it was the Mount site. In this group I believe Frank Wedgwood was crucial. No one put more time into the affairs of the Infirmary. He bitterly resented the fact that those who wished to move were having to keep the failing old building in order, while those Governors who wanted it to stay in Etruria bore little of the burden of keeping it going. The progressive group included his son Godfrey, John Heathcote, Colin Minton Campbell and Michael Daintry Hollins.

Three: Where does Mr Bishop fit into the picture?

A solicitor, he must have had his ear to the ground. He appears to have been obstructive in his insistence on the contract to purchase the land being fulfilled, but he had little to gain, he had already sold the land. I believe he was pushing the development of the Mount site for the new Infirmary in quiet support of the 'progressive' Committee, and was stopping up alleys through which the Northern party could escape from the contract. After the purchase was completed he gave £500 to the Building Fund!

Four: The motives of the the Northern Group.

These are more difficult to evaluate. Some of their opposition was due to concern for the patients who would have to travel, but the calculations of distances when finally worked out showed there was really little to choose between the sites on that ground. An ambulance was provided when the Infirmary moved to the Mount. Was it civic pride in the best sense, or was it the desire to be a big fish in a small pond, fearing the loss of status if the greater good of the district triumphed over village pump politics? This whole episode has been related because it shows most clearly how the petty battles between the towns shaped the City of today.

The writer attended many planning meetings in the 1970s and 1980s that considered possible future development of the hospitals of North Staffordshire. Should there be a greenfield site, which would have to be at the edge of the built up area, thereby placing it well away from any notional centre of the district? Should there be two hospitals, one in the North and one in the South? Stoke-on-Trent does not have a large enough population to support two first rank hospitals with all the major specialties in each hospital. Divisions, such as the provision of chest surgery say in the North and of neurosurgery say in the South would mean that patients with multiple trauma would have to be shuttled back and forth by ambulance. A modern hospital is expected to be able to deal with virtually everything which arrives through its doors. The Vicar of Tunstall was absolutely right when he said the district 'needed one superior institution securing the best possible attendance in serious cases.'

Five: Was there no warning that the site in Etruria might not be ideal, was there no 'Gypsy's warning' which should have alerted them to future problems?

An irritating habit in the early 19th century was that of newspaper editors accepting a nom de plume attached to what were effectively anonymous letters. It is impossible to know if *'Veritas'* or *'Subscriber'* or even *'A Friend of the Working Classes'* were what these names implied, if they were serious contributors or whether they hid disappointed commercial interests. On the back page of the *Advertiser*, October 14th 1815, is a communication, printed in the paper's very smallest print. It complained that the new site for the Infirmary in Etruria was not the best available, there was another (unspecified) within half a mile, and sectional interests had opposed consideration of its merits. The crux of the letter was that the supply of spring water, so vital before the coming of a reliable piped supply, would be drained away by the mining activities of Earl Granville, an event that as we have seen did come to pass. *'As it is pretty well known that Viscount Granville has lately obtained an extension of his leases for upwards of 30 years... giving him full power to get the mines in any place and to any extent he thinks fit; and at the same time binding him annually to get a certain quantity..'.*

Why did this not ring a warning bell? I can only suppose that it was thought that the water shortage could be circumvented by the deepening of the well. The prospect of severe subsidence is not even mentioned in this article because the small scale of mining had not yet shown how much damage could be caused.

Six: As I have tried to disentangle the story of the Etruria Infirmary a thought constantly recurred. Why did the Infirmary building suffer so badly from subsidence?

The Wedgwood factory, Etruria Hall and chapels in the area were affected, but they soldiered on into the 20th century. Even the old House of Recovery whose structure had been regarded as too fragile for extension in 1814 survived until 1870 when it was pulled down in order to make way for enlargement of the gasworks. You will recall that the raising of money for the first Infirmary was a constant worry to the Governors, the plan drawn up by Mr Haycock having to be steadily scaled down to keep within the budget. When the work was handed over to Mr Potter of Lichfield, Mr Haycock commented on the lightness of Mr Potter's bid - the Governors were *'indeed fortunate if they could get the Infirmary built at Mr Potters price'*.

The Governor's search for the best value is understandable, but we may ask, did they pay later for the decision? We have seen how small were the contributions to the North Staffordshire building fund in comparison to the sums donated to the hospital in Derby. The collection of money in tiny increments is immensely laborious; their tenacity in carrying it through is enormously praiseworthy. The smallest weekly Establishment Contribution was a farthing, at that rate it took 960 weeks to collect one pound! (18$\frac{1}{2}$ years)

The Potteries seem to have been underfunded for at least 200 years. As Arnold Bennett says of Darius's printing office in his novel *Clayhanger* *'it was a fine example of the policy of makeshift which governed and still governs the commercial activity of the Five Towns'.*

Seven: What came of the proposals to provide branch hospitals or local dispensaries?

In the end, the Northern and Southern extremities of the Potteries were served by new hospitals. The gift of the Haywood brothers paid in 1886 for the hospital in Moorland Road which bore their name, being replaced in High Lane in 1930 as the Burslem, Tunstall and Haywood Memorial Hospital. In Longton, in 1868 a small hospital was built, which was replaced in 1890 at Normacot. Both the Haywood and Longton hospitals had their own staffs, which included members of the consultant staff of the Infirmary, and both hospitals continue to serve the district as integral parts of the National Health Service to the present day.

CHAPTER 10
Trials and Tribulations: The Chaplain and the Dancing Nurses

This chapter looks at the Governors' attitude and response in cases where they were faced with 'moral' dilemmas that concerned the well being and good name of the Infirmary.

Christian belief was a defining influence in 19th century Britain and intolerance between its branches was still prevalent. But during the Victorian age the North Staffordshire Infirmary stands out as a beacon of tolerance. There is no suggestion of any patient being excluded on account of their religious beliefs, or even their lack of them. An early rule indicated that there should be no bar to an appointment of the medical staff on religious grounds. This does not imply a lack of moral principles in the management of the Infirmary, rather that it was based on a consensus regarding rules and acceptable behaviour.

Another powerful determinant of the acceptability of behaviour was the effect it would have on the good name of the institution. As early as 1827, the then Matron Mrs Massey was dismissed for *'having disseminated reports with regard to an Inpatient prejudicial to the interests of the institution'*. This was a matter of great importance, for the income of the Infirmary depended on the level of subscriptions being maintained and therefore on the subscriber's good opinion.

The Governors could be equally strict upon the Medical Staff. In 1809, Mr Cleavin the second Apothecary at the Dispensary and House of Recovery was tried and adjudged guilty by the committee of *'committing indecent and improper conduct against a woman attending the Dispensary for medicines.'* Mr Cleavin was dismissed.

In 1846 the rather Bohemian life style of the House Surgeon caused problems for the Governors. Dr John Mackenzie, no relation to the consultant physician of that name, threw his weight about, kept dogs, inconvenienced the domestic staff and quarrelled with Matron. An enquiry was held, it was found that the individual offences were trivial, and in the words of Francis Wedgwood who chaired the sub-committee, could have been avoided by courtesy on both sides. It is remarkable how balanced the Governors could be in their judgements, but even their equanimity was defeated when a patient died in the middle of the night and Dr Mackenzie declined to leave his bed to attend to him: he left the Infirmary precipitately to join a ship of the East India Company.

It must be admitted that the Governors were not keen to wash dirty linen in public, they would blandly smooth over complaints, but then would come down on offenders with a heavy hand. I can only ascribe this ambivalent attitude to their desire to keep the Infirmary afloat when the finances were often very straitened.

This rigour could apply to the senior staff. Dr Gooday, a physician at the Infirmary from 1862 to 1866 was a 'character'. W.D. Spanton in his autobiography describes Gooday as unkempt, and with a dread of infections, who would, in the presence of an infectious patient, put his head round the ward door and call out *'Well good man, getting on alright?'* and disappear at speed.

Dr Gooday was soon in trouble with the Governors, being accused in October 1862 of having told an outpatient of the Infirmary to go to see him at his consulting room in his home, and to bring 5/- with him. This of course was absolutely against the principle of a voluntary hospital, to recruit an Infirmary patient into a private patient. The committee examined Dr Gooday on the matter, and:

'Resolved that the course taken by Dr Gooday was a violation both of the practice and spirit of this Infirmary, and wholly opposed to its principles as a charitable institution, and that any repetition of this conduct on the part of Dr Gooday that may come to the knowledge of this committee, will be deemed by them inconsistent with his remaining a Physician of this Infirmary, and will make it imperative upon them to take the necessary steps for his removal.'

After this blast from the committee, Dr Gooday appears to have avoided trouble; he resigned in January 1866 *'being unable to devote sufficient time,'* and disappeared from our story.

We know that the experiment of appointing a Lady Superintendent for the new building in Hartshill was short-lived. The Governors took the side of the male patients against the Lady Superintendent when she complained of their indelicate language and behaviour. Reminding her that the Infirmary was actually there for the patients, most of whom would be making a contribution to its upkeep, the Governors were acting against the stereotypical picture of Victorian grandees

The patience of the Governors was severely tested in 1886. In March of that year the *Sentinel* carried a terse notice of a Special Meeting of the Governors. The meeting was to consider claims of abuses at the Infirmary, that had been presented by nurses who had recently been dismissed for misconduct and by the Chaplain, the Rev Mr Tovey. A committee had been convened, meanwhile Mr Tovey was requested to absent himself from the Infirmary.

The *Sentinel* reported the findings of this committee on August 21st, 1886. The committee consisted of Frederick Wragge, Chair, Charles Adams, F.E. Kitchener, William Keary, Joseph Knight, W.D. Spanton and Godfrey Wedgwood. This was a very experienced and hardworking committee. They held 13 meetings each lasting between 3 and 5 hours. The evidence was so voluminous that they employed a shorthand writer, *'regardless of the expense'*. In the final analysis it came down to a dispute between the Governors and the Chaplain, Mr Tovey. For Mr Tovey 31 persons gave evidence, against him 37 witnesses appeared, including Miss Annan the Superintendent of Nurses and Mr Hordley the Secretary of the Infirmary.

The accusations were that patients had been mistreated. The Chaplain said that poor patients were required to hand over little delicacies which had been brought in by friends in order to bribe the nurses to treat them well, while the nurses had luxuries on their table. Modest women were strapped to a table and forced to have unnecessary operations at the whim of a nurse. There were cases where dead bodies were mutilated. Patients were deprived of Bibles.

In reply Miss Annan reported that one nurse had indeed been dismissed, another had received a sovereign as a present, which was given to Miss Annan who returned it to the patient. Generally any present was given when the patient *left* the ward, and usually consisted of *'articles of crockery ware'* or a piece of fabric.

The accusations about specific treatments forced on patients were flatly refuted. They could refer to a gynaecological procedure, or perhaps to the passing of a catheter. Procedures performed *'at the whim of a nurse'* are difficult to understand, there is no reference to any episode in the records which refers to any similar complaint. *'Mutilation of bodies'* probably refers to post-mortem examinations, an interestingly old fashioned view for 1886.

Mr Tovey's next complaints refer to the behaviour of the nurses. There is a prurient flavour to his accusations. Men had been seen in the nurses rooms. All the investigations showed that they were seen in the sculleries but not the bedrooms, some were brothers and fiancés. Further accusations were that nurses had been seen coming and going at all times (of the night), one had been seen masquerading about the building in men's attire, and there had been dancing in the public parts of the Infirmary, apparently in tights!!! Tights of course led to thoughts of sin, the stage, of dancers and actresses, who were then still seen as loose women by polite society.

The committee found that one nurse had dressed in male attire in a *'foolish freak'* and run along the corridor. The tights were found to be garments worn by a nurse being fitted for underclothes by another nurse who had made them for her. The windows of the Infirmary were found to be securely closed (and all external doors at night) preventing any unauthorised coming and going by the nurses.

Perhaps the most interesting aspect of the long report in the *Sentinel* is the stance taken by the reporter. Clearly he had little time for Mr Tovey, who had not captured his sympathy. The summary of the Sentinel's report is quoted in full:

'Mr Tovey's picture of that nurse in tights and the committee's reply make instructive reading. We do not wonder that the committee use the phrase grossly exaggerated. As to the masquerading in mens clothing, we have heard of man millinery. It is impossible not to wonder what sort of expression the faces of the venerable committee wore when Mr Tovey detailed his particulars about the tights and they turned to hear the rebutting evidence about the undergarments. Here again we enquire, did Mr Tovey see any of these venturesome nurses after a surreptitious wandering about, climb through the windows? Did the immaculate Tovey seize the delinquent Magdalen, and arouse the staff to behold the culprit who was getting the wrong way into the sheepfold?'

This, remember was 1886. The appellation of the chaplain as the *'immaculate Tovey'* is indeed scornful. By using the phrase *'delinquent Magdalen'*, it would be obvious to every reader that Mr Tovey had implied that the nurses were 'fallen women'. At a time when strenuous efforts were being made to improve the standard of recruitment, training and status of nurses, Mr Tovey's accusation was insulting not only to the nurses but to everyone associated with the Infirmary. There can be no doubt that the *'venerable committee'* were on the side of the nurses, and in spirit were not as venerable as all that.

The real source of the grievance was that Mr Tovey did not get on well with the staff; they didn't go to chapel. Miss Annan did not encourage them to do so, as she disapproved of Mr Tovey's mode of taking a service. He complained that the staff were not provided with improving literature. The Committee felt this was a religious rather than a medical matter. He complained of not being allowed to visit a ward. The ward in question proved to be the Victoria Ward, admission to which was severely limited to allow aseptic surgical practice to be carried out, and no unnecessary visitors were admitted. There is a suggestion in the report that the patients, being captive in the wards were subjected to over zealous evangelisation, which may not necessarily have been to their taste.

Mr Tovey was found to be guilty of making reckless allegations that would damage the Infirmary. It was agreed that discipline should be tightened, that in future Miss Annan's visits should hold an element of surprise in their timing. The women had danced in the ward, but there had been no undue levity or impropriety, and it was felt to be advisable that this practice should cease. This seems so sad. Life for the nurses was hard and closely regulated, by 1886 nurses were expected to adhere to the rules, modest deviations from them being followed by dismissal. There was no evidence of great laxity. We do not know whether or not the dancing women included ambulant patients. Patients spent long periods in hospital at this time, an average stay of 30 to 35 days, so any break in the monotony must have been welcome. To see the women dancing in the ward as wickedness and a disciplinary matter suggests wishful thinking on the part of a rather humourless cleric.

The census of 1851 had included a survey of church and chapel attendance, a survey recognised as marking the high point of religious observance in Britain. Working people had more education, more information, and less deference, they no longer had to attend at church to satisfy their employer and landlord, and in a long working week wished to use their free time as they chose. The efforts of Mr Tovey to evangelise his captive flock may have been driven by falling attendances.

In many industrial areas, as in North Staffordshire, non-conformity presented a great challenge to the Anglican Church. Believing that there should be accommodation in Anglican churches for the whole population should they choose to use it, barriers to Anglican church attendance were being removed. Rented pews were being abolished. Town centre churches were left empty by the movement of people to distant housing developments. This shift of population led to the continued building of large satellite suburban churches that would never be filled.

This movement to increase the provision of buildings for worship extended itself into the Infirmary. When the Reverend Walter Sneyd of Keele Hall, the President of the Infirmary, offered, in October 1875, to provide a chapel for the use of the staff and patients, he surely did not expect the reception that greeted his offer. He offered to build a chapel at the cost to himself of £1,200; it was to be consecrated for worship according to the Anglican rite. The sum of £500, which had previously been set aside for this purpose, could now be used to pay a chaplain. At the Annual General Meeting in November, it was agreed to accept Mr Sneyd's generous offer. Mysteriously, the Annual General Meeting having been adjourned, when it was resumed the minutes were marked *'not passed'*, though the votes were recorded as 20 in favour of accepting Mr Sneyd's offer and 17 against. In January Mr Sneyd wrote to the Governors withdrawing his offer. It had never occurred to him that such a provision could give umbrage to anyone, he had no desire to cause feelings of illiberality or lack of feeling. He did not wish to do anything that could cause damage to the Infirmary.

The issue in question was whether or not the chapel would be for the use of Anglicans alone or whether it could be inter-denominational. The correspondence in the press descended into a discussion of whether or not the chapel was for the use of the whole Infirmary, and finally if they were not included, whether the excluded Non-conformists should withdraw their subscriptions. The argument hinged on the word consecrated. If the chapel was only licensed as a place of worship, then it could be used by all denominations, but if it was consecrated, then it could only be used for Anglican worship.

The payment of the (Anglican) Chaplain had caused friction on a previous occasion. In 1872 a letter had been received from the Dissenting Churches complaining that money from the Sunday Collections had been used to pay the Chaplain. They had no objection to the Chaplain, only to his being paid from the *'misuse'* of the Sunday Collections. The Governors assured them that in future the Sunday Collections would only be used for the general purposes of the Infirmary. In 1875 all members of the community still had to pay tithes to the Church of England. They were bitterly resented by Non-conformists.

Passions ran high especially in the correspondence column of the papers. Dr J.T. Arlidge did not help in a letter to the press setting out the Anglican position when he used the words *'selfish, intolerant and unchristian'* about the dissenters or Non-conformists. A devout Anglican with sincere beliefs he worked tirelessly for the working potters, especially in treating the chest diseases that arose from their work. In reaction to the

Sabbatarianism of the Non-conformists in 1864, he deplored the lack of opportunity for outdoor exercise on a Sunday. He could be very outspoken, and it might be argued be that he would have exerted greater influence in his dealings with manufacturers if he had exercised more moderation.

Both sides used the relative amounts of money that were being subscribed as a weapon, the Non-conformists threatening to withdraw their contributions, while some Anglicans suggested that the Non-conformist subscriptions were so small that they would not be missed anyway. This was really becoming very silly and in danger of causing real harm to usually harmonious relationships among the Governors and supporters of the Infirmary. It was fortunate that Mr Sneyd abandoned his plan. Nevertheless, £1200 was a great deal of money at that time and would have built a substantial church; the decision to withdraw the offer is clear evidence of the strength of feeling which had been aroused.

Christian belief was a defining influence in 19th century Britain and individual choices as to the form of worship were of great concern to individuals. It is interesting to see in the Infirmary a broad spread of belief that generally worked for the common good. Occasionally the peace was disturbed. When, in the arguments over the choice of the Mount site for the new Infirmary it was suggested that the Governors should ask Mr Bishop to cancel the contract that they had signed, the President, Mr Heathcote refused in these terms: '..to ask Mr Bishop to cancel the agreement that had been entered into would be un-gentlemanly and un-Christian...' He felt that to renege on the agreement would be degrading, and rather than do so he resigned the office of President. Here we have a clear statement of a most important ideal of the Victorian era, that of the Christian gentleman, and that if the choice was between falling from that ideal and resignation, there really was no choice.

Reading through the surviving minutes, letters and newspaper reports of the Infirmary's affairs, I have consciously looked for the hypocrisy frequently attributed to the Victorians. I have to say that I have been struck with the enthusiasm of the active Governors of the Infirmary, and cannot point to any evidence of their dishonesty or the misuse of their position. Those who were Ministers of Religion appear as enthusiastic members of the committees, and usually are to be found contributing their advice as members of society in general rather than propounding a narrow dogma.

There was always an awareness of the balancing act needed to steer the Infirmary through so many conflicting opinions and interests. These episodes remind us how a thoughtless act or an unguarded sentence could threaten the well-being of an institution entirely dependent on the goodwill and financial support of the whole of the local community.

The inscription on this ceremonial trowel reads HRH Prince of Wales laid the first stone of the New North Staffordshire Infirmary at Hartshill, Stoke-on-Trent June 25 AD 1866.

Images of nurses in the pre-Nightingale and pre-photographic era are rare, and none have been found for North Staffordshire. Nevertheless this engraving of 1808 shows a ward layout that is likely to be similar to that of the Infirmary and familiar to the Governors in the early years in Etruria.

The engraving is by the architect Pugin (Senior) with figures drawn by Thomas Rowlandson and is of a ward at Middlesex Hospital. It is unusual in that it shows a ward in operation, and with curtains around the beds still remarkably recognisable to modern eyes, although it is a vivid contrast with photographs of the later 19th century that show all the patients in bed, with Sister to the fore and the nurses grouped gracefully behind her.

The nurse on the left (see below), airing a garment, is clearly a servant, wearing cap, apron and the slightly shorter dress of the lower servant. The group on the right is apparently a ward round, the physician in knee breeches and a wig, the apothecary in his apron, a visitor in black, perhaps the chaplain, and the older female figure who is marked out as an authority figure, perhaps matron, by her large bunch of keys.

CHAPTER 11
The Nurses 1802-1869

'The nurses one and all, appear to be obliging, kind women, but overworked and depressed.'
Dr, later Sir, Benjamin Ward Richardson,

The history of the Infirmary is inextricably bound up with the story of its nurses. In the 19th century the evidence is sketchy, and we have to make the best of the snippets of information that survive. These include advertisements, minutes, newspaper reports, even census returns, but cumulatively they give a sense of the progress in nursing from very early days and very humble beginnings.

The nursing profession today is determined to shed the image of a nurse being the hand-maiden of the doctor, but there is no doubt that for many years she was just that. This does not imply a totally subservient relationship, at times the Infirmary records reveal a power struggle being played out below the surface.

In the beginning the nurse was not perceived as anything more than a servant, performing the menial tasks of cleaning, bed making and feeding the sick. The Matron might be in charge of the nurses, but her function was more nearly that of the housekeeper of a large house. She had control of the female staff, the cook and the laundry, the ordering of supplies and linen laundry, indeed experience of such work was a necessity to hold the position.

Matrons were selected from household servants, or those who had run large institutions, such as inns. They were not always expected to perform caring functions other than washing and feeding patients though they could be expected to perform basic duties such as assisting patients with toilet functions, and watching a patient at night.

The Matron received a salary plus her board and lodging, or an allowance instead. She was expected to be unencumbered by a family, i.e. children, though at times a husband could be considered acceptable especially if he could undertake duties in the hospital. The salary of the Matron was the highest awarded to the nursing staff, but it never approached that of the Apothecary or House Surgeon. Like the House Surgeon, the Matron could have her salary augmented by bonuses voted by the Governors to acknowledge particularly meritorious service. The Governors required that the Matron and the House Surgeon be full time servants of the hospital, and that they should arrange any absences so that one of them was on the premises at any one time.

The first Matron of the House of Recovery was Mrs Mary Birch of Cobridge, she was paid £15 per annum, and allowed a servant/nurse to work under her direction. This servant was to be approved by Mr Byerley and paid £6-6-0 a year. At that time Messrs Wedgwood and Byerley of Etruria provided the nascent institution its business address, and acted as treasurer. In 1807, the Apothecary was paid £5-5-0 for his extra attendance on Fever patients, but no such payment was to be to made to the Matron, although there was a suggestion that a promise of such a payment had been made by Dr Bent.

Mrs Birch was replaced when she declined the suggestion that she should act as day nurse to the fever patients. Martha Gallimore was engaged at 8 shillings a week to undertake these nursing duties. Thanks were offered to Mrs Birch for her services, but go she must.

Wanted: a steady woman who will undertake 'to nurse and undertake the household concerns of the Establishment...', and 'no objection will be made to a married man without encumbrances who will reside in the House.'

On these terms, and a salary of £21 per annum, exclusive of coals and candles, Mary Birks was appointed. Clearly the provision of nurses for the Fever patients was a problem. One nurse was hired for a period from Manchester, while another came from Trentham, for four shillings a week when unemployed and seven shillings a week when employed. This arrangement acknowledges that the occurrence of fever was intermittent, so she was paid a retainer to be available, and more when required to attend patients, an arrangement that soon broke down; the Apothecary was ordered to *'engage whoever he can'*. These were the years before the decision was taken to build a proper infirmary and in which only a few patients were admitted as inpatients, the main work of the Institution being carried out through the Dispensary, treating outpatients.

In 1815 it was agreed to fit the House of Recovery up for the admission of accidents and surgical cases needing important operations. The House of Recovery could thus be used for 'Infirmary' patients, while a nearby house was rented to receive any Fever patients. These changes allowed continuity of care during the time the new building was being erected.

In November, Mary Harrop was appointed Matron, and the temporary 'Infirmary' opened for 20 patients, and a staff of 2 nurses and 1 housemaid. Alas, on February 20th 1816 Mary Harrop resigned, to be succeeded by Mary Campbell on three months trial. Meanwhile, the Governors instructed that the Matron should provide a flannel gown for the Nurse, the first mention of a uniform being provided. The Governors also required the Matron to keep the male and female patients apart, a recurring concern for the next hundred years. The Housemaid was considered to be surplus to requirements. Mrs Campbell oversaw the move to the Infirmary in Etruria, but in 1825 the minutes record her failing health. The Governors obviously thought well of her and made every effort to see she was well cared for.

In 1827, the next Matron Mrs Massey was dismissed for *'having disseminated reports with regard to an Inpatient prejudicial to the interests of the institution'*. This had led to *'unhappy discussions'* between Matron and the House Surgeon; Matron declined to resign, but was dismissed. It was perhaps in order to establish cordial working relations that the Committee ordered that *'in future the House Surgeon and the Matron are uniformly to dine together.'* This is the start of the practice of the staff eating at Matron's table. Mrs Massey was succeeded by Mrs Sarah Brown.

The amount of food and drink consumed by the staff was soon to become a constant preoccupation of the Governors. Soon the rules began to appear, *'servants shall not be allowed ale with their meals, except the nurses, who may have it when Matron sees fit, and the washerwoman on washing days.'*

An interesting instruction appeared in December 1829, when Josiah Wedgwood II signed a minute thus: *'Matron be instructed to employ only chimney sweeps that use machines (brushes), and on no account to let any boy go up any flue in the Infirmary.'* Fittingly, his son Francis formed and was the secretary of the Chimney Sweeps' Association that got rid of the employment of climbing boys in the Potteries in the 1850s. Nationally, legislation forbidding children being sent up chimneys only became effective in 1875 when sweeps had to be authorised by the Police.

In 1837 Mrs Brown retired due to ill health and infirmity; it was resolved that her successor must not be above 50 years of age. Further, it was agreed that with the increased number of patients the existing salary was too low to attract good candidates. Raised to £40 pa, the post was advertised in the *Birmingham Gazette* and *Manchester Guardian*. Mrs Cotton, who formerly kept the Legs of Man Inn in Burslem, was appointed. For the first time a set of *Rules for Matron*, indeed a job description appeared. It is remarkably similar to rules issued for the Matron of the Manchester School for the Deaf and Dumb at the same time, an organisation with close connections to many associated with the Infirmary in North Staffordshire.

(1) Matrons was a full time appointment.

(2) She was not to leave the Hospital unless the House Surgeon took charge.

(3) She was to keep the Infirmary economical, clean and efficient.

(4) She was to exercise economy in her purchases, but seek good quality, vouchers for the purchases to be passed to the Committee

(5) She must keep a weekly account book, noting the weight of food, its price, the number of patients, and work out the average cost per patient.

(6) She could take advantage of bulk buying.

(7) She must observe the prescribed Diet Book.

(8) She must visit each ward in the morning and evening, check that chambers, beds, clothes and linen be kept clean. *Every Inpatient to have clean sheets on admission, changed every 14 days or oftener if necessary.* If the weather was satisfactory, in rotation mattresses, blankets and quilts to be exposed to the sun and well aired: patients were to help if possible.

(9) She must take care that the nurses scour their wards with soap and warm water or lye on a Wednesday, before 9 a.m. in Summer, before 10 a.m. in Winter. They are to mop the wards on another day, and constantly clean by sweeping. (Lye was a caustic scouring material derived from wood ash.)

(10) The nurses must scald the chamber pots and night tables every morning, and scour them every Thursday before 9a.m. and see that they are kept out of the ward during the day time except in cases of necessity.

(11) Matron should visit patients morning and evening, enquiring had medicines been regularly given, had the patients been properly attended and well used by the nurses. She must also enquire into the conduct of the patients and report to the Inspector.

(12) Matron must see that the food was properly cooked, and served punctually: Breakfast at 7-30 a.m., Dinner at 1 p.m. and Supper at 6 p.m. No food was to be served at other times, except on Doctors orders.

(13) She must personally superintend meals, see that the patients receive the quantities specified, that the patients have clean hands and faces, that conduct is orderly, and that Grace is said.

(14) Matron must see that patients are to be uniformly treated by all the attendants of the house with good nature and civility, and Matron should never suffer any degree of cruelty, insolence or neglect in the servants towards them to pass unnoticed.

(15) She must not employ the patients in the wards without the permission of the House Surgeon.

(16) Nurses and servants must obey the rules, or be reported to the Committee.

(17) Matron must keep an inventory of effects.

The Governors had a good record of care towards sick members of staff, although when it was pointed out that the previous Matron was occupying a whole fever ward on her own, it was decided to move her to a General ward.

At this time, the wages of the Cook and Laundry maid were increased. 36 new metal bedsteads were purchased, with pillars to carry curtains 7ft 6inches from the ground. Iron bedsteads were generally superseding the older wooden frames that harboured vermin. Two water-beds were also repaired.

In 1840 there was a gradual increase in activity, nursing wages edged up, the nurses' rooms were improved to give more air, and at Matron's insistence the new laundry had to be further enlarged six feet further than originally planned. The Auditor, Francis (Frank) Wedgwood, son of Josiah II, drew attention to the parlous state of the finances - attempts at retrenchment may be considered to be rolling on for the next twenty years in the background to our story.

Matron was in charge of the house, and the senior staff ate at Matron's table. In addition to strict economies in the use of fuel, and the purchase of food, investigations were undertaken to determine whether it was cheaper to bake and brew 'in house' or to buy in. Gradually, attention focussed on the consumption of food and particularly alcohol at Matron's table, and this forms a running minute in the Committee books.

In 1841, it was decided to resume brewing, but only of beer, and at a prescribed strength of 15 gallons to each bushel of malt. Bread had to be weighed after 24 hours. In August, Matron and the House Surgeon were summoned to the Committee, the need for the strictest economy was emphasised. No visitors (who would eat and drink) were allowed to the staff, and there was to be a regular account rendered of the consumption of porter by the patients and staff.

The supply of butter was reduced to the point, 4oz a week, at which the Physicians complained it was insufficient to feed the patients; the ration was then raised to 6oz.

In March 1842, the Committee noted with regret the *'extra consumption of Bread, Meat and Ale at Matron's table'*. More economy was urged. Alas, by June the monthly *'consumption of Ale at Matrons table was 26 gallons'*, having been 21 gallons in May. Matron was to be held responsible.

Through the list of materials ordered for the house, we can gain a rare view of the colour of the interior of the Infirmary. Brown sheets were ordered for the patients, white for the House Surgeon, calico pillow cases and bolster covers for patients. Grey counterpanes were ordered for the servants and nurses, white for the House Surgeon. Later, (1849) we see that sheets continued to be brown, but the coverlets were always blue.

By 1844, the immediate financial pressures were eased by the personal fund raising efforts of one the physicians, Dr Thomas Mackenzie, when £854 was raised in small sums.

Sadly, the sewers were now palpably defective, and adversely affecting the atmosphere of the entire Infirmary. The bedrooms of the Dispenser and House (medical) Pupil were used in the daytime as the place where outpatients were seen. Four servants (nurses) shared a bedroom 16ft by 10ft 6inches, worse, three shared a room 16ft by 6ft. This room was on the ground floor, built as a cellar, next to the Dead House (mortuary), it had two beds used by day nurses at night and by one night nurse by day. In hot weather the foetid effluvia from the Dead House was often very offensive. The wards were too small, and everyone suffered from the overcrowded and deteriorating state of the building. In 1845, it became necessary to accommodate the servants in a ward appropriated for the purpose. A recent article has shown that poor accommodation for nurses was a widespread problem at this time, and a limiting factor in recruiting and retaining good nurses.

The wards were becoming untidy, Matron was reminded of the rules of the house, but it was noted the nurses were overworked. It was found that the washing of the floors was damaging them and keeping them damp. It was resolved to have them sealed and to rely on dry rubbing after a trial on one ward. By 1846 it became clear that the internal organisation was failing as much as was the fabric of the hospital. The Committee was informed that *patients went 10 to 13 weeks without clean sheets,* patients who were not confined to bed being the worst off. Matron and the nurses were questioned and it was admitted that this could be true. It was affirmed that sheets should be changed every three weeks or more often - note the change from the two week interval prescribed in the Rules for matron of 1837. Matron said that stocks had become very low, but the Committee did not feel that this was a complete justification of Matron, as it was her duty to forecast need and avoid a deficiency. In future sheets were to be changed every three weeks, whether they were dirty or not.

There must be some sympathy for the Matron and nurses, labouring as they were under the twin yokes of attempting to run the hospital and the need to satisfy demands for ever greater economy. Nonetheless, they did appear to be failing the patients. In June 1846 a departing House Surgeon (Mr Alford) took the opportunity to tell the Committee some home truths. He had found it hard to attend diligently to the patients on account of inefficient nursing and attendance.

In October the Surgeons met with the Committee, to give attention to the unsatisfactory state of the bedding in the accident ward. The present beds made of chaff were uncomfortable under any circumstances, becoming solid and lumpy, giving rise to bed-sores, worst in patients with lower limb fractures. The Surgeons suggested best quality horsehair, 6 inches thick laid on a well made straw mattress; the Committee agreed.

In August 1847 the committee sought a porter, duties and payment as follows:

He had the use of Porter's Lodge in which to live.
His pay was fifteen shillings a week.
His wife was to attend to the gate.
His duties were:
    To have charge of Accident and Faith Wards as NURSE.
    To use his best exertions to ameliorating the suffering of Patients with civility,
    kindness and attention to the printed rules.
    To clean the Infirmary on Wednesday and Saturday
    To assist the Dispenser in preparing his medicines-when not occupied
    To have charge of the Boiler and Steam engine. The House to have constant hot
    supply of Hot and Cold Water, and the Laundry a proper supply of steam
    (The steam engine's boiler supplied hot water, while the engine itself pumped water
    around the building and to the upper floors.)
    To clean the engine at least once a week
    To assist the other Porter carrying the coals.
    To clean the pavement around the Infirmary on Saturdays
    To keep the windows clean, with such patients as may be fit so to be employed.
    To shave patients when necessary
    To sweep the front steps every morning, and wash them twice a week
    To answer front door bells.
    To be generally useful to other officers.

Particularly interesting are the duties he had as the Nurse in the Accident Ward. A male presence there seems very reasonable when many of those admitted are described in the Garner notebook (1854-56) as being the worse for drink. In general, male nurses do not appear until the 20th century. He would certainly have little time left after performing his other duties, and there is no mention of free time.

Patients were employed and paid for undertaking work in the wards. In the days before telephones, fit patients were sent out to fetch the consultants to the Infirmary in the event of an emergency.

During the last days of this year, 1847, a select committee reported its findings on a complete review of the workings of the entire Infirmary. For the first time the impracticability of improving the present building was mentioned, together with the need to consider the erection of another Infirmary in a more safe and healthy situation.

In 1848, Matron was for the second time in hot water, having allowed skimmed milk to be supplied to patients, conduct which was *'very censurable'*, and would not be overlooked again. Whether or not some 'scam' was involved is not stated. At the end of the year, Matron's table was again under scrutiny; it was to have an allowance of 3 pints of beer a day, while further controls were applied. Meat was apparently unaccounted for, even if an allowance for shrinkage was made, the losses accounted for £110-120 a year, a vast amount of meat at the prices of the time. Matron was permitted to offer food to medical officers when they attended the Infirmary, but four consultants (honorary staff) decided it was wiser to formally decline this offer in case of confusion. They recognised that there were cash flow problems, there was no stock control and *'it might be implied or imputed that Medical Officers are participators of the thousands of pounds of flesh meat and other provisions the sub-committee are unable to account for..!'* (Allowing 6 old pence per pound this equates to 2 tons of meat)

So it continues: candles were rationed, only rushlights allowed in the wards, meat marked by weight, and now only patients were to be supplied with ale. The letter from the consultants about the missing meat indicates that the internal management of the Infirmary is getting out of control, but there is an implied criticism of the incessant dictats from the committee urging ever more economy. We must remember these were the 'Hungry Forties' - the Governors sanctioned the use of rice in patients' diets if potatoes became scarce, especially in Ireland.

In 1850 a report from the sub-committee on the duties of servants and nurses was produced. The sub-committee interviewed the House Surgeon, Matron and the nurses. They found there were enough people employed to do the work, but there was *a total absence of system*. Matron was found to have no fixed plan of doing the work, so that female servants were moved from job to job. The force of nurses were sufficient if they were efficient and qualified for their situation. The nurses should include the scourer, who was appointed to assist the nurses. The wards were scoured every 2-3 weeks, instead of weekly as the rules required. It was proposed that Matron should draw up a code of laws, and specify the work of each member of staff; at this time the scourer became an under nurse.

Radically it was proposed that *'an intelligent female, accustomed to nursing'* should superintend the wards and act as head nurse. Here we have a complete review of nursing, crucially separating nursing the sick from cleaning the building and from the administrative work. The salaries were rearranged to reflect these changes; that of the head nurse rose substantially from £12 to £20 per annum, while Matron took a pay cut to reflect her lightened duties. It may be no surprise to see that soon after this that a report from matron was delayed due to her sickness. It was pointed out that the total number of staff would remain the same, but comprise a *'different class of persons.'* This review took place a decade before Florence Nightingales proposals for the reform of nursing, and recognises the need for an intelligent person to become a nurse, indeed a better class of person.

The minutes have frequent entries detailing payment for new bedding, but Matron was again accused of neglecting the inventory, and in1853 the House Surgeon protested about the state of the linen and blankets, *'much is so ragged as to be useless.'* The problem lay with the want of a good supply, and the impossibility of one woman (in the laundry) supplying so large an Institution. Soon afterwards, Mrs Cotton resigned as matron, to be replaced by Mrs Eliza Ledward.

Soon there were rumbles of discontent between Mrs Ledward and a pupil, Mitchell. By May 1854, Mr Folker, the House Surgeon wrote to the Committee: two patients had been allowed meat and cheese for breakfast for doing the night nurse's work. Worse, Matron had come to table excited by liquor and insulted Mr Folker, Mr Mitchell and Mr Bache the

Dispenser. She further stated that Mr Folker and Mr Mitchell were no gentlemen, Mitchell was an infidel and the Infirmary would never be right until he was got rid of, and she bore him ill will. She was further accused of having made faces at Mitchell and called him names in front of the servants.

The charges against Mrs Ledward were considered by the Committee to be proved to a certain extent; she then overplayed her hand. She charged that Mr Folker was alone in his bedroom with a woman in suspicious circumstances: the Committee saw not the slightest ground for imputing improper conduct to Mr Folker, indeed he and his son successively served the Infirmary as Surgeons over the next 60 years. Three days later Mrs Ledward returned to the attack with more charges, but she was informed her resignation was expected.

Miss Derry took up the post of Matron on May 22nd 1854. Committee meetings continued to reflect the continuing deterioration of the Infirmary building, and this problem becomes the dominant concern for the next 10 years. Perhaps as a result of this preoccupation with the state of the building, and the realisation that Matron cannot be expected to overcome all deficiencies herself, Miss Derry rarely appears in the Minutes. As an appearance in the Minutes is usually evidence of a problem, we may assume that Miss Derry performed her duties satisfactorily. This supposition is confirmed by the fact that in 1858 her salary was raised from £40 to £50 per annum.

We have seen that the sleeping accommodation of the nurses was very unsatisfactory, and in 1854 the room was considered so close and the stench so bad that it was unfit for a human being to sleep there. The women who slept there were weak and unwell, and were apprehensive that the air was injurious to their health. They must have been obviously unwell, for, 'in their present condition,' Matron was to obtain a charwoman on two days a week to help with their work.

Plans were approved to move the Dead House, and to improve the accommodation of Matron and the Nurses. Under these conditions it was not an easy task to maintain discipline among the staff. Cook was dismissed for drunkenness after two warnings.

The public perception of nurses at the time would not have been improved by Dickens portrayal of Sarah Gamp and Betsy Prig in *Martin Chuzzlewit.* The illustration by Phiz (H.K. Brown) shows the nurses drinking a toast from a teapot which contained rather more than tea.

Constant improvements continued to the sanitary facilities and attempts were made to improve the ventilation of the building. Problems continued with the sewers and their outflow. The problem of damp and rotting floors was addressed by treating them with boiled oil and sand, followed by beeswax. New wards, including one for female syphilitic patients increased the capacity of the hospital. Patients were at times pressed into service, painting floors, work for which they were paid. It is good to know that those patients who helped to carry lifeless bodies to the Dead House were allowed a little ale! Disposable materials were a hundred years in the future, but the appearance of oil cloth to be spread under phials and gallipots are the first steps to the use of waterproof materials to protect bedding.

In January 1858, the depressed state of trade was a concern, even so, deeper mattresses filled now with coconut fibre were supplied, and it was reported that the wards were free from bugs. Gas lighting was installed in the corridors of the Infirmary, but not yet in the wards.

Visitors had been appointed by the Committee since the earliest days of the institution to enquire as to the well being of the patients. In 1859 their numbers were augmented by a panel of twelve Lady Visitors. Although lady subscribers had always had a vote proportional to their subscription they had been expected to exercise their right by sending proxy votes; for the first time ladies were able to play an active part. Soon, it was agreed that the Lady Visitors should be informed of the presence of Fever Patients in the ward, whether in order that they should be visited by the ladies or avoided by them is not immediately clear.

It must not be thought that economy was a dead letter. The sub-committee on increased expenditure was very concerned by the quantity of extra nourishments and diets given to patients. A table was produced comparing the period July to October in 1858 and 1859. Fewer patients had consumed more food in 1859 than in 1858. The eternal tension between the Medical staff and those responsible for the finances may be read in the note that *'the sub-committee do not comment on Medical staff orders* (for extra food and stimulants, wine and brandy for patients), *but urge economy'*. On safer ground they turned on the staff consumption of food, and Matron's table. They noted that the officers of the Establishment ate two dinners, meat and vegetables, puddings and pastry and cheese each day at 1pm and 5pm. It was therefore resolved that in future there should be a cold luncheon, involving no cooking, and only one cooked meal would, in the evening. Meals were only for members of the Establishment and Medical Officers. Malt liquor was only to be served with meals.

1860 brings the first minute that mentions the Nightingale reforms. The paper *'Regulations as to the Training of Probationer Nurses under the Nightingale Fund'* was received and ordered to be preserved by the Secretary for future reference.

In December of that year the setting up of a fund to provide comforts for patients is most informative about conditions in the Infirmary. It was recognised that the *'ordinary income of the Infirmary was insufficient to provide many almost indispensible requirements necessary for the decent accommodation of patients.'* Hair mattresses were now found in all well regulated hospitals, instead of those filled with chaff still found in this Infirmary. The arrangements for the reception of clothes in the wards was *'unworthy of such an institution.'* It was noted that many patients would benefit from sea bathing in their convalescence, and many left in a very destitute state, *'a little relief might remedy this evil and prevent relapses.'* It is cheering to note that William Taylor's wages as Indoor Porter were to be paid for the period of his being an Inpatient. The Special Fund was raised, £ 330 in six months, clothing was given, patients were sent to Buxton and Southport, and better mattresses purchased. There is a note of £25 being subscribed to help patients purchase surgical apparatus required in cases of deformity, perhaps the first appeal focused on a particular disability.

In 1854 accounts arrived in London from the *Times* war correspondent, W.H. Russell, concerning the lack of medical attention and supplies for the troops in the Crimea. As a result Florence Nightingale decided to lead a party of nurses to the war.

The image shown here, from *Punch* November 11 1854, is the first to feature Miss Nightingale. The addition of a human face to an appropriate animal or bird was a common form of caricature at the time (and still is).

The nurse offering a drink to the soldier has wings to indicate her status as a ministering angel.

The text accompanying the picture was ambivalent, stating that never again should there be a lack of nurses in military hospitals - in future it must not be left to young ladies to supply the deficiency! It questions the nursing skills of the young ladies, who have *'never even nursed a baby'*. It proposes that *'a day's* (my emphasis) *experience at St Bartholomew's Hospital would be advisable'* before they set off.

When dealing with the staff, their delinquencies usually seem to have centred on excessive consumption of alcohol and failure to perform their duties, though in February 1862, the housemaid was dismissed, being pregnant by Mr Bate the senior pupil.

In 1863, Ann Parry had died from fever contracted in faithful discharge of her duties as a nurse at the Infirmary. The Governors paid her wages for the next six months, for the benefit of her children, and paid her funeral expenses. As two nurses were required at this time, it was agreed to write to the Liverpool Training Institution to ascertain if any are to be obtained from there, though we do nor know the result of this application. This Institution was the result of collaboration between William Rathbone, a Liverpool philanthropist and Florence Nightingale. Two years later, a trained nurse was sought to

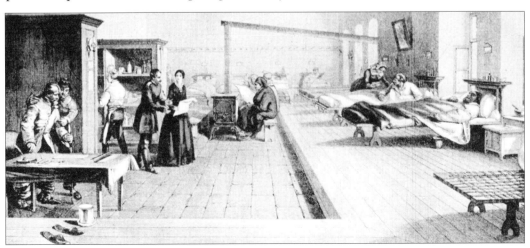

Another image of Florence Nightingale, this at Scutari Hospital in the Crimea.

replace Nurse Davenport who was given a years salary, £14 as a gratuity, in recognition of the fact that she had lost her health in the performance of her duties.

At the same time, a letter was received from the secretary of the Nursing Association of the Diocese of Lichfield. The secretary had written to all the hospitals in the Diocese, enquiring whether they would undertake the training of nurses, if so, how many and on what terms? This may be taken as a starting date for the formal training of nurses in North Staffordshire.

The Diocese of Lichfield included three counties, Derbyshire, Shropshire and Staffordshire. Fund-raising committees were formed to raise funds for the training and provision of qualified nurses for hospitals, families and the poor. Initially training took place in London. At St Thomas's Hospital training was free, being paid for by the Nightingale Fund. At Kings College Hospital a charge was made for training. The St Thomas's Nurses were intended primarily to work in hospitals; the training at Kings College Hospital was more broadly based for nurses intended for work in the patient's home. Training at Kings took one year, it included midwifery, childcare and advice and education for mothers, much as might be expected of a Health Visitor in later years. It was expected that each Parish would be responsible for raising money to pay for 'their' nurse. The scheme was particularly advanced for its time in that proper remuneration was insisted upon and even more remarkably in that a superannuation scheme was incorporated.

By 1870 the scheme split into three County Associations. From Staffordshire the early supporters who were also associated with the North Staffordshire Infirmary include The Rev E.J. Edwards of Trentham who was the scheme's first secretary and Sir Smith Child. The Smith Child Ward had been built in the grounds of the new Infirmary at Hartshill to accommodate those patients excluded by the Rules, the chronic sick and incurable patients. It was soon converted to provide a home for the Association's Nurses, under the supervision of the *'Lady in Charge'*, Miss Harding. The Nurses' Home moved to new premises in Hartshill in 1876, after which the Smith Child Ward served as the Children's Ward.

Thus trained nurses appeared in Staffordshire in the 1860s. The Diocesan scheme was originally organised to serve parishes, which would support their nurse. The scheme had elements of all voluntary schemes with regular subscriptions from the better off. For those who could afford to pay there was a scale of charges levied by the Association who then employed the Nurses. We can see how these nurses were perceived in Arnold Bennett's novel *Clayhanger*: one of these nurses came to nurse Darius in his last illness. We can encounter an early representative in Longton in 1863 when a nurse noted as being trained was employed by the Rev Adam Clark to look after patients in their homes. Her salary was paid by a collection of money from trades people in Longton. It was from this initiative that Longton Cottage Hospital developed. This nurse gave young ladies in the area an opportunity to accompany her on her rounds to discover whether or not they felt an aptitude for nursing. Nurses trained under these schemes would be especially important in the growth of professional nursing and the setting up of training schemes and schools of nursing in hospitals across the country. Those employed in hospitals were in effect contracted to the local Association, which received their pay from the hospital and passed it on to the nurse; thus they were able to keep an eye on the nurses' interests. In December 1865, Nurse Smith was engaged from the Bath Nursing Association as Superintendent Nurse.

These were the last days of the Infirmary in Etruria, the new building was nearly complete in Hartshill, and the Governors, following the precept of Florence Nightingale, felt that only a Lady Superintendent would suffice to head their nursing staff.

CHAPTER 12
The Nurses 1870-1948

The new Infirmary was nearing completion. It was time to improve the training and status of the Nursing Staff. Naturally, the Committee turned to the principles advocated by Florence Nightingale. The results were not those that might have been expected, and though her advice was sought on several occasions, the Infirmary followed its own path.

A Better Class of Person.

In February, 1869, just as a specially ordered load of five tons of coal was being used to dry out the plaster in the new Infirmary building, the following advertisement appeared in the newspapers:

> 'The Committee are anxious to obtain the services of a Lady who will be competent from her practical acquaintance with nursing under Hospital Training to Superintend the Nursing and to manage with the aid of a Housekeeper the Domestic Department of this Infirmary.
>
> Salary £70 per annum, Board, washing and service are provided. It is expected that the new infirmary will be opened before May, next, at which date it will be necessary for the Lady who may be appointed to enter upon her duties as Superintendent.
>
> Further particulars could be obtained from Mr Hordley, at The Infirmary, Etruria. It was wished that applications be sent in not later than March 30th that sufficient time may be allowed for making the requisite enquiries.'

The concept of a Lady Superintendent of course arises from Florence Nightingale's personal view that while nurses had to be trained, they, or at least their leaders had to be morally superior to conduct the war against disease. Disease was seen as a breakdown of order, a failure of organisation that allowed dirt and uncleanliness to flourish and encourage disease. Sin played its part in that it was responsible for the failings in the system which encouraged disorder. At the same time it is helpful to recall that lady-like nurses were needed to attend the Private Patients that St Thomas's Hospital began to admit after 1867. It was the first hospital to do so and these paying patients provided a considerable part of its income. Certainly Florence could be very directive when it came to her protégés, and when Godfrey Wedgwood asked her to recommend one of them to North Staffordshire as Lady Superintendant, she refused, saying that they would be wasted there. As we shall see, she may have been right, but not in the way she imagined.

At any rate, there was no great rush of applicants, two in fact. Miss Jane Watson had undergone Special Training at St Mary's; the Committee needed references and further information. Miss Nicoll had nursed in the Crimea, having worked at the Civil Hospital in Smyrna; the Committee wanted to know what she had done since that time. They decided to readvertise the post in the *Lancet*, the *Times* and the *Manchester Examiner*. Meanwhile, they took the opportunity of the move to the new Infirmary to appoint the first House Physician who would look after patients in the Medical Wards.

Dr Arlidge headed a Nursing Committee to appoint a Superintendent. Miss Nicoll was appointed, but within 5 months she resigned as she was about to be married to a gentleman from Stafford.

The previous Matron, Miss Derry was now the Housekeeper. This demotion was an uncharacteristically unkind act by the Committee; Miss Derry had served them well.

Their action can only be explained by the Committee being dazzled by the prospect of employing a Lady Superintendent.

The next advertisement for a Lady Superintendent attracted 22 applications. It was agreed to follow up three: Miss McLaughlin from Walsall Cottage Hospital, Miss Duck from Bristol, and an offer from Mr Bonham Carter (Florence Nightingale's cousin and secretary of the Nightingale Fund) of a Lady and staff trained under the Nightingale fund. Mr Edwards (Vicar of Trentham) was to see Miss Duck, and to see Mrs Wardroper, Matron of St Thomas's Hospital in London as to the Lady Superintendent recommended by Mr Bonham Carter. Miss Duck was preferred. She would not accept a full time appointment, but would come with two friends to keep her company to give temporary assistance in organising the staff and perfecting the arrangements. Her offer was accepted. The Committee hoped she would accept the salary.

Mr Folker reported to the Committee on the number of nurses required for the central wards, eight were hoped for. Three came from the old infirmary, H. Haggith, *trained, £19 per annum*, Mary Ann Rowley (£17pa) and Ellen Wood (£15pa), both *'untrained but good.'* Nurses Joyce and Dawson were recruited at £25pa, as were three others at £19pa. All were appointed.

A committee was formed to consider the relationship between the duties of Lady Superintendent and the previous post of Matron. Meanwhile the House Surgeon was to be the Master of the House, and the Lady Superintendent the Mistress. The Housekeeper and servants were to be subordinate to them.

Miss Duck saw the Infirmary opened by the Duchess of Sutherland in December, 1869, but by the end of January it was clear from her letter to the Committee that she wished to move back to Bristol. She said she did not think that she had the strength to be a full time Lady Superintendent, she had come as a guest to help organise the new Infirmary. She had not received the hoped for support, perhaps she had been using the wrong channels of communication.

She reported some serious defects: she disapproved of the nurses taking meals together, the patients were greatly inconvenienced by the manner in which meals were served. The meat might follow the pudding by half an hour. She believed that there was a want of system, of economy and waste amounting to extravagance. There was a misuse of bedding and a want of inventories. She said that economy did not consist of stinting necessities but being careful of materials.

She then turned to a graver matter *'affecting health and humanity.'* When a death occurred the *'ghastly spectacle of a coffin'* appeared before the patients, who were subjected to all the sights and sounds of the preparation of a corpse. Patients would then carry it to the Dead House, and sometimes have *'to take their dinner in the presence of a corpse'*. More, female patients, even young girls walked in the garden at the same time as men, some of whose character was too bad for women to nurse them.

She then expounded her views on the place and duties of the Lady Superintendent. The first principle of a well ordered hospital was to have an Educated Gentlewoman at the head, in reality the position of Mistress, the representative and co-adjutor of the Committee. From the nature of the women's work in hospitals, it was in the interest of these women to have as a Superintendent a woman of cultivation, a friend and counsellor and protector of those under her care, who had at heart the cause of order, decency and morality. Some circumstances, which she would not detail, *would cause gentlemen who were present to be shocked. The relation of the Lady Superintendent and the Medical Staff should be based on close cooperation, not from rules but regard for knowledge and experience. The strength of the Lady Superintendent lay in studious attention to the minutest instructions of the Medical Staff. She had exclusive responsibility for the economy, morality, order and comfort of all under her surveillance within and without the wards.* She concluded by saying that she was returning to hospital nursing in Bristol. She declined any payment.

At a Special Meeting of the Governors on January 25th, 1870, Miss Cartwright was appointed to the post of Lady Superintendent. It was agreed that she should appoint one or more Probationer Nurses, but was requested to bear in mind the (limited) amount of sleeping accommodation available. A Housemaid (£12pa) was appointed, together with two competent laundrymaids (£14), in addition to the laundress, an additional servant as a waitress, and a charwoman employed for three days a week.

On March 17th, Miss Cartwright and Miss Derry, who had been the previous Matron and was now the Housekeeper, were seen by the Committee. In the case of Miss Derry altered circumstances, indeed exceptional circumstances caused her to submit her resignation. She must have been highly valued by the Committee, or was it that they felt they had placed her in an impossible situation by placing her under the lady Superintendent, for they gave her a gift of £50, a whole year's salary. Miss Cartwright was to advertise for a replacement Housekeeper at £30 per annum, while the salary of Cook was to be £20, with board, lodging and washing, but NO perks. Miss Oakden was appointed as Housekeeper.

There was soon friction with the Governors, when Miss Cartwright was reminded that the appointment of the male servants was a matter for the Committee. Economy was still important, the housemaids were reduced in number from four to three. Mr Lynam, the Honorary Architect was asked to investigate dampness in the bedrooms, which was blamed for sickness among the staff. It is worth noting that new hospitals in several other towns were afflicted by outbreaks of infectious disease at this time. The probable cause was that the early 1870s were years when streptococcal infections were particularly virulent. There were those who had opposed new buildings, and doubtless they saw themselves as being vindicated.

It must have been alarming to the Governors and Staff when there was an outbreak of typhoid fever in the Infirmary. They had left the dilapidated old Infirmary for the new ideal building on a most salubrious site, but the health of the staff was not satisfactory, and now there was an outbreak of typhoid! There were 18 cases among patients, of whom 8 died, and 3 among the staff, of whom 1, who significantly worked in the laundry, also died. The cause of typhoid fever was still unknown, not until 1884 would the causative organism be discovered, and there was much debate as to the nature of the disease itself. The minutes note that *'while many great authorities believe that it is non-contagious there is quite sufficient evidence of its communicability to behove us to be careful.'* The Fever (Albert) wards had not yet been opened, an investigation suggested that *'there had been no more spread of the disease in the wards than if the fever wards had been open.'*

Relations between the Committee, the Medical staff and Miss Cartwright were now in sharp decline. Reports were received on the employment of probationer nurses and the wages and dress of nurses. Miss Cartwright was warned *'not to part with nurses on the account of dress'.* Uniforms were only to be worn by nurses, night nurses and probationers. Miss Cartwright had given notice to Nurse Joyce, and declined to withdraw it, despite being informed that, *'Nurse Joyce is highly valued by the Medical officers.'* She was one of the best paid at £25 per annum.

The Committee now recorded that they regretted *'that Miss Cartwright has continued her notice to Nurse Joyce despite the recommendation of the Medical Committee.'* While unwilling to put further pressure on her in this case, they had to impress upon her that the management of the nurses and servants in the institution is *'one which required great judgement, kindness and discretion, and they hope that the frequent changes of nurses and servants, which has marked her administration of the Infirmary will cease as it implies want of discernment in engaging them or hastiness in dismissing them.'* The Committee approved a new rule, whereby the Lady Superintendent could engage staff, but not dismiss them without reference to them.

A Special Meeting of the Committee was called, with Robert Heath in the chair, to consider a letter from Miss Cartwright, in which she complained of the conduct of patients in the Accident Ward. A patient had wanted to obtain a pint of brandy. A previous nurse used to subscribe one shilling and sixpence and drank with the male patients. Miss Cartwright considered such conduct *'insufferable, generally disgusting and shockingly indelicate';* the nurse had resigned. The Medical Committee had questioned those involved in the current episode, and felt that the condition of the patient explained his conduct. Miss Cartwright now wrote to Mr Heath:

'Sir,

Understanding from the Rev. Sir Lovelace Stamer the tone of discussion which took place yesterday after I left the Boardroom - I fully concur with his advice to resign my appointment.'

At the next Committee meeting, it was resolved that the post of Lady Superintendent should not be filled up, but a new post of Superintendent of Nurses be created. So it was that North Staffordshire's brief fling with a Lady Superintendent came to an end. In the nature of things, those for whom the Infirmary existed were those who could not afford to pay for medical attention. Anyone who could pay would do so to avoid admission to hospital and to be treated at home or in a nursing home, thus the patients inevitably came from the working classes. Good-hearted they may well have been, but they would contain some not amenable to the niceties of Victorian etiquette. The Governors were not sympathetic to Miss Cartwright's strictures. Many of them, like Robert Heath, who owned large businesses, understood these patients and knew how to deal with them. The Medical Staff would also have understood their patients, and recognised that the nurses would

Rev Sir Lovelace Stamer Bt. Vicar of Stoke, Bishop of Shrewsbury and grandson of John Tomlinson.

have to manage these men by befriending rather than bullying them. The Committee members were not a soft touch, they *did* expel patients for violent conduct and gross disregard of the rules, but they did understand the people with whom they dealt.

Nevertheless, there were limits and to give a balanced view of the world in which the Infirmary operated, and indeed to be fair to Miss Cartwright, we must recognise that not every patient was automatically a paragon of virtue. The Infirmary had a duty to help the needy, but there was an implied contract that those in receipt of treatment should behave in a reasonable manner, not abuse the system and not make life impossible for the nurses and, be it noted, for other patients. Being an independent charity rules could be set, and if the transgression justified action the Governors could say 'enough is enough'.

Other than the Gamer notebook, our best resource for the later 19th century is an admission book for the years 1879 to 1882. It lists the patient's name and address, and the source of the recommendation, in the case of an Establishment contribution, the recommendation would be in the name of the employer. Some details of treatment were included together with the name of the Surgeon or Physician in whose care the patient was placed, and, best of all, the outcome and details of discharge. The majority of the patients were discharged to their home, many being made Outpatients to complete their treatment. A substantial number went away for convalescence to St Anne's or New Brighton, under the aegis of the North Staffordshire Convalescent Fund, another favourite cause of Sir Smith Child. Some patients were sent to the workhouse when no more could be done for them, but these often appear to be patients needing long term care, for example a blind woman and a women suffering from paralysis.

Discharges were divided into three major categories, Cured, Practically Cured and I.S.Q. that is unimproved but implicitly no worse than when they came in. Others however left more precipitately. Some left of their own accord, often against medical advice, others were taken out by relatives or friends. One was a four year old child with burns to his arm, leg and face whose father removed him 'rather than pay two shillings a week'. Some left having 'refused to submit to treatment or operation', while a girl left after refusing to have her hair cut off, even though it was described as 'lousy'. Drinking brandy in the ward, swearing at the nurses, impudence to a nurse or the Superintendent of Nurses could all bring about expulsion, as could annoying other patients. One such delinquent was 'swearing and throwing things at other patients and threatening to murder them'.

Discontent with and complaints about the standard of food appear not infrequently in the reasons for discharge. One patient felt the meat was too fatty, another left because he was put on a milk diet while a further gentleman 'considered the food was not of a quality good enough for him'. We must however have sympathy with the collier aged 20 who 'could not make himself content away from home'.

Outpatients could also fall below the standards which could be hoped for, and they abused a system designed to help those who could not afford treatment. In 1899 a minute stated that only plain cod liver oil was to be supplied to Outpatients and then only to the 'needy'. Apparently 'there appeared to be a traffic in the (much more palatable) cod liver oil emulsion'; some patients, having received it free of charge proceeded to sell it on.

The titles Lady Superintendent and Superintendent of Nurses are superficially so similar as to seem a quibble about words. The key words are of course lady and nurses. The lady was not necessarily trained or experienced in nursing, she was there to supply an elevated tone to the establishment, and her approach was directed to this end. Conversely, the Superintendent of Nurses was expected to be educated, trained and experienced. In most cases she would have been a lady, but she had to be a nurse first and a lady second. She would be expected to manage the nurses as well as train them and by doing so raise standards of education.

It would be useful to think about the changes taking place throughout nursing at this time. Since the return of Florence Nightingale from the Crimea no one could be ignorant of the problems in Britain's hospitals. The outcry had led to a call for trained nurses, and we have seen that in London this had led to the opening of Schools of Nursing at St

Thomas's, Kings College and other hospitals. The local response came with the Lichfield Diocesan scheme of 1865; all the hospitals in the diocese were asked to take and train probationer nurses. Expectations were rising, new surgical techniques were being developed, and adequate numbers of trained nurses were needed to provide these improved standards of care. This was a time of change, the old ways were no longer acceptable, certainly not nurses drinking brandy in the wards. One may sympathise with the Lady Superintendent in that she clearly was not equipped to manage change satisfactorily. The Board's choice of words to Miss Cartwright are a masterly summing up of that which is required, regretting the frequent changes of staff and the lack of judgement and kindness which have caused them.

The minutes that have survived are chiefly a record of decisions taken at 'Board' level, and many of the day to day details are lost. The census returns taken every ten years give us a rare snapshot of the staff, as they record all who were in the Infirmary on the appointed night. We must accept that there are many opportunities for error when taking a census and there were additional rules specific to a large institution such as a hospital or a workhouse. Only those present on the designated census night were counted, those who were away for whatever reason were not counted, thus the House Surgeon, being resident, was always counted, the Consultants were not. We know that until the Nurses' homes were built at the turn of the 20th century the Infirmary was always short of accommodation, therefore we do not know if any nurses slept outside the Infirmary, and if they did, what numbers were involved.

In 1861 in the old Infirmary in Etruria there were six nurses and ten domestic staff to look after 99 patients, 6 patients for every staff member. By 1891 there were nine nurses, four night nurses, 18 probationers and 31 domestic staff, a total of 67 staff for 186 patients, or 2.8 patients for each staff member. Thus the ratio of staff to patients had doubled in thirty years. While originally recruitment had been mainly of nurses whose place of birth was Staffordshire, a state of affairs which always continued to be the case with the domestic staff, there was now a wide spread of nurse recruitment from across the country. By 1871, there were nurses who had been born in Brighton, Dublin, Gloucester, London and Scotland, presumably drawn from the training schemes in London. By 1891, two thirds of the trained nurses were born in Staffordshire and probably most of them were trained at the Infirmary. The Infirmary had attracted trainees (probationers) from Derbyshire, Cheshire, Lincolnshire, Warwick, Liverpool and Yorkshire. The remainder, nearly half the total, were born locally. This suggests that the training offered in North Staffordshire was proving attractive to candidates from well outside the Potteries.

Miss Crawford was the first to hold the new title of Superintendent of Nurses. She resigned after a year citing poor health and thanking the Committee for much kindness, to be succeeded by Miss Simmonds in 1872. This lady soon offended the Committee, for during the following year her conduct was investigated. Her conduct had been 'indiscreet', causing the committee great fear that the nurses were not under proper supervision; she was warned to be more careful in future. Worse than this, Mr Neale's constant visits to the infirmary were the cause of grave scandal injurious to the best interests of the institution: he was requested to abstain from these visits. Miss Simmonds resigned in the following year, 1874.

It was difficult to find a replacement. Miss Harding, the delightfully titled 'Lady in Charge of the North Staffordshire Nursing Association' declined the post, and Miss Edwards, the daughter of the Vicar of Trentham deputised temporarily. Eventually Miss Annan was appointed. This was a most successful appointment. She was open to new ideas coming from other hospitals, for example we know she visited the Children's Hospital in Birmingham and drew on the experience of their staff when the Children's Ward was opened at the Infirmary and we have on record that she recruited probationers recommended by the Superintendent of District Nurses in Manchester and from Nursing Associations in Lincolnshire and Nottingham. She remained for 17 years, resigning in 1891, having presided over the formative years of Nurse Training in North Staffordshire. She had been well regarded and when she left she was presented with a purse of sovereigns by the Governors and Staff.

In 1884 we find the Governors voting a pension of half a crown a week to Mrs Ecclestone, an old and faithful servant of the Infirmary, and considering the case of Nurse in Charge (Sister) Hulme, who had contracted pulmonary tuberculosis. She was granted £5 for her expenses and seven shillings and sixpence a week and sent to a sanatorium. More significant was the discussion of the propriety of paying pensions to disabled staff, especially from that scourge of young women, tuberculosis. The practice of other hospitals was investigated; the principle was not settled yet, but seems to have been dealt with on an individual basis.

The problem of an adequate supply of bedrooms for nurses, who were expected to be strictly resident in the hospital was being addressed piecemeal. It was quite usual for ward sisters in 19th century hospitals to have their bedroom attached to the ward. Such bedrooms were later used as the Sister's office on the ward. Six bedrooms were built above the kitchen block, while later the upper floor of Albert Ward was converted to sleeping quarters for nurses.

In 1891 Miss Wilkinson who came from the Women's and Children's Hospital in Leeds succeeded Miss Annan. The Committee, taking the opportunity of a change of Superintendent investigated the conditions of nursing in other hospitals, increasing the number of probationers, ie trainees, from 13 to 19, and increasing their wages and that of the sisters, though these ladies had to wait another ten years for that title. The question of a pension scheme was again discussed; it was thought that a pension would remove the embarrassment of the nurses being dependent on a gratuity when they retired. In 1893, there were further problems: Night Nurses were often a law unto themselves. Other hospitals also had problems because the night nurses frequently formed a separate team from the day staff, and saw themselves as a separate entity, perhaps even as an elite who operated in the hours of darkness. Generally, matters improved when the staffs were integrated, and the night duty was performed by all the nurses in rotation. The workload and the use of untrained probationers also caused resentment.

Miss Wilkinson seems to have ruffled some feathers, perhaps the inevitable result of a new broom. She appears to have been rather more keen on discipline and came into conflict with the House Surgeon and the nurses when she altered off duty rotas without warning. It was agreed to increase the number of nurses and establish a hospital certificate for nurses, based on that of the Leeds General Infirmary, to be obtained after three years. It is a marker of the importance attached to these new certificates that initially the order was placed for them to be printed on paper, and then changed to parchment. A programme of lectures given by the medical staff was instituted, as were local examinations. In 1895, a nurse received a year's salary as a reward for twenty-three years service. In 1896 we find the appointment of a permanent Surgical Nurse, a definite step towards specialised nursing. More bedrooms were added above Albert Ward, which was then used for infectious diseases. At long last pensions were funded for nurses; the provision of pensions was another area where the diocesan scheme was in advance of current practice.

In 1897 Miss Wilkinson resigned to become matron of the new Derbyshire Royal Infirmary. She was followed in quick succession by Miss Warburton, Miss Jessop and Miss Pearse. A further enquiry into the Engagement and Training of Nurses looked into the examinations, lectures, duties and pay.

In 1899 Mr H.H. Folker proposed that an appeal be started to provide a proper Nurses' Home. He recognised that the present accommodation was inferior to that of other hospitals, and that only the provision of good quality accommodation would attract and retain first class nurses. In order to set the fund in motion he offered a donation of £100, on the condition that the design was thrown open to competition. In 1902, Lord Dartmouth, the Lord Lieutenant of Staffordshire laid the foundation stone of the new home, which contained fifty bedrooms.

So ended a momentous thirty years in the history of the Infirmary and of its nursing staff, perhaps the most important years, for everything else followed from and depended on these developments. A recent article in the journal *Medical History* has reviewed the development of nursing throughout the 19th century as it was seen from the point of view of the 12 London medical schools. It offers a valuable yardstick to compare our provincial Infirmary with the London Teaching Hospitals. As with our Infirmary, the nurses began as servants, offering a degree of domestic care to the patients. Many of their duties involved cleaning the wards, supplying laundry and food to the patients, nursing care came lower

The North Staffordshire Nursing Association Home in Hartshill.

in the scheme of things. Many were drawn from the class of lower servants, poorly paid and often overworked, immortalised by Charles Dickens in the shape of Sarah Gamp and Betsy Prig, and preserved for all time in their teapot full of gin. The improvement in the quality of entrants into nursing began with the separation of the cleaning from the nursing duties, though this did not begin until 1850.

The besetting difficulty in obtaining and retaining staff in most hospitals was the poor quality of accommodation offered. In the Infirmary in Etruria in 1854 the bedroom was so crowded as to be thought dangerous, while Richardson in 1864 described the nurses as being all *'obliging, kind women, but overworked and depressed.'* There were 106 patients being looked after by four day nurses and two night nurses, aided by two scourers. *'The reason for this is want of accommodation. In a Hospital where, as it sometimes happens, two patients have to be put into one bed, where is there room for nurses and attendants.'* (The only reference I have found to patients having to share a bed in the Infirmary minutes and records, though it is unlikely to have been a unique event as evidenced by the casual mention of it.)

Thus the nurses were overworked, particularly the night nurses, and urgent action had to be taken to increase the accommodation. Pay was another problem, only when it rose to acceptable levels was it possible to recruit more suitable candidates. At least we have no record of the nurses in North Staffordshire having to pay a substitute when they were ill, as happened in London until the 1860s.

As with the London hospitals, it was the medical staff that drove the advance of nursing. They wanted well trained staff to cope with the advances being made in treatment, nevertheless they were unwilling to lose those who had the natural gift of being good nurses. Equally, training in good centres was important for the future of the profession. The dilemma as to the 'class' of candidate most suitable is well illustrated in the chapter on the training of a theatre nurse in Spencer Wells' book on ovariotomy. Clearly he favoured the nurse who was increasing her attainments rather than the employment of the lady nurse. (see chapter 12)

We know that Florence Nightingale gave specific advice on one occasion about the provision of nurses in North Staffordshire. The question was on the advisability of providing a separate children's ward. Traditionally if any children were admitted at all to hospital they were found accommodation in the adult wards, and treated according to their particular disease, be it medical or surgical. It was considered that they would be mothered or mentored by older patients in the ward who had experience of looking after the younger members of large families. From these patients the children would receive the personal care that could not be provided by the scarce nurses on the wards.

Godfrey Wedgwood had written to Florence Nightingale to seek her advice. Sir Smith Child had offered to convert the building he had previously provided into a Children's Ward. The correspondence was printed in the *Advertiser* in January, 1876. It was lengthy, the matter had obviously caused Florence Nightingale some concern, for she took the trouble to lay out both sides of the argument. She appreciated the problems and potential benefits of the old system of admitting children to adult wards, she was concerned that a child in an isolated children's ward, where no other adults were present, could be at the mercy of an unsympathetic nurse. Miss Nightingale came down on the side of preferring to stay with the older mixed system where adult patients would mentor a child. Today's patterns of thought would probably see the opportunities for abuse in the adult wards, whereas she saw the possibility of cruelty in a children's ward. In the event, the decision was taken to accept Sir Smith Child's offer of a Children's Ward, the ward being described in the standard work on hospitals as one of the earlier children's wards to be set up in a general infirmary.

The appropriate title for the nurse in charge of a ward exercised the minds of the Infirmary Committee for many years. In the Crimea, there had been friction between Florence Nightingale and groups of nurses from religious foundations, and she had not taken too kindly to them. Much of the problem resided in the fact that they felt more of a

KING EDWARD VIIth NURSES HOME,
North Staffordshire Infirmary and Eye Hospital.
(FROM THE ARCHITECTS' DRAWING.)

Improved accommodation for nurses 1902. An essential component in the raising of the nursing standard.
This was the first Nurses' Home, destined to be extended in the future. That this splendid building could be
built for £5000 gives us an idea of the value of money in 1902.
The building on the extreme right with 'pepper-pot' roof is Ward 7.

Night Duty!

Male Medical Ward 1890s.

Male Surgical Ward 1890s.

The Infirmary seen from Hartshill fields in 1881.
The haystacks emphasise the rustic character and clean air of the Mount to which the Infirmary moved in 1869 so different to the former Etruria site. This 1881 photo was taken from the present site of the Central Pathology Department, by Mr Allinson, the Infirmary's pharmacist.

loyalty to their religious Superior than to herself, at any rate she saw them as a potential threat to her authority.

The title Sister smacked of such religious groups, and as such offended some shades of religious opinion, particularly the Low Church wing of the Church of England and the Nonconformists. Nonetheless, the nurses of the St John's House, an Anglican sisterhood of nurses, had won great respect for the quality of care they offered in the Crimea. Under the leadership of Sister Mary Jones they took over the nursing of Kings College Hospital in London. Nonetheless, the use of the word Sister as the title for the Nurse in Charge of a Ward still alarmed many members of the Committee.

Thirty years later, Nurse in Charge of the Ward was proving an unwieldy mouthful for day to day use, so in 1891, the proposal was put forward that in North Staffordshire they and the Night Superintendent should be called Sister, and given a distinctive uniform. This was also the wish of the Superintendent of Nurses, Miss Annan. This proposition was defeated in Committee by 15 votes to 3. Nothing more was heard of the matter for 10 years. In August 1901, at a review of Nursing, it was agreed that nurses with three years experience or more who were in charge of a ward could at long last be called Sister, but only after the nonconformist subscribers were reassured that the title had no religious significance!

The same review considered training and recruitment of nurses, their duties and pay, and lectures and examinations. A printed form (1894) to be completed by an applicant to become a probationer asked was she Married, Single or Widowed, had she any children, and what was her father's occupation. She was informed that candidates must be *'well educated, active, industrious, thoroughly trustworthy, possess an unexceptionable character and be between 21 and 32 years of age.'*

Gradually, nursing education became standardised, local certificates of competence achieved after three years training gave way to nationally recognised qualifications and centralised registration by 1920. Nonetheless, hospitals still vied with each other to provide the best accommodation and training in order to attract the best candidates.

The successful Matron, a name that returned in the 20th century, was immensely influential, and gave a 'tone' to the hospital. Miss MacMaster's title when she was appointed in 1904 was Superintendent of Nurses, but her title changed to Matron as was recorded in the Annual Report for 1910-11, and was part of a Revision of Rules that was undertaken as one of the major reforms of 1910. When Miss MacMaster retired in 1930 a speaker at the Annual General Meeting said *'anyone who knows the Infirmary knows Miss MacMaster'*, while another said that she was respected *'not only for what she did but for what she was.'* Others who served in that post with particular distinction were Miss Annan and Miss Blakemore. The appellation Matron went out of fashion again in the latter years of the century, to be replaced by Director of Nursing Services or a similar title reminiscent of the Superintendent of Nurses of one hundred years earlier.

Now in the 21st century there are calls for Matron to be recalled: *'she'd soon sort things out'* people cry. The Matron whose return is dreamt of today is a reincarnation of the early to mid-20th century model. In charge of all aspects of a nurse's life, professional, personal and moral, *she had the power to hire and fire with immediate effect and usually without arguments or appeal.* More than that, she was often a commanding personality who was as much respected for her personal qualities as the tremendous power that she wielded. As well as the nursing staff, the medical staff fell under her spell, indeed a great matron could make a senior doctor feel like a naughty small boy. In spite of this, the doctors appreciated her contribution to the good name of the hospital, and came to hold her in high regard.

The main entrance to the Hartshill Infirmary.
Below the word 'Infirmary' is a light which now warns of the approach of a helicopter.

MISS MACMASTER AND HER NURSES 1920

MISS MACMASTER AND HER NURSES LATE 1920S

North Staffordshire Infirmary. Hartshill, Stoke-on-Trent.

An unusual view of the Infirmary. On the right in the foreground is the Victoria Ward, the single-storey building partly hidden by the bushes.

CHAPTER 13
Advances in Abdominal Surgery

The 146 years covered by the life of the Infirmary in this book include so many developments and so many new ideas and techniques. The best documented in the Infirmary archives are the changes in abdominal surgery, so these are chosen to illustrate the developments taking place in hospitals in general, and in the North Staffordshire Infirmary in particular. The development of 'clean' surgery was one of the landmarks of medical history. The key to all the surgical operations performed today, it remains a clear and logical process that can be readily understood by a general reader.

The following extract from a textbook of surgery of 1901 shows a surgeon looking back at the changes of the previous 30 years, indeed the years since the Infirmary arrived in Hartshill in 1869 and reflecting on the revolution that had taken place. From *Manual of Surgery*, Rose and Carless, 4th edition, 1901:

> *'Wound Phagedena and Hospital Gangrene are conditions affecting wounds which were seen often enough in the pre-antiseptic era, but are now practically unknown thanks not only to antisepsis, but to the increased care directed to ventilation and hospital hygiene. They consisted of a rapidly spreading ulceration or gangrene, which attacked operation wounds a few days after their infliction, and as a rule led to rapid death. It is fortunately unnecessary to describe or discuss them nowadays'.*

That the most feared of all outcomes of surgical treatment, infection leading to rapid death, which represented the most powerful argument for avoiding major and particularly abdominal surgery, should no longer merit description in 1901 is truly remarkable. Less than twenty years previously the mortality of a 'clean' operation such as ovariotomy (the removal of an ovary, usually performed because of massive cysts) regularly exceeded 50%. This is a measure of the revolution that had been wrought in surgery between 1861 and 1901.

From the records that survive for the North Staffordshire Infirmary, we know that all the early operations were peripheral, usually arm or leg, none involving the major body cavities, the head, chest or abdomen. These might be approached when they had already been injured, but never by choice, such operations being seen as a death sentence. Even up to the 1860s this rule was nearly always observed.

In the 1860s, and more widely in the 1870s, Joseph Lister, a surgeon in Glasgow, began to publish the results of his researches on antiseptic surgery. Aimed at the elimination of airborne infection, his method depended on the sterilisation of the air by a spray of the antiseptic carbolic acid, and the continuous application of dressings soaked in carbolic solutions until the skin had healed. The spray made the operating theatre an extremely unpleasant place in which to work. The patient's dressings were soaked in carbolic acid and they needed to be changed frequently. Even if the treatment was successful patients could be in hospital having daily dressings for a year or more. They sometimes became ill from absorption of the toxic carbolic solution which was a poison to the liver and kidneys; at least one death from carbolic acid poisoning was reported in an Infirmary patient. When, by the 1870s, bacteriology had advanced sufficiently, investigation revealed that carbolic acid was not a very effective disinfectant, especially against spores which occurred in the type of germs that caused tetanus and gas gangrene. Mercuric chloride was a better but a very toxic agent. All these factors, added to the expense involved caused dissatisfaction with antisepsis. The Governors complained that this one treatment alone was costing 2.5% of the Infirmary's annual income. Nonetheless, however imperfect it was, Lister's method showed that death from sepsis was not an inevitable consequence of surgery.

This method of prevention of infection by the use of agents to kill any germs that might enter the wound was called antisepsis, meaning against sepsis. Gradually the alternative method of asepsis, meaning without sepsis, of elimination of germs from the wound, grew apace, largely in Germany as a result of experience gained in the Franco-Prussian War of 1870. William Spanton and Charles Orton, both on the staff of the Infirmary, visited the hospitals on both French and Prussian sides and their visit influenced their thinking about wound infections. The method of asepsis meant that instruments and dressings were carefully cleaned and sterilised by heat, hands were washed and techniques refined. Antiseptics themselves caused inflammation of the peritoneum and this discouraged their use inside the abdomen. With asepsis there was no such irritation, and abdominal surgery forged ahead, principally led by surgeons in Germany.

In Britain, surgical progress was concentrated on the need to treat huge ovarian cysts. Although they were not malignant, these cysts killed the patient by virtue of their size, they could contain gallons of fluid, filling the abdomen and making it impossible for the woman to breathe. They presented the perfect opportunity for pioneering surgery, from a surgical and ethical standpoint, for the patient would certainly die without surgery, and success meant the patient could enjoy a normal lifespan. An additional attraction of the operation was that the removal of the cyst with its narrow pedicle (where the blood vessels entered the cyst) was relatively straightforward.

W.H. Folker.
House Surgeon, Surgeon and President
of the North Staffs Infirmary

The initial results of abdominal operations in North Staffordshire were not encouraging. Until the 1880s the overall mortality for abdominal surgery varied from 50% to 80%, results common to many other hospitals including famous London teaching hospitals. 'Listerism' was often advanced as the cure-all for hospital sepsis, but there were other changes essential for success. However clean the operating theatre, poor technique, dirty dressings or infected patients in the ward would kill the patient. Progress required that surgeons really had to believe in asepsis, and build a team that would follow instructions meticulously.

In the Medical Institute Library is a textbook *Diseases of the Ovary* by Thomas Spencer Wells (1872). This volume, published two years after the Franco-Prussian War, is of particular interest in that it was owned by W.D. Spanton, Surgeon at the Infirmary, a man who would become very influential in the development of abdominal surgery in North Staffordshire, and was a disciple of Spencer Wells. Remembered today for the arterial forceps named after him, Spencer Wells had served as a surgeon in the Crimean War and became an eminent teacher and researcher. He was known as a stickler for cleanliness, it was known he cleaned his own surgical instruments himself before they were packed away, but until antisepsis was adopted even he could not better a mortality of 25%.

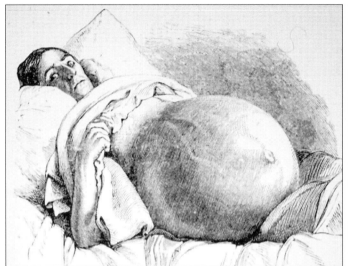

William Spanton, the surgeon who collected the money to build the Victoria Ward

TOP: a massive ovarian cyst

MIDDLE:
The removal of the cyst was technically easy because of the narrow pedicle

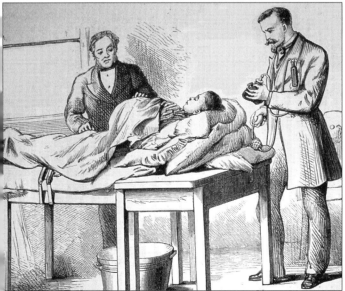

The three illustrations left were taken from Spencer Wells's book *Diseases of the Ovary* 1872. The surgeon is Spencer Wells and the assistant is Dr Junker, who drew the illustrations. Note the improvised operating table indicating an operation in the home. Dr Junker is using his chloroform inhaler which remained in use until WWII.

Fissure and Painful Ulcer of Anus	3		
Fistula in Ano	9		
Foreign Bodies in Nose and Ear	1		
Hæmorrhoids	7		
Hare-lip	2		
Herniotomy	10	d3	d Two of these 3 died from the effects of Peritonitis existing before the Operation In the Third Case, an Internal Strangulation existed. One died from Bronchopneumonia.
Hydrocele	32		
Hydrocele of the Cord	3		
Ischio Rectal Abcess	2		
Ingrowing Toe Nail	4		
Lithotomy	11	1	
Necrosis and Caries	4		
Nævus	9		
Oöphorectomy	1		
Ovariotomy	5	e4	e In One Instance, the Complete Removal of the Tumour was Impossible. Two Died from Effects of Pre existing Peritonitis.— The last Died, presumably, from Carbolic Poisoning.
Osteotomy	2	f1	
Paracentesis Abdominis	3		
„ Thoracis	8		
Patellar Bursitis	2		
Paraphymosis	1		
Phymosis	11		
Pericæal Section	4		
For Prolapsus Uteri (plastic)	1		
Plastic Operations for Cicatrices	6		f Died from Septicæmia.
Radical cure for Hernia (Mr. Spanton's method)	4		
Carried forward......	234	12	

An extract from the Annual report.
Many cases were admitted when very ill, and infection was a problem - and one patient died from carbolic poisoning, absorbed from the dressings soaked with the substance to reduce infection

Spencer Wells reflected on the problem of sepsis. He referred back to the work of Sir James Simpson in Edinburgh. Simpson, the obstetrician best remembered for his part in the introduction of chloroform, had looked through the records of Scottish hospitals back into the 18th century, and demonstrated that the operative mortality had been much less in the smaller hospitals then than the huge institutions of the mid 19th century. Simpson named this decline in standards 'hospitalism'. Spencer Wells found his own results were better when operating in a small hospital and compared his results in hospital and in private practice - often undertaken in the patient's home. He argued that the best results would be achieved in a unit with single rooms, away from the large ward with its infected cases, abscesses, erysipelas and scarlet fever, which we now know were all teeming with germs, usually streptococci.

These views clearly influenced Spanton. Appalled with the mortality of abdominal surgery undertaken on the general wards of the Infirmary, 80% in some years, Spanton looked for single rooms, and borrowed the only ones in the Infirmary, those in the children's ward. Sir Smith Child who had largely paid for the children's ward was not at all pleased to see it used for adults, and said so. As a result Spanton raised £900 (of which a large part actually came from Sir Smith Child) to build a two-bedded surgical ward for female cases needing abdominal surgery, the Victoria Ward, in 1882, named after Mrs Victoria Spanton not the Queen. Within a short time he was able to publish much improved

VICTORIA WARDS.

THIS BUILDING WAS ERECTED IN 1882, TO BE DEVOTED EXCLUSIVELY TO THE TREATMENT OF SURGICAL DISEASES OF WOMEN. SIR SMITH CHILD, BART (PRESIDENT) AND HIS FAMILY, CONTRIBUTED ON THIS EXPRESS CONDITION, A LARGE PORTION OF THE TOTAL SUM SUBSCRIBED FOR THE PURPOSE, WHICH WAS COLLECTED BY W.D.SPANTON, F.R.C.S. HON, SURGEON.

Plaque from the Victoria Wards built in 1882 to house clean operations for women.

Year.	No. of Cases.	*Recoveries.	Deaths.	Mortality per cent.
863 to 1867	9	5	4	44.44
868 to 1872	6	3	3	50.00
873 to 1877	5	4	1	20.00
878 to 1882	21	10	11	52.40
	41	22	19	46.34 Average of 20 years
883 (only)	15	13	2	13.00
Total ..	56	35	21	37.50 Average.

*This is giving former years credit for recovery in 5 cases which cannot be traced in the books.

Figures quoted by W.D. Spanton in the Annual Report.
The mortality rate for 1883 was down to 13% after the opening of the clean Victoria Ward.

results in the *British Medical Journal.*

Between 1863 and 1882 the overall death rate for ovariotomy was given as 46%. It may in fact have been worse than this, for 5 patients *'were unaccounted for'*, and *'giving the Infirmary the benefit of the doubt, were presumed to have survived'*! In 1883, the first year of operating on patients in the Victoria Ward, 2 out of 15 patients died, a mortality of only 13%.

To be fair to an earlier generation of surgeons, Richardson in his account of the Infirmary of 1864 does report that the surgeons were having some success in reducing sepsis by isolating surgical cases from the general ward in the years just prior to Lister's discoveries.

With the accommodation sorted out, the next link in the chain was reorganisation of the nursing staff. The reforms advocated by Florence Nightingale were not yet sufficiently advanced to supply the new requirements of the surgeon. In 1869 it was resolved that the splendid new building in Hartshill should be presided over by a Lady Superintendent. As we have seen, this arrangement was never comfortable and in 1871 the Governors parted company with their Lady Superintendent and replaced her with a Superintendent of Nurses.

Spencer Wells devoted several pages of his book to the selection, training and duties of a surgical nurse. By this he meant a nurse who would look after the patient, prepare and attend the operating theatre, and superintend the post-operative care, either in hospital or in the patient's home. His observations are worth quoting at length. Of the *'Lady'* nurse he wrote:

'As a rule, ladies in search of an occupation for a livelihood, or who take to it because they know not what else to do, or fall into it by sentiment or accident, seldom succeed in nursing well. There is generally a lurking sense of degradation which takes the spring out of their work, and throws over it an undefinable but appreciable air of taskiness which has its influence both upon patient and surgeon.'

He advocated the recruitment of a young woman trained in domestic service, who would be used to the disciplined performance of her duties that the new clean surgery would require. In contrast to the Lady, *'a nurse who has changed from the business of ordinary domestic service feels she is taking a step upward in life, and goes about what she has to do with a kind of professional elan and personal interest in its success.'* What could be a better personal profile of a nurse than this, even today: *'what is especially wanted for this kind of work is a calm quick way of doing it; an intelligent understanding of its nature; a readiness in comprehending the instructions given; punctuality and exactness in carrying them out; and a discriminating carefulness in observing and reporting all that passes under her notice, and may be of importance in judging the progress or regulating the treatment of the case.'* The nurse so described is much more than a servant, her observation of the patient is valued, she is a vital member of the team.

The ladylike character of the nurse was important in the perception of the Nightingale reforms, but recent research by nurse historians suggests that the real motor for the advancement and improved training of nurses was the hospitals' need for young women who could learn the techniques essential for the success of the new treatments being developed. Clean surgery was crucial among these techniques, for the lessons learned in the operating theatre and surgical ward had important implications for the control of infection throughout a hospital.

Having demonstrated that the operations could be now be successfully performed in the abdomen to remove ovarian cysts, it was natural that other conditions should attract the surgeon's attention. Appendicitis is a condition which epitomises this change. Virtually unknown as a disease in 1890, it 'exploded' both in the number of cases being diagnosed and the number of operations performed. Illnesses formerly treated by rest, pain killers and diet, treatment that had been firmly the province of the physician, were now treated surgically. For many years ill defined conditions of pain, tenderness and upset bowel function more or less corresponding to appendicitis had been known and given twenty different names, a sure sign that no one really knew what was happening. The most reliable figures indicated that 95% of cases got better by themselves, either by the infection becoming walled off or discharging into the bowel, or occasionally externally as a faecal fistula, the abscess discharging through the skin. Nonetheless, in the remaining 5% the outcome was the spread of pus and faeces throughout the abdomen, leading to peritonitis and death. Worst of all, there was no way of certainly predicting which cases would prove to be in the 5% that would suddenly deteriorate and die. Now that surgery no longer presented a considerable risk of death from infection, it was a sensible suggestion that an operation should be carried out in an attempt to reduce this mortality. The hope was to remove an inflamed appendix before it 'burst'.

Appendicitis was thrust into the public's attention by the postponement of the Coronation of Edward VII in June 1902. A few days before the Coronation, the King developed the signs of intra-abdominal infection. Initially it was hoped that the condition would settle under a 'wait and see' regime, but the reappearance of pain and swelling in the lower abdomen on the right hand side suggested that a large abscess was forming, and that operation was indicated. Sir Frederick Treves, (the surgeon who cared for the Elephant Man), incised the Royal abdomen and encountered a large abscess at the (considerable) depth of four and a half inches. This was drained. The King made a good recovery, and he was crowned three months later. Appendicectomy became the wonder of the age - although the Royal appendix was not actually removed. In the next few years the operation became as fashionable as cosmetic surgery is today - and was probably performed to excess.

All this is fully reported in the medical journal *The Lancet*; indeed in the week of the King's operation *The Lancet* had fortuitously included the full report of a lecture given by Treves on the very subject of appendicitis. But the press was puzzled by this 'new' disease. Then as now, it matched the certainty of its statements with the inaccuracy of its content. The *Daily News* told the world that the King suffered from *'Perityphlitis, an inflammation of the kidney'*. Many papers carried a report that had originated with the Press Association. This had confused the use of tubes to drain the abscess with tubes used to restore the continuity of the bowel, from this they deduced that bowel had been cut out, and that was a sure sign that the King had cancer. (wrong again!)

We can watch the changes in the results of treatment of appendicitis in North Staffordshire as knowledge about its diagnosis and surgical treatment evolved. The surgical returns published in the Annual Reports of the Infirmary are particularly helpful. They divide up the cases into those in which:

(1) there is inflammation of the Appendix alone,
(2) there is the formation of a localised abscess, where the infection is walled
off around the Appendix
(3) the infection has already spread throughout the abdomen, i.e. where
generalised Peritonitis has developed.

For example:

In the Annual Report for 1908-9, of 57 patients admitted with appendicitis where the infection had NOT spread throughout the abdomen 1 patient died. **1 death from 57 patients**. These were the patients from Groups 1 and 2

But of 38 patients who were admitted with appendicitis where infection HAD spread, 15 patients died. **15 deaths from 38**. These were the patients in Group 3.

It becomes clear that those patients in whom there was no spread of infection much beyond the appendix, ie those which were intrinsically clean, could expect to survive. They were no longer being infected in hospital, or more accurately by the hospital. Those in Group 3 had peritonitis, where infection had already spread from the leaking bowel; they had a substantial mortality, and even those who survived often had a long and stormy convalescence.

The final reduction of this death rate would have to wait for the coming of antibiotics and the full range of intensive care. In 1936, before antibiotics were available, the Infirmary was proud that the mortality of patients that had been admitted with appendicitis was only 4%. We should remember that recent national figures show that about 80 people still die each year in Britain of appendicitis, mostly the very old, debilitated patients or cases of self-neglect.

Aseptic surgery really was a watershed in medical history and in the story of the Infirmary. In order for it to succeed, the use of buildings, and the method of work of doctors and nurses had to change and become integrated. Traditional patterns of work had to be broken down, and new ones established.

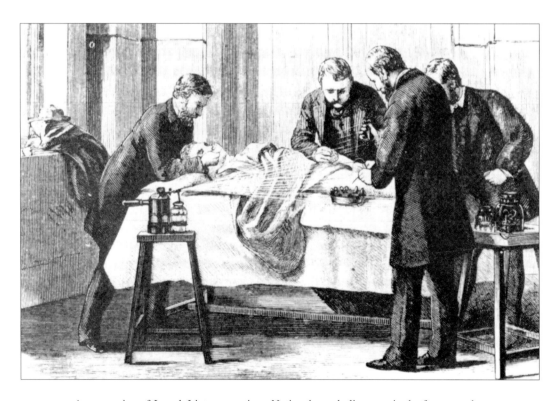

An engraving of Joseph Lister operating. Notice the carbolic spray in the foreground.

CHAPTER 14
A successful Caesarean Section in North Staffordshire, 1876

This is the account of the first successful Caesarean section performed in North Staffordshire. A coincident tragedy that occurred in the surgeon's family meant that the operation never received the acclaim that was its due. The methods available at the time to deal with obstructed labour are considered.

While sorting the contents of a battered suitcase in the library of the Medical Institute, a sepia-tinted photograph, a *carte de visite* was found. The photograph showed a diminutive couple, carefully posed next to a dining chair, to emphasise their short stature. On the reverse was a note, giving the height of the husband as 41 inches (104cm), and that of his wife as 43 inches (109cm). The handwritten annotation stated *'Successful case of Caesarean Section both to Mother and child performed in 1876 by J. Alcock, Surgeon Burslem at the N.S.I. They travelled with a show. This photograph was given me by the patient.'*

The proud parents of the child born in 1876 by Caesarean section in which
both the mother and baby survived - a very rare event.

The Annual Report of the North Staffordshire Infirmary for 1876 was checked: *'The list of operations calls for no special mention, except for the very rare operation of Caesarian (sic) Section, which was successfully carried out in the case of a dwarf, with the happy result of saving the life of the mother and infant.'* The next step was to obtain a copy of the birth certificate.

This was made simple as only one baby was registered as having been born in the Infirmary in 1876. The child had been born on June 23rd, and the birth registered by his father, whose occupation was given as Showman. Delightfully he had been christened William after his father, and given the middle name Hartshill to commemorate his place of birth, an act in keeping with the giving of the photograph to the surgeon as a 'thank you'.

An examination of the *British Medical Journal* and *Lancet* for 1875-7 showed that Caesarean section was indeed a rare operation, and its successful outcome as regards the survival of both mother and child could lead to three publications in these prestigious journals: a preliminary report, a detailed step by step account of the circumstances and the procedure, and a follow-up communication confirming the outcome. The reporting of a successful Caesarean section in the 19th century is reminiscent of the

John Alcock, Surgeon.

triumphalist reports which appeared in the press following the first heart transplants. A search for a full report of John Alcock's case was fruitless. Eventually a book was found that contained the *Proceedings of the Staffordshire Branch of the British Medical Association for 1876*. At the bottom of a page, in very small type was the statement that Mr Alcock reported a successful case of Caesarean section. This report had appeared in the *British Medical Journal* of December 16th, 1876, overlooked in a similarly unremarkable position on the page.

Here was definite evidence that the operation had taken place and the outcome had been successful - and yet the expected detailed national publication could not be found. To put this in perspective, 14 years later, in 1890, a report of a successful section that had been performed in Glasgow was awarded 5 full columns in the *BMJ*, and included two pictures of the mother to show her rachitic pelvis (deformed by rickets), and a picture of the baby wrapped in a shawl!

The details of the birth certificate of the baby delivered by John Alcock appear in his entry in *People of the Potteries* by Henry Allen Wedgwood. From this I noticed that John Alcock's first wife had died on June 24th 1876, the day immediately following the successful operation. A copy of her death certificate, gave the cause of death as *Puerperal Insanity and Phthisis* (postnatal depression and pulmonary tuberculosis). That his wife had died as a late consequence of childbirth was surely the reason that Alcock did not feel disposed to trumpet his triumph, and why his colleagues and friends did not press him to do so. It is now more than 100 years since John Alcock collapsed and died while walking to his home in Burslem having seen his patients in the Haywood Hospital, and it seems proper to recall one of the most important operations performed in North Staffordshire in the 19th century.

Delivery of a baby by the mothers own efforts has always been seen as the ideal outcome. Nonetheless, sometimes obstetric assistance has been required, be it manipulation of the foetus to change the position , or, since the 1740s, the use of obstetric forceps. But in some situations the baby could not be delivered even with assistance, usually because of small maternal stature or deformity, very often a consequence of rickets due to vitamin D deficiency. The result would be the death of both mother and child. The choice here lay between the destruction of the baby, making it small enough to pass through the pelvis, or Caesarean section.

Unless surgical intervention was required, obstetrics was a matter for the midwife or general practitioner in the patient's home, or for the Medical Officer in the workhouse hospital. There was no obstetrician on the staff of the North Staffordshire Infirmary. Had such a post existed, its holder would have been seated 'well below the salt', *'No person shall be eligible to, or allowed to retain the office of Physician who practices surgery, pharmacy or midwifery; or who is connected in partnership with any gentleman in those branches of the medical profession.'* (Law 21 of the North Staffordshire Infirmary, 1877 edition).

Until the 1940s a considerable body of opinion remained in favour of the destructive operations in obstructed labour, occasionally even if the child was alive, as it was believed that the results of Caesarean section were so poor that sacrifice of the child was the least worst option. It is possible to believe from some texts that it was a trivial procedure with minimal suffering on the part of the mother. This was not necessarily so, for if there really was no room in a grossly deformed pelvis for a normal delivery, there could be little room in which to manipulate the destructive instruments. The largest part of a baby is the head, thus it was necessary to 'open' the head, allowing the brain to escape and the skull bones to collapse. Should it still prove impossible to pull the child through the pelvis, the next option was to dismember its body. This exercise was conducted inside the uterus without anaesthesia. It not infrequently led to a ruptured uterus, allowing infection to be scattered throughout the abdomen. Cases were described in which the operator gave up exhausted, and allowed the mother to die undelivered.

The sufferings of the mother were considerable. She would know her child was dead or soon to die. She would suffer the protracted manipulations, following on from the fruitless exertions of an obstructed labour. Her general condition would deteriorate from loss of blood, dehydration and from rapidly advancing fever as the uterine contents and traumatised tissues became infected. At some point along this downward slope a Caesarean section might be proposed as a last resort. The patient would often consent to the operation, even without an anaesthetic, seeing in it a foreseeable end to her sufferings. The greater the delay, the worse the outcome, and in many series the mortality of Caesarean sections performed under such conditions reached 100%. The high mortality of these desperate operations influenced the profession in Britain against Caesarean section. Nowadays where Caesarean section is readily available, it is the method of choice. In some Third World countries, far from any hospital, the choice today may still be a destructive operation - and with sterile instruments and anaesthesia the operation is satisfactory as a means of saving the mother's life.

In Continental Europe, largely composed of Catholic countries, Caesarean section was resorted to with greater readiness than in Britain. The medical profession in England said that this was due to a desire to secure the soul of the baby for the Church, even at the expense of the mother's life. Perhaps because of their greater experience or because they allowed less delay in performing the operation, surgeons on the Continent claimed better results. Most embarrassingly, by the 1870s a comparison of the results of Caesarean section in Britain and America showed them to be much better in America.

These were the considerations that faced John Alcock when he performed his operation in 1876: There was a great body of opinion ready to criticise him in the event of failure. He would surely have been wise enough to follow the rule of the Infirmary *'No important surgical operation shall be performed, without a previous consultation of the Honorary Medical Staff (consultant staff) convened by the House Surgeon for that purpose, unless an urgent occasion require it'* (Rule 48, 1877).

The results of abdominal surgery at the North Staffordshire Infirmary at the time showed a mortality of about 50%. Thomas Radford of Manchester was a great advocate of Caesarean section, and considered destructive operations barbarous. He collected details of cases with their outcomes. I am much indebted to J.H. Young's classic book, *The History of Caesarean Section* (1944), based on Radford's collection.

In his own book, published in 1865, Radford listed 11 maternal survivors from a total number of 77 operations performed in Great Britain (14% surviving). In the 1880 edition the totals had risen to 23 survivors from 131 operations (17%). One of these 23 maternal survivors from 131 recorded cases was John Alcock's patient who was additionally a member of a still smaller elite group of 16 patients, in which both mother and baby survived. According to Radford's book, the information sent to him did not come from John Alcock himself, but from Dr Walter, who was House Surgeon at the Infirmary at the time. The entry is noted *'now related for the first time'*.

Some clinical details were included. The patient had been in labour for 24 hours and the presenting part was a knee. The antero-posterior diameter of the pelvis was one and a half inches. The patient is described in the book as having a rachitic pelvis, but she was described in the Annual Report as a *'dwarf'*, and the photograph suggests achondroplasia. Perhaps rickets was so prevalent that all cases of contracted pelvis were ascribed to it - or perhaps both conditions co-existed.

By 1876 the use of general anaesthesia was well established at the Infirmary; and it is reasonable to assume that chloroform would have been chosen. *'The House Physician shall attend at operations; and shall be responsible for the administration of anaesthetics.'* (Rule 55) In the *Centenary Brochure of the North Staffordshire Medical Society*, John Alcock is recalled as a meticulous surgeon who favoured the use of liberal quantities of iodine to disinfect the patient's skin and the surgeon's hands. The incision would have been made in the body of the uterus and this may well not have been sutured. Catgut at that time was not a reliable product. There was a great fear of leaving sutures in the abdomen where they might become foci of infection. The danger posed by not suturing was fatal haemorrhage as the womb relaxed.

It seems reasonable to claim that John Alcock's case was among the first twenty operations in Britain in which mother and child survived. It was a considerable achievement and it is sad that circumstances denied him the renown that would otherwise have accrued. In the 30 years 1876-1906, there were seven more Caesarean sections recorded at the Infirmary, of whom 3 survived, a mortality of 57%. John Alcock continued as a surgeon at the Infirmary, and was also on the Staff of the Haywood Hospital in Burslem. He was President and Secretary of the Burslem District Nursing Association. Two of his sons by his first marriage became members of the consultant staff of the Infirmary. From his second family a link continues to the present day.

CHAPTER 15
Illness in the Potteries

This chapter presents an exploration of the medical wards of the Infirmary, particularly in the latter part of the 19th and early 20th centuries. Beginning with those diseases especially relevant to the pottery worker, including Potter's Rot and lead poisoning, it continues with an overview of the many illnesses which were common to all those who lived in North Staffordshire. Infectious diseases were often especially virulent in the 19th and early 20th century. The chapter looks at illnesses that were admitted to the Infirmary and at those that were not admitted, at least in theory.

Surgical cases were less specific to North Staffordshire, being common to the injuries attendant on all heavy industries, and following the gradual pattern of developments in surgery that followed the adoption of aseptic techniques.

All accounts from the 19th century are remarkably consistent in describing the typical pottery worker as an unhealthy looking specimen. Indeed the one detailed account of actual cases, R.C. Garner's casebook 1854-6, routinely describes the patients from the pottery industry as '*unhealthy looking potter*'. It does not use this adjective for labourers, ironworkers or miners.

Richardson visiting the area in 1864 concurred, but was puzzled as to the cause. He referred to reviews of income levels in different industries and in other towns and felt that many people in England were paid less than the potters and appeared to be fitter than them, so he felt lack of money was not the principal cause of their inferior health. Nor was housing the obvious cause, there were pockets of bad housing in North Staffordshire, but these were not as extensive as those in Manchester, and there were very few back to back houses and no cellar dwellings.

It must be said that anyone living in the Potteries in the 19th century would suffer from the general background level of smoke pollution - asthma and chronic bronchitis are the lot of any population living in such conditions. Even the medical staff of the Infirmary seem to have been particularly afflicted by illness, and a surprising number resigned to seek a more salubrious climate on account of their health. Until the coming of the Acts which controlled atmospheric pollution from 1956 onward, any person resident in Stoke-on-Trent, whatever their occupation, would be expected to have some form of respiratory disease.

The potter stood out from the local population due to his or her poor state of health by virtue of their occupation. The principal cause of chest disease was dust, and not just any dust but silica dust. This came from the flints and the clay used in the making china. The death rate soared in the 1720s when flint was introduced to the industry. At first the practice was to grind it in a dry state so the dust flew everywhere. In 1732 Thomas Benson of Newcastle took out a patent for grinding flints under water, specifically claiming the advantage of his process to be the prevention of chest disease. His patent application details the appalling damage to health consequent on dry grinding of flints; no one reading that document could argue against the connection between dust and chest disease. Nonetheless, further measures to control dust were long in coming, two hundred years, and only really effective by the mid-20th century. To quote the *Victoria County History* on the subject of attempts to control dust: '*such methods as did exist were rendered ineffective by the indifference and contempt of the pottery workers*'.

The first legislation to control dust had to wait until 1891, and major progress until the

1940s. The most important single source of silica dust was the powdered flint used to pack the ware for firing, and the process of removing it from the ware afterwards. These placers worked in clouds of pure silica dust and the problem was only ameliorated in the 1930s when less irritant alumina dust was substituted. Of course, the dust was not confined to the placers and blew about throughout the works, so everyone in the factory was exposed to this silica- containing dust to some degree. Even those who dealt with dusty clothes at home and workers in a local commercial laundry were not immune from inhalation of silica.

Silica dust damages the lungs because it is a powerful irritant of lung tissue, which responds by trying to wall off and isolate the silica by forming masses of fibrous tissue around the particles. This fibrous tissue gradually displaces the lung tissues needed for breathing, while the lymph glands in the chest become involved and enlarged. These can become so hard and so large they compress the windpipe or the gullet, their large size making breathing or swallowing difficult and necessitating an operation to remove the obstruction. The fibrotic lung will be made even less efficient by bronchitis or tuberculosis. Once in the lungs, the silica dust continues to irritate the tissues long after the patient has left the source. This is the disease known as Potters' Rot or Potters' Asthma. The only practical action to reduce the disease is prevention, to avoid exposure to silica dust altogether.

Ultimately the destruction of lung tissue makes the patient very breathless, and this symptom is made worse as the fibrous tissue damages the blood vessels, making it harder and harder for the heart to pump the blood through the lungs. Eventually the patient develops heart failure. The Infirmary could do little for these patients, apart from the usual provision of rest and good food. Inhalations of steam eased the patient's cough, while digitalis was available to treat heart failure. The coming of X-rays into general use in the early 1900s helped to make the diagnosis more certain and to allow the progress of the disease to be followed, but of itself did not lead to a great advance in treatment. In the 1940s antibiotics arrived to control infections, drugs helped to alleviate the asthmatic component of the disease, physiotherapy and oxygen helped, but they still could not cure the patient.

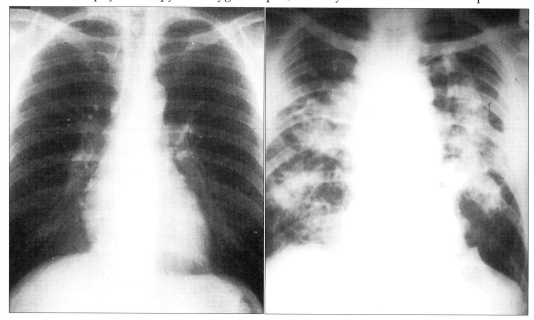

The X-ray on the left is normal, the lungs, filled with air 'let' the X-rays through and appear black. The ribs obstruct the rays and appear white. The chest X-ray on the right shows white masses in the lungs, dense tissue formed in response to inhaled silica dusts. This is silicosis, known as 'Potter's rot'.

Tuberculosis could be added to silicosis, but of course tuberculosis itself was a disease of young people, and a major cause of death in that age group in all sections of the general population. There is a romantic glow cast by 19th century literature over the death of the heroine from tuberculosis. In opera, La Traviata and La Boheme both end with the death of the heroine from that disease. Novels give the idea of the consumptive patient slipping serenely away surrounded by their family. Researchers who have explored diaries of the period tell us that many patients died after days and nights of racking coughs, coughing up alarmingly copious, even fatal volumes of blood, in severe pain and with desperate shortage of breath.

It is true that many such patients were recorded as being surprisingly calm under this sentence of death. The years 1800 to 1850 were the period of most fervent religious belief in the virtues of a 'good death,' which allowed sufferers to be reconciled to their destiny with an unshakeable belief that the family would be reunited in the after life. This comforted the patient and the family in an otherwise unbearable situation.

In practice there was no treatment other than the usual rest and good food. The patient's cough may have been improved by leaving a smoky town for the country or seaside, but the improvement was often marginal. The sufferer's cough must have disturbed the whole family, especially the other children who might well see their brother or sister's condition foretelling their own fate, as it did in the Bronte family. A note made in the 1920s by the Medical Superintendent of the Workhouse (now the City General Hospital) described how the booming cough of the tuberculous patients echoed across the site in the night disturbing the sleep of patients in distant ward blocks. It could well be that sending the patient away did most practical good for the other children by removing a source of infection and distress from their midst. Tuberculosis of the lungs was known as consumption because by the last stages of the disease the patients health was totally destroyed. It was a major killer in North Staffordshire until the later years of the 20th century.

Out of all proportion to the numbers of deaths it caused, lead poisoning is the illness that has always exerted a great attraction for historians of the Potteries. The condition has long been known and efforts to remove the use of this toxic substance from industrial processes in general and from pottery manufacture in particular date back to the 18th century. In terms of the total numbers of deaths, diseases of chest and the infectious diseases were much more significant. Nonetheless for the individual, and mostly for those relatively small numbers actually 'working in the lead', it was disastrous.

Lead was held to be so much superior to any substitutes that any attempts to dispense with its use were unsuccessful. Lead is a component of the glaze, a glass like film that covers the pot and confers many of the attractive properties to the finished article. The process of dipping, coating the biscuit ware in the glaze that contained large concentrations of lead, involved plunging the ware into a container filled with the liquid. There were no safeguards such as rubber gloves, so the process guaranteed that the hands and arms of the dipper were constantly coated with the glaze, which could be inhaled, pass through the often broken skin and be swallowed with food, particularly if there were no facilities for the washing of hands before eating. At the worst period, it was reckoned that a dipper had a life expectancy of 29 years. In the late 18th and early 19th centuries, Benefit Societies did not admit dippers into their membership, classing their work as a dangerous trade, along with coal mining. Other trades in the pottery industry were exposed to lead, particularly painters of ware, especially Majolica ware in whom it was thought that the practice of pointing the brush with the lips was particularly injurious.

We can most readily understand lead poisoning if we recognise lead as a heavy metal and therefore a tissue poison. It is particularly damaging to nerves, and the clinical diagnosis can be made from the characteristic pattern of those nerves that are particularly susceptible to the damage, such as the nerves that control some of the muscles in the forearm. If the patient were to stand, holding his arm out parallel to the floor, palm facing the floor, the muscles that were paralysed were those that will bend the wrist upward. The hand may droop downwards at the wrist - the characteristic sign of 'wrist drop'.

Another set of nerves particularly sensitive are those in the wall of the bowel which coordinate the contractions which propel the food along. The action of the bowel became irregular, the patient suffers from severe colic and from constipation.

Other sources of lead were water pipes, household paints and lead toys, particularly dangerous to small children who chewed them, attracted to its sweet taste. The brain is susceptible to lead poisoning and in children it could produce irreversible brain damage. Epilepsy was a common symptom of lead poisoning. The younger the child the more serious the effects of the poison. This was seen in its most extreme form in pregnancy, when small concentrations of lead could produce a severely incapacitated child. More extreme damage to the foetus produced a miscarriage. This was not lost on those wishing to procure an abortion. Just as the industrial exposure was being reduced, the deliberate ingestion of lead was said by major medical textbooks written between 1900 to 1940 to be a very common method of ending an unwanted pregnancy. So it could be that some of the cases of lead poisoning that have been unquestioningly blamed on industry had other causes.

Lead is capable of damaging most organs in the body, it is not metabolised and once in the body it remains there for many years. Its effect is cumulative, repeated small doses building up to toxic levels. Perhaps the most often quoted sign of lead poisoning was the 'blue line', a deposit of lead sulphide along the margin of the gums where they met the teeth.

Protection of workers involved keeping young and pregnant workers away from lead on account of their increased susceptibility to the poison, keeping workshops clean, providing protective clothing and washing facilities and insisting workers did not eat while contaminated with lead. Other possibilities were the reduction of lead in glazes and the substitution of less soluble forms of lead. Regular examinations of workers, and eventually blood tests, have virtually eliminated this scourge in pottery workers - the car in which the workers travelled home became the largest source of lead until the advent of unleaded petrol.

The absorption of lead caused a number of deaths each year and left many disabled people in the area. It was in the hope of offering some recovery of function to patients suffering from paralysis due to lead poisoning that the Electrical Department was set up at the Infirmary at the beginning of the 20th century. Millicent, Duchess of Sutherland, took the lead in setting up this department paid for with donations collected from her friends. Powered initially by a supply from the Potteries Electric Tramway Company, it was hoped that electrical stimulation of the damaged nerves would hasten their recovery.

Eye injuries were a staple of the industrial injuries that afflicted the local population. Metal splinters were a common hazard to the eyes of workers in the mining, engineering and metal working industries. Hot metal flew about in ironworks, splinters of stone in mines and quarries, so it is no wonder that the Infirmary added the words Eye Hospital to its title in the 1890s, and opened a specialised department. Those who tended furnaces were prone to develop cataracts in their eyes, especially the left eye due to the infra-red rays from the glowing furnace. It affected the left eye more, probably because most people are right handed and peer through 'spy holes' to judge the state of the fire with their left shoulder and eye nearest the target. Now protective glasses have eliminated this problem.

One of the most persistent concerns of the Governors and the Medical Staff was the policy to be adopted on the admission of infectious diseases to the Infirmary. The 19th and early 20th centuries were plagued by infectious diseases, often of a particularly virulent character. The Governors knew that they were administering a limited resource, the Infirmary had a limited number of beds, and treatments were much more protracted than now, a patient's average length of stay was about 30-35 days. They knew there were many diseases for which there was nothing they could offer. Smallpox cases were not officially admitted, though vaccination was made available, but it was the group of common infectious diseases that causes the greatest worry and the most frequent shifts of policy.

Childhood diseases such as measles would not be admitted although it often led to pneumonia killing young children, and left many survivors with nerve damage. Mumps and chickenpox were also unwelcome in the ward. Diphtheria was a particular concern. Some cases had to be admitted in need of urgent surgery when the membrane the germ produced in the throat had to be by-passed with a tracheostomy (a hole in the windpipe). Real dread was reserved for diseases caused by streptococci. They were present in skin infections such as abscesses and erisypelas, in throat infections such as scarlet fever, and they were the principal cause of puerperal fever. They were the main cause of maternal and post-operative deaths. Should a patient infected by a particularly virulent strain of organism arrive in a ward full of surgical patients the germs could spread like wildfire. It was to avoid such cross infections that the Victoria Ward was established for clean surgical cases. The acute diseases caused by streptococci had further problems in store, for depending on the particular strain involved they could lead to damage to the valves of the heart (rheumatic fever) or the kidneys (nephritis), bringing continuing ill health and premature death to many in early adult life.

The problem was made worse by the consideration that these patients could not be discharged recklessly from the Infirmary. Many were too ill to be sent to small crowded houses and they could still be in a very infectious state and a great danger to the other children in the family. Solutions included refusing admission to infected cases, designating wards, often the detached Albert Ward, to be fever or infectious diseases wards, limiting the number of patients suffering from certain infections such as typhoid to be admitted to any one ward, and banning certain infected patients from surgical wards. During one epidemic of smallpox an overflow ward was created in tents in the Infirmary grounds. A small prefabricated corrugated iron ward was erected in 1901 to serve as an isolation ward, only for it to be severely criticised as cold and miserable by Sir Henry Burdett in his report of 1910.

The arrival of a children's ward in 1876 had helped the staff to deal with childhood diseases, but it was not until the local authority infectious diseases hospitals were built, beginning with Bucknall Hospital in 1886, that there was an agreed policy for dealing with infectious patients. Even then, it took time to establish who was financially responsible for the care of patients admitted to Bucknall. Eventually it was agreed that patients admitted directly to Bucknall were the financial responsibility of the Local Authority in whose area they lived, and that the Infirmary would be responsible, initially at least, for patients transferred to Bucknall from the Infirmary. Patients who came from outside the area would be the responsibility of the Governors until they were reimbursed by the 'home' parish or authority (the Law of Settlement was still operating). The issue of payment for patients at Bucknall was still contentious in 1926, when a bill for medical attention to patients transferred from the Infirmary was sent to the Governors. A conference was held at Bucknall, when it was pointed out that sometimes patients came from Bucknall for emergency surgery. It was agreed that a system of reciprocity should prevail from thenceforth.

Infirmary Staff 1880s. Seated figures are D. Ball and R. Garner

Infirmary Staff 1890s. J.T. Arlidge in centre with W.D. Spanton to his right.

The Governors tried to control the spread of infection by restricting movement in and out of the Infirmary. Even today the legal position regarding a patient with an infectious disease who will not accept treatment or allow his movements to be restricted can cause major problems for those responsible for the control of infection. In 1888 an epidemic of smallpox arose in the Infirmary. The Medical Officer of Health and the Police authorities agreed that the Infirmary could detain patients who had already been admitted to the wards that contained the smallpox patients to prevent the possible spread of the disease to the other wards and out into the community. Policemen were hired to prevent these patients' departures at five shillings per constable per day. When its advice was requested, the Local Government Board in London wrote rather stiffly that they were unaware of a hospital's power to detain a patient, so presumably it was illegal even though done with the best of intentions. On other occasions, all visiting was forbidden when there was a particularly virulent epidemic of scarlet fever in the district.

In the late 19th century there were changes in the virulence of many of organisms, which altered the pattern of the diseases caused by infection, especially those caused by the streptococci. A study of maternal deaths has shown that the worst years in which to have a baby, certainly from infection, were the 1870s and afterwards there followed a very slow decline in the incidence of puerperal fever. The years when the new Infirmary at Hartshill was new coincided with a period of great virulence of infectious disease. Great hopes had been pinned on the new building getting rid of the infections that had plagued the old Infirmary. When the hoped for improvement did not appear there was a considerable concern, were the drains all they should be? was damp plaster causing disease? Increasing knowledge of the true causation of infectious disease and news of similar problems with other new hospitals built at the same time gradually elucidated the problem.

By the 20th century scarlet fever was usually a mild period of illness with a characteristic rash. The patient would be expected to recover from the initial episode of illness, although the later complications involving the heart valves still occurred. In the 1850s a 'malignant' form was described in which the infection could overwhelm the child in a matter of hours. The infection was so severe that it could destroy the tissues of the neck, some patients bled to death externally because the jugular veins in the neck had been destroyed. This malignant scarlet fever is equivalent to the 'flesh eating bug' so beloved of the editors of today's tabloid newspapers. These are the pictures we should carry in our minds when we see a Victorian tombstone recording multiple deaths occurring in a family over a brief period. One famous example, which shows how infections were no respecters of rank or station, was in 1856 when A.C. Tait, later Archbishop of Canterbury, lost five young daughters to scarlet fever in thirty-three days.

One problem facing the Governors in making provision for patients with infectious diseases was the variability of the demand. In most hospitals in the country, the total provision of beds was inadequate, so the decision to leave beds empty to accommodate a possible emergency was open to criticism. If there were fever wards, should they be kept empty for instant use, or should they be used for other cases in 'quiet' periods? This problem still has to be considered today when planning emergency services, or numbers of intensive care beds. In the 1880s there were discussions about the need to use surgical beds for medical patients in the depths of winter.

The work of the Infirmary can be traced in considerable detail in the years 1860 to 1910 as the Annual Reports for those years gave details of the cases admitted, with an account of the outcomes. When we look at the work of the medical wards of the Infirmary, it is very different from today. There *were* many cases of infectious disease in the Infirmary, despite all the rules. The numbers and particular varieties of disease varied from year to year. Despite all the instructions to the contrary there were always a large numbers of patients in the wards suffering from tuberculosis, in the majority of cases the chest being involved. The Annual Report in the 1880s said that the Infirmary was in practice a Consumption Hospital. There were always cases of acute and chronic bronchitis, pneumonia and croup, a severe form of laryngitis particularly in young children. Some patients with chest infections went on to develop an empyema, a collection of pus in the lining the lung and against the ribcage. The streptococcal diseases seen in the wards may have been recorded as acute tonsillitis, but more frequently by the complications of it - rheumatic fever or chorea ('St Vitus's Dance') and acute nephritis. There were many patients suffering from the later manifestations, damage to the valves of the heart and chronic kidney failure.

Rheumatism is a disease associated with work in the Potteries. There was a fixed belief in the Potteries that the cause of rheumatism was movement between extremes of temperature. In 1912 a Factory Inspector, making a report to the Government, explained that the fitting of opening windows in a workshop had been insisted upon during an inspection in the previous year in order to improve ventilation. The Inspector said they had recently been found fixed firmly shut *'owing to the potters' morbid fear of a draught.'* In practice, there were many heavy and repetitive operations in the manufacture of pottery, so wear and tear on joints could be anticipated, while the movement in and out of hot workshops may well have produced muscle aches.

Venereal disease was very prevalent in 19th century England, but it is not listed as one of the prime causes of admission to the Infirmary. In its later stages, syphilis can affect virtually every organ in the body, but in the absence of a specific test, the actual incidence was uncertain. It could be that many diseases of the brain, heart and circulation were in fact due to the later effects of syphilis. When a test, the Wasserman Reaction (W.R.) appeared in 1906, the author of a textbook of the time said that early in the 19th century an association of syphilis with many illnesses was suspected but not proven, by the end of the century suspicion was stronger still, but after 1906 it still came as a shock when it was understood how many cases of illness were indeed syphilitic. During the First World War it was estimated that 10% of the adult population were infected. A large proportion of the patients in the huge Victorian mental hospitals were suffering from the final stages of the syphilis affecting the brain, General Paralysis of the Insane. Eventually penicillin proved extremely effective in early syphilis. In comparison, other venereal diseases, particularly gonorrhoea were regarded much more lightly, although they could present serious health hazards and could indeed prove fatal.

The scientific investigation of illness depended on the development of new techniques. Until X-rays were available at the start of the 20th century, it was very difficult to be sure what was happening in the chest of a patient who presented with a cough, shortness of breath and coughing up blood. It could be tuberculosis, it could be silicosis or cancer of the lung, or a combination of all three. Pathology was initially a matter of individual initiatives undertaken by doctors who had an interest in particular aspects of disease. Microscopes were brought to a pitch of optical perfection in the 1840s and spread into general use. The earliest record that I have found of a microscope being used in the Infirmary is contained in R.C. Garner's casebook of 1854-6, when a breast removed for cancer was examined microscopically to see if the removal was complete. The last twenty years of the 19th century saw a rapid advance in the identification of different germs and the diseases they caused, indeed it is said that one major family of organisms was identified by researchers in every one of those twenty years.

However, a proper laboratory was not set up at the Infirmary until the beginning of the 20th century. The Infirmary's first department of pathology was huddled into a store room and was described as being a danger to the pathologist - and anyone else - who entered. Mr F.J. Harrison of Maer Hall, President of the Infirmary, gave £3000, £500 was to be used to improve working conditions in the department, and £500 a year for five years to provide the revenue. However, Dr Myott, who was the pathologist, was called to the First World War, and the department was left without a pathologist during those years, indicating the low priority accorded to the subject at the time. Many specimens had to be sent to commercial laboratories for examination. It was not until the return of Dr Myott in 1918 that the pathology service could be said to be on a permanent footing.

It is evident that until the 1920s many diagnoses had to rely solely on the history and a clinical examination. Physicians of that period were remarkably skillful in the interpretation of physical signs, and one should not decry this. In practice their diagnoses of such diseases as those of the heart and lungs, where there were clear signs to be detected with a stethoscope, were very accurate, but in those cases where detailed pathological or X-ray analysis were required they could be in difficulties. Thus we should be cautious when examining retrospectively the annual analysis of cases; while these may be relied on to give a broad understanding of the diseases admitted, detailed diagnoses may vary from current opinion.

Good food and rest were the basis of the treatment of many medical illnesses. Chest diseases were treated with drugs to thin secretions, steam was inhaled, and portable 'bronchitis tents' were bought in 1893. Digitalis was available for the treatment of heart failure. The first electrocardiograph or ECG machine was purchased from London for £273 in 1922. It was given a room of its own in the basement, where it could be dust and vibration free. It was provided with a nurse trained in its use and was the responsibility of Drs Sowry and Gill. The minutes spoke of it with the same awe that the first computers inspired - like them it was probably large, unreliable and temperamental, needing a room to itself.

Replacement therapies, such as insulin for diabetes and thyroid extract for underactive thyroid had arrived by the 1920s, while cortisone was not available until the 1950s. Perhaps the greatest medical advance of the first half of the 20th century was the development of treatments which could kill bacteria without harming the patient. These fell into two groups, those based on harnessing immune reactions to prevent or treat infections, and chemicals which would kill germs inside the body without harming the patient.

Vaccination was the first of the immunising treatments, while towards the end of the 19th century specific anti-toxins and anti-sera were prepared. The organism that causes diphtheria killed by flooding the body with a toxin which affected the heart and nervous system. Anti-toxin was prepared by injecting increasing amounts of the toxin into a horse, and extracting from its blood the antitoxin it had developed. Given in adequate doses and as soon as the diagnosis was made it was life saving in very many cases. In order to get it to patients as soon as possible, before the toxin had reached the vital organs, local authorities supplied antitoxin to general practitioners, who were paid a fee (one shilling and sixpence) for administering it. This was important as the first treatment to be financed in such a manner. Its introduction was closely followed by antistreptococcal serum given in the hope that it would cure severe infections. In an Infirmary patient's notes of 1897 there is a record of the use of this serum to treat a patient with septicaemia, where the streptococci had invaded the blood stream. This very early use of the serum saved her life, though the notes indicate that she probably did not escape the later effects of the infection on her heart. From the year 1900 we have a minute permitting the use of the boardroom at the Infirmary for the inoculation against typhoid fever of volunteers on their way to the Boer War.

In 1909 Ehrlich described salvarsan, the first of the antibacterial drugs. This became the routine treatment for syphilis during and after World War I. By 1917 the Infirmary had a Salvarsan Department that held a clinic on Thursday afternoons. The first sulphonamides appeared in the 1930s, and antibiotics arrived with penicillin during World War II.

The Governors were always anxious to keep up with advances in medicine and surgery, although at times conflicting demands on the finances meant that difficult choices had to be made. In the early days, 200 years ago, there was little standardisation, even if the treatments were agreed there was no guarantee of the quality and uniformity of drugs which depended on the skill and honesty of the local pharmacist or hospital dispenser. Everyone was 'doing their own thing'. As communication, travel and journals became more available, so it was possible to develop a consensus on what was the appropriate treatment in a particular case. Clinical meetings among doctors were common by the middle of the 19th century, giving opportunities for dissemination of new ideas and criticism and review by other members of the profession; we know that the staff of the Infirmary participated in such meetings both locally and in London. The Infirmary's library has been in continuous use since 1825.

Coroners became more knowledgeable about medicine, newspapers more adept at detecting failures of care, and gradually the public came to have increasing expectations. The staff at the Infirmary can be seen responding to these demands, the minutes often express a desire to keep up with the latest equipment and treatments available. The wording of appeals for money often centred on the need for improvements in equipment and training and the sums required *'to keep up with London standards.'*

Making a fair judgement about the treatment offered so many years ago must involve an assessment of the extent of knowledge at that particular time. In any hospital much depended on the desire for excellence to be found on the part of the staff and the Governors, and the constraints on available funding. There can be no doubt that there were wide variations in the standard of care offered from hospital to hospital across the land, and that the greater the distance between a provincial hospital and a 'centre of excellence' the further that hospital could fall behind. Certain factors helped to keep up standards. The adequate size of a hospital, the number of staff and the number of junior members of staff preparing for examinations for higher qualifications all helped to maintain standards. If the hospital was not a Teaching Hospital, the appointment of visiting honorary consultants from London, as in the case of the Infirmary in the 1930s and 1940s, kept everyone up to scratch. We may notice here the long held wish to have a Medical School in North Staffordshire, as detailed in other chapters.

External events brought a degree of standardisation. We may quote reviews such as Sir Henry Burdett's, the exposure of a hospital to scrutiny in return for central funding and overall supervision brought about through the unified system of the Emergency Medical Service in World War II. The coming of the National Health Service led to a standardisation in training and accreditation of doctors. Under the eye of the Royal Colleges applicants for senior posts have to have undergone nationally approved training.

When we look at the record of the Infirmary throughout the century and a half in which it had to plough its own furrow and maintain its own standards I believe the Staff and Governors of the North Staffordshire Infirmary can be seen to have performed very creditably (but not always with the financial resources enjoyed by some other similar provincial hospitals).

CHAPTER 16
Illness in the Community

This chapter looks at some of those conditions that the Infirmary chose not to admit, believing that there was little to be done in those cases, and that they would occupy beds that could be more usefully employed. In particular the admission of children was not favoured although a change of heart occurred in the 1870s, even though the available treatments were still very limited. The fight to improve the appalling state of children's health had to be fought in the community. The Infirmary could not make much impression on the enormous mortality among the children of the Pottery towns other than by education of parents. The illnesses of childhood would affect the health of many Infirmary patients in later life.

Obviously, there were ups and downs in the life of any organisation surviving nearly 150 years, but I believe that over the years, as medicine advanced the staff made every effort to offer to the local people the best treatment available. Certainly, from the mid-19th century all voluntary hospitals were anxious to publish their results, and entered into public competition with other hospitals to demonstrate their utility to the community. Driven by the need to generate income from the local people, year in, year out, voluntary hospitals were scrutinised as much as any modern successor.

The Infirmary had for much of the later 19th century about 200 beds, rising to 420 by 1948. This was generally agreed to be far less than the number needed to properly serve the needs of the population, even though there were many fewer treatments available in those earlier days. This was not due to a lack of appreciation of the need but an expression of the difficulties involved in raising the capital and revenue needed to expand.

Thus, throughout the life of the Infirmary as an independent institution there was a list of conditions that patients who were suffering from would not normally be admitted. If they were inadvertently admitted, they could be sent home or sent to the Workhouse Infirmary, located on the site of the present City General Hospital. There was no secrecy about this policy, it was all laid out in the Annual reports. It may seem hard and Victorian, but at least it was honest, and there was no pretence of giving a service that could not even be attempted.

Medicine had little to offer to patients who were afflicted with mental illness, other than sedation or restraint; an order to pay an invoice for £1-10-0 for a strait jacket was authorised by Josiah Wedgwood II as early as 1804.

An exclusion that upsets some historians today is the rule that only those cancer patients for whom an operation offered a reasonable prospect of treatment were admitted to the Infirmary. Before the days of radiotherapy or chemotherapy, if the cancer was not amenable to operation, there was little to be done.

The remaining exclusion from the Infirmary that seems particularly strange to us today is that of pregnancy. In order to understand the Infirmary Governors stance in this, we must consider the position of midwifery in the country as a whole. 19th and early 20th century midwifery was to a large extent a domestic activity. Babies were born at home whenever possible, under the care of family members, a midwife or a handy woman, or the general practitioner. Only if the domestic circumstances were unsatisfactory, often in the cases of extreme poverty and often illegitimacy, the woman would be delivered in the Hospital Ward of the Workhouse, cared for by the Workhouse doctor, using instruments (forceps) if necessary, for which service he could claim a fee. A patient was only likely to be admitted

The Infantile Mortality Rate was 134 per 1,000 births, compared to 98 in 1920, and 111 in 1919. In 1920 the rate was the lowest ever recorded. In the 96 Large Towns of England and Wales the Infantile Mortality Rate for 1921 was 87. This year the rate for the County Borough is the highest recorded in any large town in the country. It is due to the excessive number of deaths from Epidemic Diarrhœa which occurred in the third quarter of the year. It will be remembered that the year was remarkable for the long, hot, dry summer and autumn, and though the Infantile Death Rate did not rise to the same height as it did in 1911 it is evident that no efforts in the campaign against Infantile Mortality can yet be relaxed.

The scheme for the abolition of cesspit closets in the Borough is now in full operation and satisfactory progress is being made; in two years time few of these insanitary conveniences should be in existence in the Federated area, though the large number in the recently added areas will still have to be dealt with. A complete scheme has been formulated for the satisfactory disposal of the whole of the ashpit and ashbin refuse in the area. It is desirable that it should be carried out with as little delay as possible.

The Medical Officer of Health's report for 1921.
The Infant Mortality rate varied from year to year. In 1924 it was 134, that is for every 1000 children born in Stoke on Trent, 134 had died by the age of one. Stoke on Trent had the worst figure for any large town. Between 1900 and 1912 the IMR in Stoke on Trent was over 200 three times. Large numbers of deaths were associated with hot summers and related to diarrhoea due to flies fouling food.

to the Infirmary if surgical intervention was proposed, as in a (very rare) Caesarean section, or if the woman was brought to the Infirmary in danger of death.

In those years the status of obstetrics was not high within the medical profession, nor in the mind of the public. A doctor engaged in midwifery thus was seen as a man who worked with his hands, and more than this he lost status by associating with midwives who certainly were not professional people, however skilled they may have been in practice. We recall that even in 1877, the printed rules of the Infirmary still stated that should a Consultant Physician even enter practice with a person who practiced Midwifery, he would have to resign. It was not until the 1930s that the specialty of obstetrics gained its proper place as a specialty in its own right, with its own Royal College

The story of obstetrics in Britain and in Stoke-on-Trent does not directly affect the Infirmary, but it is important for an understanding of the attitude of the Governors who largely left midwifery to be provided by other agencies. Into the 20th century the obstetrics for Stoke-on-Trent as elsewhere was practiced in the patient's home, in private nursing homes or in the hospital wards of the Stoke Workhouse, and after 1927 at the City Maternity Hospital (the Limes). During the 1920s the Workhouse become a Public Assistance Institution, the Wards of which became successively the London Road Hospital, and having passed into the administration of the City Council in 1929, the City General Hospital. Additionally after 1930 the new Haywood hospital offered beds for maternity care.

I have mentioned some of the apparent inconsistencies in the care offered at the Infirmary. One particular group should be mentioned here, the children. The people of 19th century Britain were ambivalent in their view of children. There was a sentimental regard for children, seeing them as epitomising innocence, greatly revered in such a religious age, but the loss of children at an early age had to be borne by all families, regardless of rank. At the same time the birth rate was very high, reaching a maximum in the 1870s, before entering a long decline in common with other industrialised nations. It

SMITH HILL CHILD BUILDING.

A donation of £1,000 which was offered by Sir Smith Child, Bart., about this time for the erection of a separate building in memory of his eldest son, to be called "The Smith Hill Child," for the reception of such patients as the rules of the Infirmary oblige the Committee to discharge, was accepted by the Governors. Plans were adopted, and the Committee were authorized to enter into a contract for its erection.

was a long held belief that there was little that could be done for sick children; the first children's hospital, Great Ormond Street Hospital in London was not founded until 1852. The Children's Ward at the infirmary dates from 1876, and is quoted as an early example of such a provision in a provincial infirmary. The ward was originally built with a gift of £1000 by Sir Smith Child to provide accommodation for those who were not eligible for admission under the rules we have discussed, and he paid for the conversion of the building to create a Children's Ward.

The Governors were concerned that the children's ward should not be a burden on the finances of the main Infirmary, perhaps because they too doubted its usefulness. Uniquely for a ward at the Infirmary it was decided that there should be a charge imposed on the parents of those children who were admitted to the ward. There was in fact a means test, which took into account the income of the parents and the number of children in the family. It is hard to know all the details at this distance, but from the raw facts in the minutes I suspect that it was generously interpreted by the committee that decided such matters. Sir Smith Child took a leading part in the affairs of this ward, and we know of his actions in relation to other charities that he supported, for which he would personally make up any financial shortfall rather than see children go without. Of course, this was 'his' ward, associated with the memory of his son who had recently died.

The Smith Child Ward in use as a children's ward around 1900.

Even more than with adults, medicine seemed to have so little to offer to sick children. There was no knowledge of the special metabolic needs of small children until the beginning of the 20th century and the major surgery for tiny babies regularly performed today is a development of very recent years. Infectious diseases were treated in infants much as they were in adults, indeed all children were viewed and treated as little adults. Surgical treatment was similarly confined to the reduction of fractures, incision of boils and abscesses and treatment of burns.

One operation that was performed on newly born infants with some frequency, and dates back to well before the advent of anaesthesia, was the repair of a hare-lip. The defect in a case of hare-lip prevented the child's lips from closing round the nipple to get milk from the breast. Of course, in early days this was a rough and ready procedure, closing the defect with a few large stitches. This would save the child's life, but many people lived with severe disfigurement before the development of plastic surgical repairs.

The coming of aseptic surgery in the 1870s made it possible to gradually extend the range and number of operations being successfully performed. One of the first of these new operations was aimed at the care of infected joints in children. Many children suffered from deformities of the hip joint, usually a consequence of infectious disease, often tuberculosis. An effective operation (osteotomy) was designed to reduce the deformity and consequent limp, but not until surgeons became sufficiently confident that patients would not be infected were they prepared to perform this operation.

We have seen that the range of services for children were limited in hospitals of the 19th century, equally the numbers treated were very small. This is ironic when we consider that throughout the Victorian era, and even after the First World War, a veritable holocaust was raging outside the hospitals among children, especially those who lived in the large industrial towns of this country. *During the First World War, it was less dangerous to be a soldier at the front line than to be a small child in an industrial town.* The large figures of mortality from long ago tend to be met with polite incomprehension, as with the ten millions who died in that war, or the twenty-five millions thought to have died in the flu epidemic which followed it. How can we comprehend such figures, make them relevant to our story?

If we are to understand the story of the Infirmary we must know what was going on outside its walls. In order that we shall not drown in figures, I have concentrated on the Annual Report of the Medical Officer of Health for the new County Borough of Stoke on Trent for the year 1911. This is the first full year after Federation of the Six Towns, the returns are those drawn up by Dr Petgrave Johnson, Medical Officer of Health for the whole of the new borough, instead of the six separate returns of the Medical Officers of Health of the six towns.

Looking through the return we see that although Stoke-on-Trent had not yet absorbed neighbouring authorities such as Smallthorne: it had a population of nearly a quarter of a million people. The statistic which most interested the Council was the Infant Mortality Rate, the IMR. This is the number of children who died in the first year of life expressed as so many deaths for each thousand live births. If there were 5,000 babies born in a town and 500 babies died there before reaching their first birthday, for every 1000 births there were 100 deaths, so the IMR was 100. The IMR was a most important figure for comparison between towns. It was then, and is now, the standard for comparison and used nationally and internationally. It was published and was there for all to see. It is recognised to this day that the Infant Mortality is a very sensitive measure of the quality of health provision in a town or a country.

Today the IMR for the United Kingdom is 5.3, for Japan it is 3.3 per thousand, in USA 6.8, Pakistan 76.5 and in Mozambique, the country which has the worst all, it is 199 per

Causes of Death	Net Deaths at the subjoined ages of "Residents" whether occurring within or without the District.								
	All Ages	Under 1 year	1 and under 2	2 and under 5	5 and under 15	15 and under 25	25 and under 45	45 and under 65	65 and upwards
All Causes { Certified...	3611	942	176	110	146	172	436	832	797
Uncertified	36	17	1	...	1	1	2	8	6
Enteric Fever	7	...	...	1	1	1	2	1	1
Smallpox	...	...	...	...	...	...	...	...	...
Measles	1	..	...	1	...	...	...	...	..
Scarlet Fever	14	1	1	3	6	3	...	...	...
Whooping Cough	22	9	7	5	1	..	...	...	..
Diphtheria and Croup	20	2	5	7	5	...	1	...	..
Influenza	87	10	6	3	3	7	26	17	15
Erysipelas	14	3	...	...	..	...	2	5	4
Phthisis (Pulmonary Tuberculosis)	292	1	4	1	10	68	115	85	8
Tuberculous Meningitis	25	8	3	1	7	3	1	2	...
Other Tuberculous Diseases...	49	14	5	4	10	6	6	4	..
Cancer, Malignant Disease	252	...	1	...	3	2	25	135	86
Rheumatic Fever	9	..	...	..	3	2	1	2	1
Meningitis	27	8	5	3	8	2	1	...	..
Organic Heart Disease	285	1	...	2	5	15	41	100	121
Bronchitis	430	68	24	17	4	2	16	121	178
Pneumonia (all forms)	263	64	49	28	17	14	43	34	14
Other Diseases of Respiratory Organs	34	6	3	3	4	..	4	7	7
Diarrhœa and Enteritis	339	282	30	6	...	1	8	5	7
Appendicitis and Typhlitis	22	...	...	1	6	5	3	6	1
Cirhosis of Liver	16	...	..	...	...	...	...	12	4
Alcoholism	1	...	...	...	...	...	...	1	..
Nephritis & Bright's Disease	84	3	1	..	5	4	12	38	21
Puerperal Fever	12	...	...	...	...	6	5	1	...
Other accidents and diseases of Pregnancy & Parturition	21	...	...	...	...	3	18	...	...
Congenital Debility and Malformation, including Premature birth	366	354	6	4	2	...	...	...	...
Violent Deaths, excluding Suicide	94	6	4	10	17	9	17	21	10
Suicide	25	..	..	...	.	2	10	10	3
Other Defined Diseases	820	117	19	10	29	16	79	231	319
Diseases ill-defined or unknown	16	2	4	...	1	2	2	2	3
TOTALS	3647	959	177	110	147	173	438	840	803

Deaths in 1921 in the County Borough of Stoke on Trent.

Thirty-three women died from diseases related to childbirth, twelve of these recorded as being due to puerperal fever, the others would include eclampsia and haemorrhage. Note the high proportion of deaths from chest diseases, bronchitis, tuberculosis and pneumonia.

We see also that in the first year of life 282 children died from diarrhoea and enteritis, while a further 354 died from congenital debility and premature birth, markers of poor maternal nutrition.

thousand live births. So we can see that the towns with the worst records one hundred years ago, a list that includes Stoke-on-Trent, had a worse IMR than any country in the world today.

In 1911, a very bad year, the IMR for the Borough of Stoke-on-Trent was 203/thousand live births, that is1495 children of those who were born alive in the Borough had died by their first birthday. It was the second highest figure in the country. In comparison, the average IMR for all the large towns in Britain in 1911 was 140. Worse, there were a further 679 children in Stoke who died between their first and fifth birthday. To add these together, we find that of all the 4636 people who died in Stoke in 1911, 2174 were less than five years of age. To these we should add the burials of 379 stillborn babies (babies which were born dead) In other words, of all the people who were buried in Stoke-on-Trent in 1911 nearly half had not reached the age of five years, a figure little improved over that of the 1850s.

What then was killing these children? The 19th century was undoubtedly swept by epidemics of scarlet fever, diphtheria and measles that were of extraordinary virulence. Gradually this decreased as the 19th century passed. There was a gradual fall in the death rate nationally, but this was a trend rather than a smooth decline - there were wild variations during epidemics; in Longton in 1898 the incidence of diphtheria was 14 times the national average. Effective treatments with antitoxins and sera only began at the end of the 19th century, when the death rate was already falling.

There was another group of diseases killing children about which a great deal could have been done without waiting for major scientific advances. These were diseases that related to inadequate nutrition, and to infections of the bowel caused by dirty food and water. Associated with poverty, poor housing and overcrowding they were summarised as filth diseases. When we look at deaths from these causes, the numbers of deaths vary both with the season and from year to year. Diarrhoea was always present to some extent, but in late summer frequently there were major outbreaks. It acquired its own name, summer diarrhoea, though the disease was always present.

From time immemorial there had been attempts to determine whether natural phenomena, the nature of the soil, climate, rainfall, even the prevailing winds were associated with illness, particularly with epidemics. In the case of summer diarrhoea one general rule did apply: when a thermometer was placed in the ground at a depth of four feet and the temperature recorded reached 56°F (13°C), a severe epidemic of diarrhoea could be expected. Even after this association was confirmed, some time elapsed before the connection was made between the larger number of house flies present in hot summers and the occurrence of major outbreaks of diarrhoea. In fact, the summer of 1911 was particularly hot, temperatures then were not exceeded until the 1990s. Eight people died in Stoke-on-Trent from 'sun stroke' (probably heat stroke in the furnaces). Certainly, the high infant death rate of 1911, largely due to diarrhoea, agrees with the theory that high temperatures and summer diarrhoea were causally connected. In 1912, which had a cold summer, the IMR fell from 203 to 128 per thousand, the lowest figure that had ever been recorded in the district.

The house-fly was ideally placed to spread diarrhoea, moving between the piles of rotting manure, human and animal, and the family's food in the house, food for which there was no adequate provision for storage. The fly has particularly unpleasant habits, not only does it walk on people's food, but it vomits its own food, derived from the open closet and cess-pits, onto that of the family. At that time, and for many years to come, milk was produced in many small cowsheds, often in cramped and unhygienic conditions within the large towns and travelled around the streets in open churns. From these churns milk was ladled out on the street into jugs, which then stood uncovered in the kitchen. The kitchen was only a few feet away from the midden across the yard. Most foods were susceptible to fouling by flies, sugar basins were particularly attractive to them; these are described in contemporary accounts of housing conditions as being *'black with flies'*. Interspersed with houses were stables housing the horses which still provided the motive power of most of the road transport and provided more fouling of the neighbourhood.

Small children are particularly at risk from diarrhoea, they cope very badly with the fluid lost from reduced intake, vomiting and copious diarrhoea. Very many children died as an immediate consequence of such an infection. These cases presented little difficulty in diagnosis, and we may assume that they were reasonably accurately recorded. However, there were other categories of deaths that should be added in to find the true toll of diarrhoea. The connection with diarrhoea was not recognised because there was an appreciable interval between the obvious bowel infection and death. Of those infants who survived the initial attack of diarrhoea it often happened that the infection had inflicted long term damage on the bowel making it inefficient in absorbing food. Children whose bowel had been damaged were susceptible to other infections, their immune systems being poorly developed. When they died after an interval, the attacks of diarrhoea having been forgotten, they could be recorded as having died from *'debility'*, or *'wasting'* or *'marasmus'*. The wasted children with swollen bellies that we have seen on television screens in Africa were no different from many children in the Victorian inner cities. A recent estimate gives a death rate of 12,000 children dying each day worldwide from protein energy syndrome to give its proper name.

There were many children who suffered impaired health throughout their lives through the effects of malnutrition. Apart from the consequences of infant diarrhoea, many more suffered in the womb due to their mother's poor diet and inability to breast feed her children well. When these children were weaned their diet often continued to be poor, especially if largely composed of the infamous 'pobs', mainly bread and lacking in essential vitamins and minerals. It may reveal itself by failure of intellectual development or in obvious physical deformities. The association of spina bifida with a lack of folic acid in the mother's diet is now well recognised.

In the Victorian towns, with small houses, large families and many mothers going out to work, childcare was always a problem. Often elderly people or small children in the family, even the simple-minded neighbour, were left to care for an infant. In such cases it was found very convenient to use a bottle that had a long tube inside it that collected the milk from the lowest part of the bottle whichever way up it was placed. A long rubber tube carried the milk to a teat. The bottle could be propped up in the baby's bed and the child effectively left to feed itself. Sadly, there was no means of sterilising

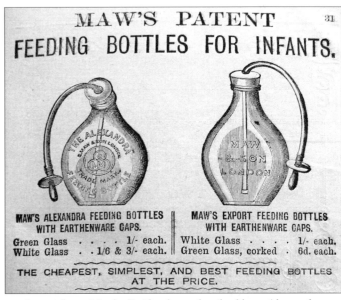

Long tube or Murder Bottles, here advertised in an Almanack published in Longton in 1871. The long rubber tube leading to the teat soon began to perish and became impossible to clean. It became a perfect breeding ground for germs.

Pavement delivery of milk from a churn. As late as 1950 the Medical Officer of Health for Stoke on Trent used this picture to support the campaign for cleaner milk.

Taken from *The Lady's Realm* in 1910, this shows a marasmic baby who had been left in the care of a 'Baby Farmer'. At this time much effort was being expended in developing 'Health Visitor' services throughout the country. The Lady's Realm was a very upmarket periodical, full of pictures of society beauties .The appearance of a picture of such a child in such a paper tells us that the implementation of the Children's Act, passed in 1908, was beginning to stir consciences.

A baby boarded out with a baby farmer for a weekly payment !

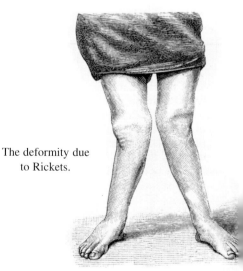

The deformity due to Rickets.

tubing made of rubber, which was a perfect breeding ground for organisms, and these bottles were popularly and correctly known as murder bottles.

By 1916 Dr Balsillie, Stoke's Lady Medical Officer, was one of the doctors campaigning for these long tube bottles to be made illegal, an action which was undertaken in France by 1907, and in America, before Great Britain took any notice. She also proposed that all illegitimate children, whose health was often less satisfactory than that of the other children, and those put out to nurse, should be seen compulsorily at a clinic to check on their progress. This was not moralising, circumstances dictated that illegitimate children were often put out to nurse and until childminders were inspected and registered after the implementation of the Children's Act of 1908 these children were at increased risk. In 1902 the IMR was 203, for illegitimate children it was 300.

All over the country reviews undertaken in the late 19th and first half of the 20th century revealed overcrowding as a readily measurable predictor of illness. Halving the room available to a family would double the incidence of infectious disease, especially of tuberculosis. Hospitals were dressing stations in the battle against social conditions. Many of the diseases which occasioned hospital admission were made worse by a poor basic standard of living, all of which added to the problems faced by those caring for the Infirmary's patients. Nothing the Infirmary could offer would correct the problems of bad diet, poor housing and poverty. The Medical Officer of Health set up emergency wards at the Workhouse (City General) in particularly bad years, but many children could not be saved.

Of course, the cure of all these ills was not in the hands of the medical profession, it would need change throughout society. Doctors certainly cannot claim to have cured these ills, but some can claim that by bringing the extent of the problems to the public's attention they have played a part in many improvements. Dr John Snow's demonstration of the water borne nature of cholera is a well-known example, even so it took years to persuade the suppliers of London's water to invest in the plant needed to provide clean water. In North Staffordshire, Dr.J.T. Arlidge, Physician to the Infirmary and a pioneer of industrial medicine, was one of the first to cast an incomer's eye on the health of the Potteries. When his paper *On the Sanitary State of the Staffordshire Potteries*, published in 1864, is examined, his analysis is remarkably acute and wide-ranging.

Arlidge's paper is always quoted as one of the first to quantify the harmful effects of working in the potteries, and relate it to the preponderance of chest disease in the population, but there are many valuable sub-texts to his paper. He was concerned that most potters worked in an enclosed atmosphere, and that although the layout of the Potteries towns meant that open country was in easy walking distance no advantage was taken of it for recreation. He pointed to the large number of Dissenters in the area, and that the Sabbatarian and other restricted views of most Dissenters opposed opportunities and means of outdoor exercise favourable to health, and lead to the necessity of indoor relaxation, one part of which is among the uneducated classes pretty sure to be indulgence in drinking. He further regretted the absence of public parks. We must recall that at that time six days a week were normally occupied by work, and Sunday was the only day available for any exercise in the fresh air.

Arlidge was concerned at the high infant mortality in the Pottery towns, and many of the concerns he raised in 1864 were still being voiced in 1920. He was concerned by the prevalence of diseases of wasting and atrophy, diseases then as now associated with poor feeding in early life. He saw this as indicative of a very numerous and feeble progeny. *"Frequently mothers have to go out to work - they do not choose poor care for their children'.* Of course, in making his point Arlidge is being unfair to the mothers in making them shoulder the blame for the numerous feeble progeny. Both necessity and domestic circumstances made women go out to work. In 1910 62% of the houses in the new federated borough of Stoke-on-Trent had four rooms or less.*

Bringing up a large family in a tiny terraced house, many with no running water, and an earth closet in the yard, must have been immensely stressful. The company and social contact to be found in factory work for the wife, and the pub for the husband, must have been awfully attractive. Arlidge advocated the benefits of breast-feeding. Breast feeding is most effective in reducing bowel infections, at the same time providing optimal nutrition for the first months of life. Unfortunately, while it has many advantages, after six months milk no longer contains all the nutrients necessary for healthy development and it must be supplemented by a properly balanced diet. In the poorest homes children were found to be subsisting for two years or more on a meagre supply of breast milk alone, and showing all the signs of relative starvation. This often manifested itself in the prevalence of rickets, due to a deficiency of Vitamin D. The bones were poorly formed and distorted. Vitamin D is manufactured in the skin on exposure to sunlight. In the Pottery towns even this source was denied by the pall of smoke that hung over the district. In the 1920s and 1930s the deficiency was treated with artificial sunlight, specially adapted electric lamps to which children were exposed in controlled conditions, a treatment offered in the Electrical Department at the Infirmary and in the Welfare Clinics.

In 1862 Arlidge recounted his surprise at the absence of mechanisation in the pottery industry, so common in other industries, to perform routine tasks in the factories, which here were left to women and children. He placed the blame on the male pottery workers, the men not the employers. He wrote of the *'blind and mischievous jealousy'* of the men, who feared that the machines would deprive the family of the earnings of their wives and children. With great prescience he saw that in the long term mechanisation would keep a price advantage, cheapness of production which would extend their trade and protect it from rivals. Reducing the need for child labour, and removing the need for work performed in unhealthy surroundings by women, would progressively improve the health of mothers and children, while increased productivity would preserve the men's employment.

There is little doubt that there was a great deal of chronic ill health in the Pottery towns. It has become customary to blame all the ills on industrial diseases. While in no way denying their ill effects, there were other causes operating to the detriment of local people, and even today the change from an industrial environment may not of itself be sufficient to transform the health of the people. The old enemies of low income, poor diet, poor education and unsatisfactory housing may still be contributing to the self same problems.

Were there no other voices to speak for the wives and children of the working class in North Staffordshire? There were some women from the upper and middle classes who led the battle against the evils they saw around them. One was Lucie Wedgwood, the wife of Cecil Wedgwood and the first Mayoress of the new Borough of Stoke-on-Trent in 1910 and 1911. Lucie Wedgwood was a remarkable woman who made a powerful impact on the lives of working women. As Mayoress she instituted the Stoke-on-Trent Infant Health Visitors Association, later renamed the Stoke-on-Trent Health Association. In 1910 there were only six health visitors employed in the whole new County Borough, which meant that each child could only ever receive one visit. The new association recruited a group of ladies who, with the agreement of the mothers visited their homes and young children bringing advice and support. They also opened clinics, named 'Welcomes' where food supplements, clothing and advice were given, where children were examined and weighed and treatment was organised. They recognised that many of the problems with premature and underweight babies were due to the malnutrition of expectant and feeding mothers. Free dinners and dietary supplements were given to expectant mothers thought to be most at risk, often with striking benefits for the mother and child. Eventually these functions were taken up by the municipal authorities, but the voluntary health visitors filled a need and gave an example to officialdom of what could be achieved. Often derided as do-gooders, we should recognise that in their time these ladies did great good.

Officialdom was represented by the Department of the Medical Officer of Health, Dr Petgrave Johnson. The doctor with responsibility for child health was the Lady Medical Officer, Dr Jessie Balsillie. She was quite prepared to work with the volunteers, and to campaign vigorously on behalf of women and children. She found younger mothers were anxious to learn, but in older women tradition died hard, '*only too often disabilities from which their children suffer are regarded with a certain amount of pride as a family inheritance*'. This agreed with a report from a Lady Sanitary Inspector in Longton that young mothers were glad to learn but the older women were vigorously resistant to change. We should note that the deprivation as measured by the mortality of children was not evenly spread across even the poorest districts. It was noted that while some families lost a majority of their children and lived in squalor, many other families, often similarly situated, battled to keep their homes clean and tidy and their families healthy despite all the odds against them.

Finally, after forcefully expressing her concerns about failures in childcare, Dr Balsillie showed that she did not put the blame on the mothers. '*One has considerable sympathy with the women who go out and leave their homes in search of recreation and enjoyment because unfortunately the majority of the working class houses in the Potteries are not conducive to happy and contented home life*'. Recent medical research suggests that those who grew up in straitened circumstances early in the 20th century may at this moment be suffering in their later life from such diseases as coronary artery disease due to the imperfect development of vital organs in early life. Further it is suggested that raised blood pressure in some older people may be a consequence of stresses imposed in infancy when they literally had to fight for life before birth. This stress may result in an increased production of adrenaline being programmed into their metabolism in early life, even while still in the womb. Such possibilities are useful to help our understanding of the history of ill-health in an industrial town such as Stoke. The word malnutrition usually implies a lack of food, but we should remember that mal- in the word malnutrition means bad, and it is possible to be at the same time badly fed and grossly overfed. Sadly all indicators show that the present health of the Potteries is still not as good as it might be, and that some of the present problems could both have roots in the past and lessons for the future

*The Medical Officer of Health reported in 1911 that 62% of houses in the new Borough of Stoke-on-Trent contained four rooms or less. The census form of 1901 asked about the number of rooms in houses, and directed that families occupying 5 rooms or less be marked on the form. In 1901 the duty of supplying this information became the duty of the enumerator who filled in the forms, often we may suppose on the doorstep. The census analysis indicates that in large parts of the Potteries 60 to 70% of houses had 5 rooms or more. Clearly these figures do not agree. Unfortunately, the Census authorities never defined a room, thus it was never resolved that a closet, a landing or a washroom was or was not a room. The room count included in the Medical Officer of Health's Report for the new Borough Council would include the latest information available, which would go the Rates Department and be easily checked by Council officers. In this instance I would prefer to believe the Medical Officer of Health's Report, especially when we know that as late as 1981 a check on the Census of that year revealed that in 28.6% of households the number of rooms inhabited had been given wrongly in the return .(*A Clearer Sense of the Census*, Edward Higgs: HMSO 1996.)

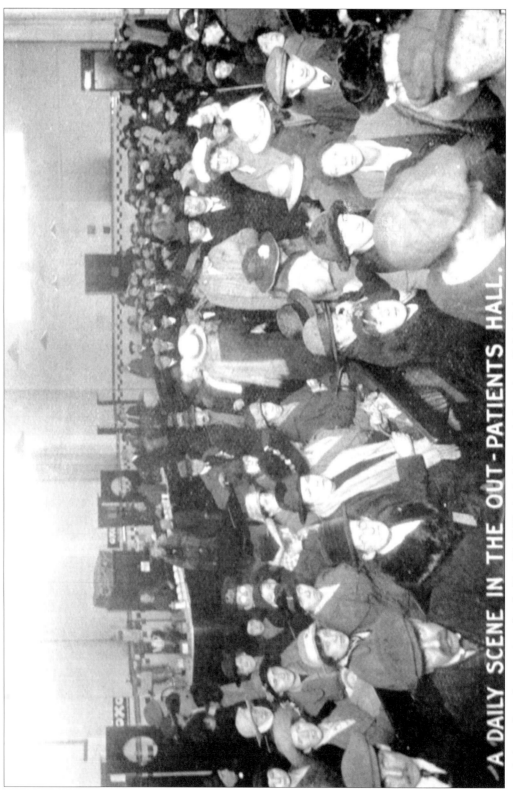

A DAILY SCENE IN THE OUT-PATIENTS HALL.

A picture from the years just after the First World War in the Infirmary's Outpatients Hall, built in response to Sir Henry Burdett's critical report of 1910. Ten years on crowding appears to be well on the way back to 'Standing Room Only'.

CHAPTER 17
ICEBERGS - or a Close Run Thing

This chapter looks at the events of the years 1908 to 1910. These years were part of the Edwardian Summer, the golden years just before the first World War. The Infirmary basked in this glow, matters went on as they had for half a century, God was in his Heaven and all was well with the world.

The Governors and the Committee running the Infirmary were largely drawn from the middle classes, many now well advanced in years. Many had begun their Committee work at the time of the move to Hartshill in the 1870s. They did not fully appreciate the pace at which medicine was moving on and that the demand for beds and accommodation was pressing. Most of all they did not appreciate that the Establishment Subscriptions and Saturday and Sunday Funds produced most of the income but had no adequate representation on the Committee.

This is the story of that crisis, of how problems were recognised and how they were resolved. The change in society during those Edwardian years is illuminated by these events, not just in the Infirmary, but also in the Country as a whole.

In 1906, forty years after Edward VII, as the Prince of Wales, had laid the foundation stone of the Infirmary in Hartshill, there had been little material change in the building or in the mode of its government. There had been improvements of course, an X-ray department, new operating theatres and the first Nurses' Home but the management was not dramatically changed. The resident staff had increased, the nursing staff was more numerous and better trained and managed. The Honorary Staff, the consultants, still gave their services free as before. The decision making body, the Governors and the Committee was still formed mainly from the individual subscribers and benefactors, drawn mainly from the upper and middle classes, even though their subscriptions had long ago levelled out at about £3-4000 a year. The contributions of the less well off, from the Establishment Subscribers and through the Saturday and Sunday Funds had steadily increased until they were by this time providing the great majority of the revenue of the Infirmary. The significance of this steady growth in these contributions, year on year, had not been accorded its proper value, without it the Infirmary would have closed long ago.

The first signs of discontent appeared in newspaper reports. To take the North Staffordshire Railway as an example, discontent arose among the engine drivers, a class usually considered the aristocrats among working men. It appeared that since 1877 they had sent a sum corresponding to a day's wage as their annual establishment contribution. By 1906 they had become concerned at their lack of representation in the affairs of the Infirmary and were reported to be considering obtaining legal advice on their future conduct. They wished to know the extent to which they were bound by this agreement. Had the Infirmary lost the support of these men, it would have been a very severe and a very public blow.

1906 was politically a watershed year with the Liberal landslide at the election. It was a time of considerable unrest, and it was a time in which there was a re-evaluation of the status quo. The imbalance between their contributions and their representation on the governing body was not lost on the leaders of the working people. The issues resolved into two questions. Could working people obtain representation on the Committee that reflected the importance of their contributions? - or should they withdraw their support and try to find an alternative means of supplying their medical needs?

On one hand were the Individual Subscribers who, although their total annual subscriptions had fallen behind, had as a group over the years been generous donors to the Infirmary. They had built up the invested funds and the interest on these funds often provided the only means by which the books could be balanced. They could also point to a continuing tradition of service on the committees of the Infirmary and lastly but not least, they were men used to dealing with large sums of money, with investments, building works and Government regulation. The value of such experience and expertise, if lost, would not be easily replaced.

On the other side was the sheer volume of the income from the working people. The work they undertook in regularly collecting the money from the works, and raising it in the Saturday and Sunday funds represented a huge investment in time in support of the Infirmary and its aims. To jeopardise all this goodwill would be equally damaging. The resolution of this conflict was thus of absolutely crucial importance. We have seen earlier how bitterly divisive a falling out over the Infirmary could be.

Local feeling was shown by changes in the level of Saturday, Sunday and Establishment contributions. In 1908, the Saturday Fund brought in £2159, and from the Establishments came £5704. By 1909 the sums were £1793 and £4606, showing substantial falls. After the reorganisation in 1910, the Establishment subscriptions were £6712, £1359 of it arrears withheld from the previous year, evidence of a protest in 1908, and a satisfactory resolution in 1910.

In calling this chapter 'Icebergs', I have acknowledged the folkloric status of the *Titanic* and its Captain Smith of Hanley. Certainly, those in charge of the Infirmary found themselves in waters as threatening as those facing Capt Smith. In 1909 a critical article appeared in the influential journal devoted to hospital design and administration, appropriately called *The Hospital*. The article was written by Sir Henry Burdett, 1847-1920, who edited and owned the magazine. He was one of those Victorians at whose energy we can only stand amazed. He started life as a bank clerk in Birmingham in 1863, he then became Secretary and General Superintendent of the Queen's Hospital in Birmingham. He completed the course to become a doctor, but as he did not wish to practice medicine, preferring public administration, he did not take the final exams. He went on to be Secretary of the Share and Loan Department of the London Stock Exchange. He compiled definitive books of information on financial securities worldwide. He set up the Prince of Wales's Hospital Fund for London to celebrate Queen Victoria's Diamond Jubilee, which we know today as the Kings Fund. He also produced an annual directory of charitable institutions, which developed into today's Health Services Journal. To be criticised in print by Sir Henry was, in terms of a voluntary hospital, to have incurred the wrath of God.

The article about the North Staffordshire Infirmary was published in the *Hospital* in October 1909, and duly copied into the *Sentinel*. The principal objects of the attack on the Infirmary were the out-patients and casualty departments, but through these criticisms was a scarcely veiled attack on the management of the Infirmary. Sir Henry felt that the lack of administrative care was shown by the recent trouble in connection with a member of staff (the Secretary had recently gone on leave and disappeared.) The outpatients department was criticised, outpatients clinics for ordinary (general) patients were only held on two days a week (in addition to two days for eye cases and one for an increasing number of ear, nose and throat cases). Four clinics were suggested, which would need an increase in the medical staff, adding two physicians and surgeons. The Honorary (consultant) Staff was seen as inadequate in number in relation to the increasing numbers of in and outpatients. The article notes that half the income (actually three quarters) came from the Establishment Subscribers, '...*it speaks volumes for the forbearance and patience of the men of the Potteries that they should have continued to subscribe so handsomely to this hospital, having regard to the present lamentable condition of its outpatients and casualty departments...'*

Sir Henry recalled that when the Infirmary had been examined after the opening in 1869 it had been at the forefront of hospital design. He admired the work of Charles Lynam the architect, his wards were good, and are *as good today for the treatment of disease as they ever were, so the hospital authorities have good cause to be grateful to Mr Lynam for the excellence of much of his work.* However, he was very unhappy about the state of Ward 14, which was almost underground, that there were no separate eye wards, eye patients being treated in the general wards, and about the state of the children's ward. He noted an empty room at the entry to each ward, which was formerly the Ward Sister's bedroom, harking back to the time when the sisters lived on the ward. He proposed their conversion into dayrooms. The isolation wards were inadequate, cold and built of iron. *'It would be cruel to think of putting any patient on any pretence into these wards as they exist today'.*

If that seems harsh, Sir Henry was merely working up a head of steam for the outpatients department, *DISGRACEFUL.* He found it grossly overcrowded, patients were seen in small cubicles, boxes, one of which housed three doctors and their three patients, of mixed sexes. On outpatient days there was not even standing room for patients, nowhere for a doctor to see a patient who was lying down, no separation of the medical and surgical outpatients, and conversations were audible from one room to the other. Sir Henry felt no satisfactory work can be done due to the noise and overcrowding. He hoped that the working men and other governors would go to see the outpatients department in action, noting that it inflicts cruelty on both the medical staff and the patients, who, in recognition of the support they give to the hospital deserve better service from it.

So far so bad! But it got worse: *THE WORST CASUALTY ROOMS IN ENGLAND. They exhibit an absence of conveniences, a want of privacy and decency, and a callous disregard of what is due to the reputation of the hospital and the feelings and rights of patients, which we feel justified in declaring is to be found in no other medical institution in the United Kingdom at the present day.*

Many operations were performed there, although there was no operating theatre and no recovery room, patients were herded together, those awaiting surgery listening to their fellow patients being anaesthetised. There was no place to examine gynaecological patients, they had to wait a long time until operating was finished at the end of the day and the surgery eventually became available. Again Sir Henry appealed to the Governors to visit this department, and see for themselves what is going on.

The defects of other departments were recorded. The hospital had a pathology department poorly housed in the basement, a source of danger to the pathologist and to others. Sir Henry recorded that the pathologist saved the Infirmary £30-£40 per year; at this time commercial laboratories offered a pathology service to doctors and hospitals, but of course, for a fee.

Other services were reviewed. The laundry, the boilers and the supporting services all came in for criticism. The resident doctors were effectively isolated in the Infirmary, and he urged proper recreational facilities, while the porters should have their own room to keep them away from the female servants.

He believed that the number of patients that Individual contributors could recommend was too generous when the cost of treating a patient was considered. He encouraged an urgent review of the finance and running of the Infirmary, pointing out that there were investments of £60,000 in reserve, with the implication that this should be spent to rectify the worst problems.

The Governors set up two subcommittees to examine every aspect of the Infirmary's affairs. Sir Henry Burdett's article appeared on October 2nd, the new subcommittees were formed on the 14th. One was to examine the administrative, staffing and committee structure, the other to examine the buildings in light of the criticisms and recommend improvements.

That was the internal response. In the *Sentinel* the correspondence columns were soon filled on a daily basis with letters about the Infirmary. The President, Mr Guy Knight defended the Governors and the Committee. Sir Henry Burdett had been welcomed at the Infirmary, he had been shown everything he asked to see, afforded all the information he needed. Mr Knight protested that Sir Henry had been unfair in that he concentrated on the defects without reflecting the good work done by the staff. He listed the improvements made in the past ten years. Electric light, new drains, an X-ray department and a new nurses' home had been built at a cost of more than £5,000. The problems with the outpatients department were largely due to the marked increase in the numbers who were attending each day. The inadequacies were recognised, but their solution came down to money. The investments referred to by Sir Henry were the reserves, the interest they generated being a permanent endowment.

The letters flew back and forth, sometimes Sir Henry wrote to the *Sentinel*, sometimes he replied through leading articles in the *Hospital*, then copied by the *Sentinel* - while he himself kept an eye on the correspondence in the *Sentinel*! On October 11th a letter appeared supporting Sir Henry. It said the Infirmary had attained the status of a sacred institution, beyond criticism, operating in a medieval manner. A new committee was required. As so often happens, useful detail is buried in unlikely places. The letter goes on to graphically describe post-operative patients being brought out into the waiting room, bleeding and vomiting, and left to recover among those awaiting surgery. A leading article in the *Sentinel* was supportive of the Infirmary: it thought the Infirmary had been unfortunate in that Sir Henry's series of articles had started with North Staffordshire, thereby achieving maximum impact. The Infirmary was getting old (in 1909!) and he could have started with a newer hospital.

Next day, there was a meeting of Burslem Town Council. Mr George Wade thought there should be representation on the Committee of those who paid, by a body such as the Town Council. They would seek an improvement in the civility and punctuality of the medical staff. The Haywood hospital was in the process of rendering their committee more representative of subscribers.

On the 13th a letter from Sir Henry was printed in the *Sentinel*, replying to Mr Knight. He felt the expenditure of which Mr Knight had written was small over ten years. He felt that they had missed the most important point, the most pressing change needed was an increase in the medical staff numbers, and a reformed and vigorous management. A correspondent signing himself *'Onward'* pointed out that the Infirmary was not purely a charity, but through the Establishment Scheme was in fact a subscription hospital and representation was needed for the working population who provided all the patients and 80% of the income.

On the 14th, another letter urged the involvement of the Trades Council from which more incidental details emerged. The writer had been one of 4 patients on the open air ward, at the far end of Ward 2. He had found it boring, and being at liberty to roam in the grounds and the ward, occupied himself feeding patients and emptying bedpans, due to the inadequate numbers of nurses and doctors. As he almost certainly was on the open air ward for treatment of tuberculosis, his case was very likely to be open and infectious so his excursions onto the ward may not have been as beneficial to other patients as he appeared to

Two pictures of the Open Air or Consumption (TB) Ward added to the end of Wards 1 and 2 about 1902.
The interior of the ward shows the very large windows and the patients huddled in their blankets

BELOW
The number of openable windows gave the benefit of 'outside wards' as in a sanatorium. Outside, beyond the
right hand edge of our picture, a grove of pine trees, thought to benefit chest patients, was planted, the gift of
Mr Phillips of Tean. The wards have disappeared, but the pine trees remain.

believe them to be.

On the 15th, in a report from the week's *Hospital,* Sir Henry said that the Governors had little knowledge of the workings of a hospital. He praised the *Sentinel,* but said he felt that it showed its lack of understanding of hospitals when it commented that an increase in staff was a matter for the existing staff to sort out.

On the 21st the Rev Granville Bailey, Vicar of Goldenhill, wrote in support of the committee for their zeal and long service, and defended them against the attacks of Sir Henry and anonymous attackers, which made his blood boil. The Rev Bailey had brought Blondin, the high-wire walker, and the band of the Royal Artillery, to his church fete, from the proceeds of which he maintained a Parish nurse! He said *'The excess numbers of outpatients were due to too many tickets* (recommendations) *being given to people who could well afford to pay for their own treatment and should not have been in the outpatient department in the first place.'* Another letter addressed to the Rev Bailey asked how many Governors attended meetings? W.H. Folker was ill, and C. Adams was between 80 and 90, the implication being that the Committee were now too old and infirm to attend to business. The Rev Bailey said he would not reply to anonymous letters, only to those who would sign their names like a man.

At this time a visit to the general practitioner entailed the payment of a fee to the doctor unless one was in a 'club', while a visit to outpatients together with a bottle of medicine was free providing you could get a ticket of recommendation. It was obvious from the numbers attending outpatients that it was becoming very easy to obtain a ticket and many patients were thought to be abusing the system. In London there were stories in circulation of well-to-do women borrowing a servant's clothes to plead poverty - some versions say they were thrown out when they forgot to take their diamond rings off. However apocryphal they may have been, these stories reveal a deep-seated belief that many of the problems in voluntary hospitals were due to people not playing the game. The medical staff wanted the outpatients department to be used for difficult cases, for second opinions and for specialist attention, essentially the system we see today in outpatients clinics, where patients are only seen on referral from another doctor.

The 22nd brought the news of the appointment of a new Secretary and House Governor, Dr Roscoe, to replace the absconder. He was an experienced doctor, indeed he had worked in hospital administration in Africa under Cecil Rhodes.

Undoubtedly there were problems, largely due to the excessive workload passing through the outpatients department. Remember it did not have a proper out-patients operating theatre, but in 1909 it had to accommodate 615 operations to remove tonsils and adenoids among a total of 1194 operations. Of these, 16 were to remove a rib to drain an empyema, an abscess inside the chest. There were additionally 620 general anaesthetics given for dental extractions. No wonder recovering patients were dumped unceremoniously in the waiting room, it was remarkable that there were not more reports of fatalities. The house physicians gave the anaesthetics. In order to ease their burden the first anaesthetists were appointed in 1902, *initially working in the main operating theatres, not the outpatients where most of the deaths occur, and where skilled anaesthetists are needed round the clock* - a comment from 1905.

These must have been exciting days for the patients and the staff. It is probable that many of the committee would not have been familiar with all these problems. They represented an older order, and none of them nor any members of their families would have personal experience of being treated in the conditions that prevailed in the outpatients department.

Any organisation has to face up to the ageing of those who have given it good service.

The Outpatients Hall of 1911, a memorial to Edward VII, and built after reorganisation consequent to the strictures of Sir Henry Burdett in *The Hospital.* *(Page 189)*

The longer that service has lasted, the greater the sense of attachment to the organisation, and unless there is an agreed retirement age or similar limit, removing an aged committee member can be difficult and seem like treachery. There is no doubt that there were members of the committee who were advanced in age, some had served for forty years or more. I know there can be exceptions, Frank Wedgwood served for many years, but even he was in latter years content to let others, including his son Godfrey take the lead, and Frank Wedgwood was a remarkably fit and vigorous man. The comment was fairly made that *until the report by Sir Henry Burdett, there had been no sign from the committee that they appreciated the severity of the problem.*

There was no doubt that there would have to be representation of those who gave such a large proportion of the income. There were problems however. Had the Trade Unions managed to gain an ascendancy in the affairs of the Infirmary it may well have been at the price of losing the support of other sections of the population. Equally, the concept of the Town Councils being in charge was anathema to many people, including many doctors. This antipathy to municipal control would be important determinant of the way that the National Health Service was introduced in 1948. The area had recently witnessed the battle for Federation with all the recriminations between the participants; it would have done little to enhance the desire to place the Infirmary under municipal control. Thus the introduction of the Establishment and Saturday Fund Governors to the committee while maintaining continuity and independence from any particular grouping was a triumph of diplomacy.

Bringing about change in the Honorary Medical Staff was not as simple as it might appear. The consultants were not paid, so why not appoint as many as were required? Sir Henry chided the *Sentinel* for suggesting that the existing members of staff should have the decisive voice, after all, the more there were the less work each would have to do. Although they were not paid, their appointments as members of the Infirmary Staff represented a considerable cachet when it came to attracting the private patients on whom they depended for their income. They were consultants, but they were also in practice on their own account.

For example, W.D. Spanton was a Consultant Surgeon to the Infirmary, but he was also the medical attendant of the Duke of Sutherland at Trentham, and he also attended the Wedgwood family. While the growth in the numbers of hospital patients seemed endless, this was not necessarily the case in private practice. An increase in the consultant staff could lead to a fall in the number of patients each saw privately and therefore a fall in their income. As long as the hospital services relied on the 'Robin Hood' system, the Honorary Staff cannot realistically be blamed for choosing not to vote themselves a decrease in income. The committee in general would have to take responsibility and deal with the matter.

THE DUKE OF SUTHERLAND.

THE Duke of Sutherland, who is now lying at Trentham, under the charge of Mr. W. D. Spanton, of Hanley, is suffering from a very acute attack of inflammation of both lungs, the result of a chill. The Duke has a gouty diathesis, and has long been suffering from chronic bronchial catarrh, so that his condition is one which causes considerable anxiety to his medical attendant, Mr. Spanton, and to Dr. Quain, who has been called in consultation.

An announcement in the medical press; even a senior surgeon at the Infirmary (W.D.Spanton) earned his living in part by acting as a general practitioner to private patients. Medical details of the rich and famous were discussed freely in the press a century ago.

On the 1st November, a letter from the Rev Bailey protested against anonymous attacks on the Infirmary Committee, and of the remark by Sir Henry in his last communication saying that a small clique must not be allowed to defeat the wishes of the majority. November 12th saw a more hopeful report. A Trades Union deputation had visited the Infirmary. They had met the subcommittee charged with revising the rules. Drs Alcock, Russell and Young had shown them over the Infirmary, they had been permitted to question the nurses. The delegates declared themselves well satisfied with the information they had gained. .

The Annual General Meeting of the Governors was better attended than any in recent years. The retiring President, Mr Knight handed over to his successor, Col.A.H. Heath, who had been unanimously elected in his stead.

Fortunately, the new President of the Infirmary was a man of considerable ability. He also seems to have been a man blessed with a high order of negotiating skills who could empathise and communicate with a wide spectrum of society. He was a member of the Coal and Ironworking family, the Conservative Member of Parliament for Leek, and he was widely known for his sporting achievements. He had played cricket for Staffordshire against the Australians on the County Ground in Stoke, situated then behind the North Stafford Hotel. Col. Heath had been able to assure the railway men that their complaints were being heard and attended to, persuading them not to take action until changes came into effect.

At the meeting all the grievances were rehearsed yet again. It was urged by Mr George Wade that no changes should be made nor a Committee elected until the subcommittee reports were available. Some wanted the two subcommittees to be reconstituted. It was pointed out that they were well advanced in their work, and to replace them with those with no experience of the workings of the Infirmary would be counter-productive, worse, such an action could be seen as a vote of no confidence which would damage the reputation of the Infirmary still further. The President proposed that ten additional members, drawn from those who sought reform should act as an advisory panel to assist the temporary Committee especially when they came to scrutinise the reports of the subcommittees. *At the end of the three hour meeting, this elegant compromise was gratefully accepted. In a supportive editorial, the Sentinel described the meeting as the most momentous in the Infirmary's history.*

Thus it was decided that the new Committee would have thirty elected members. Fourteen were elected as before by the general body of Governors, plus sixteen, eight of whom were elected by the Establishment Governors from their number and eight by the Saturday Fund Governors.

Having changed the composition of the Governing body, the task was by no means over. The new members of the Committee that managed the day to day affairs of the Infirmary had to be integrated into the structure. They had to learn the skills which would enable them to understand the medical necessities essential for the Infirmary to perform its duties, develop working relationships with the doctors and nurses, and perhaps most important learn the complexities of financing a large institution. Just as working men found themselves sitting next to and working with men of a class they had only known as employers, so the older governors had to work with men who might work in their factories or mines. For both groups this was a huge culture shock, with ample potential for disaster.

Col Heath seems to have been an ideal man to handle such a situation; he was elected President for the three years covering this turbulent time. Regularly in the reports from Annual General Meetings references occur to Col Heath's negotiating skills, and from those identifying themselves as representatives of the working people appreciation of his tact and courtesy in his dealings with them.

The Committee undertaking the review of administrative affairs, having settled the question of representation undertook an overhaul of the rules and regulations affecting staffing. As a consequence of this review, five new members of staff were appointed, two Honorary Assistant Physicians and two Honorary Assistant Surgeons and an Assistant Physician in charge of the Electrical Department. Miss MacMaster, the Superintendent of Nurses, found her title changed in 1910 back to that of Matron, forty years after the title had been abolished in favour of a Lady Superintendent.

The other committee, which had reviewed the buildings, under the leadership of W.D. Spanton in his last official duty before retirement, issued a report which received the approval of Sir Henry Burdett. The improved climate of opinion surrounding the Infirmary meant that an appeal for £35,000 for renewal of the buildings launched in January 1911, was successfully accomplished by January 1913. The new outpatient's building was the most prominent result of the reforms and still bears the inscription dedicating it to the memory of King Edward VII.

The Infirmary could now reasonably hope to see its affairs drop out of the public gaze, but 1909 held one more Iceberg. At the Annual General Meeting the Governors had congratulated themselves on securing the services of Dr Roscoe, as Secretary to replace his absconded predecessor. He was due to take up his duties on January 1st, 1910, he had attended the Annual General meeting and had held discussions with Col Heath. Imagine the feelings of the Governors when they read in the *Sentinel* of December 18th that Dr Roscoe had booked into the North Stafford Hotel, retired to his room and shot himself. He had just completed a term of service as a medical officer at St Edwards Hospital, Cheddleton. Earlier in his career he had to abandon a surgical career when he lost a finger due to infection and it was assumed that this had contributed to his state of mind.

On December 29th, Dr T. Basil Rhodes was appointed as his successor, a man who served the Infirmary extremely well until he left during the First World War for a distinguished career in the Ministry of Pensions.

A pair of snapshots taken during the First World War. Above are the hutted wards built where the Accident Unit now stands, to accommodate the wounded soldiers. In the background is Hartshill Church, while the houses in Princes Road are readily recognisable. The light coloured structure to the left of the huts is the Recreation Hut given by Mrs Harrison of Maer Hall.

Below is an interior view of a hut.

CHAPTER 18
War and the Infirmary

The North Staffordshire Infirmary was founded during the Napoleonic War, and war has always played a part in its history, most obviously in the two World Wars. On each occasion it treated more than 2000 casualties. Each major war brought changes, new techniques and new attitudes that contributed to the development of the Infirmary.

No man is an island, as the poet tells us, and no institution can exist in isolation from the conditions that prevail at the time. The Infirmary was born in the middle of the Napoleonic Wars which had brought problems to the Pottery industry, seriously reducing exports to America and Europe. The idea has been put forward that the signing of the Peace of Amiens was so enthusiastically received that the Dispensary and House of Recovery were founded as an act of Thanksgiving.

I believe that this is an error which came about in this way. The Peace of Amiens was agreed in 1802, and, unsurprisingly, after years of war, was greeted with massive relief and rejoicing across the country. In all parts of the country, including the Potteries, the buildings were decorated and there were bonfires and fireworks. Employers gave massive feasts for their workers and there was wild celebration. Perhaps rather too wild, for there were deaths and buildings were set alight. So when the treaty was signed, it was often decided to celebrate in a more constructive way. The *Advertiser* reported that the people of Bath had decided to raise money for their hospitals, and following this lead, a subscription list, headed by Josiah Spode, was begun to raise money for the hospital nearest to the Potteries at Stafford. We have no evidence of any other response, though it could be that the thought of all that good money leaving the Potteries for Stafford might have made the prospect of building its own hospital more attractive than might otherwise have been the case.

The Treaty of Amiens did not last, and war returned, and ten years later, when the move to the new site in Etruria was being planned, the War with America (the Second American War 1809-1815) depressed trade. The decision to advance to the building of an Infirmary was slowed by the financial uncertainties.

The North Staffordshire Infirmary may claim connections with the Napoleonic War through a Vice-President, the Marquis of Anglesey, who was second in command to the Duke of Wellington, remembered especially for losing his leg at the end of the battle of Waterloo. Earl St Vincent, of Meaford, near Stone was President of the Infirmary from 1816 to 1823. Starting life as an ordinary seaman he rose to the very pinnacle of the Navy, indeed he was Nelson's commanding officer. He quelled the mutiny of 1797, at the moment when Napoleon was assembling his invasion fleet across the channel. He was very generous to the Infirmary. When asked in 1814 to become a subscriber to the Infirmary, he sent a cheque for £300, saying that as he was eighty years of age he did not think that an annual subscription would do much for his good name!

In the 1860s, the *Advertiser* carried a report of an operation to remove a musket ball, lodged years previously under the shoulder blade of a soldier. He had acquired it in a battle in India in one of the myriad wars fought in the 19th century. The report's real interest is in the account of the anaesthetic, which while it allowed the operation to proceed, presented the surgeon with a moving target, implying the presence of an inexperienced anaesthetist who was frightened of getting the patient properly asleep. Giving anaesthetics at this time was the duty of the physicians, but W.D. Spanton says in his memoirs that they were terrified of chloroform, and more than happy to pass the duty on to anyone who would take it.

W.D. Spanton was connected with the Infirmary for fifty years, beginning as House Surgeon at the time of the battle to move the Infirmary from Etruria in the 1860s and retiring as the author of the report on the internal reorganisation of the Infirmary in 1910. In 1870 he and Dr Orton travelled in France and Germany during the Franco-Prussian War. He was able to visit hospitals on both sides of the front, and wrote of his experiences in a series of four articles published in the *Lancet*.

Surgically the Franco-Prussian War was very important. As Spanton tells us, the weapons used ranged from sabres, the cuts of which being generally clean and open healed well, to high velocity bullets which shattered bone and took fragments of clothing deep into tissues, leading to tetanus or gas gangrene. By 1870, the ideas of Lister were spreading across Europe. Spanton reported that carbolic acid was used, though in weaker solutions than those recommended by Lister, and without the daily attention Lister insisted upon. New, 'exciting' treatments can be disastrous because they induce doctors to throw away tried and trusted methods. A German surgeon, encouraged by the promise of immunity to infection offered by carbolic acid, operated on soldiers with wounds of the knee. Abandoning the time honoured course of amputation he decided to try to 'save' their legs. All but one died. The last did not die, but his knee did not heal, so amputation was called for after all - then he died. The false sense of security that the Listerian method produced probably killed them all; the majority might well have survived after amputation.

Their experiences in the Franco-Prussian War led German surgeons to seek a better solution to infection than soaking the wound with disinfectant. They chose the method of asepsis, operating in sterile theatres in sterile clothes with sterile instruments. This method remains the key to successful surgery to today. Spanton raised the money to build a small detached ward for gynaecological patients where they could be nursed in single rooms away from the general wards with infected cases. The death rate fell dramatically, and abdominal surgery became routine at the Infirmary in the last decade of the 19th century.

The Boer War was one of the last wars in which disease killed more combatants than did weapons. Dysentery was a great killer, and the Infirmary lost Dr Herbert Davies to this disease. He had been released from his post of House Surgeon to serve as an Army doctor. On the British side, 7500 men died from wounds; nearly twice that number died from disease, mostly typhoid and other bowel infections.

Perhaps the one lasting if unintended benefit of the Boer War arose through the fact that many of the candidates for military service proved to be unfit, being considered unable to carry a rifle. The implications of this were appalling; how was the country to defend its Empire, the Empire on which the sun never set? A commission was set up to look into the causes of *Physical Deterioration in the Population*. The report gave a most valuable picture of life at the start of the 20th century, with evidence from London and many large industrial areas including the Potteries.

Miss Garnett, who undertook missionary work in the Potteries on behalf of the Lichfield Diocese, gave evidence to the Commission on conditions in the Pottery towns. Perhaps the most important part of her evidence was that which helped to influence the Commission's recommendation that in future all Medical Officers of Health should be paid officers, and that they could only be dismissed by the local Government Board in London. Miss Garnett gave evidence that much of the worst housing in Fenton where she lived was owned by councillors and, fearing for their jobs, local officials declined to act against them.

Among other benefits that arose from the Commission were the establishment of School Medical Services, the provision of school meals and the encouragement of physical education. The encouragement of physical activity in childhood is still a major concern today - but now the providers of school meals are more concerned with obesity than starvation!

When the First World War began there was still a light hearted attitude to war, but it was soon extinguished by the casualty lists. The first mayor of the new federated Borough of Stoke-on-Trent, Cecil Wedgwood, was killed in action in 1916. He was the last of a notable succession of descendants of Josiah Wedgwood who had served the Infirmary and were concerned with the well being of the area. In 1909-10 the Infirmary was in serious trouble due to the urgent need to reorganise, and a real fear that the new National Insurance scheme would deter subscribers. Cecil Wedgwood led a reorganisation of the charities of the district, and encouraged increased support for the Infirmary. Lucie Wedgwood, his wife, now continued the work begun with her husband, campaigning to reduce the continuing toll of Maternal and Infant Mortality, founding the Etruria Mothers Welcome and the Health Visitors Association.

Soon the Infirmary was receiving the casualties of the war. Accommodation was stretched, and temporary wooden buildings were added, some of which remained in use until the 1980s. Over the four years of the war 2500 inpatients were treated. The Infirmary received and cared for the wounded soldiers, and although the Government paid for their care, the Infirmary was sorely tested. In the first two years of the war, the finances were running at a loss until the War Office increased the fee paid for soldiers from three shillings to four shillings per occupied bed per day.

Throughout the wars, the local population were immensely supportive of the Infirmary. The finances benefited from special appeals, such as that of 1915 which raised £9221, in 1916 £1543, and the next year £3353. In addition, the levels of routine sources of income rose steadily throughout the war. Remarkably, despite all the upheaval of the war, people kept up subscriptions, those who had not gone to the war making up the subscriptions of those at the front.

If we take the Individual subscriptions, the Sunday and Saturday Funds and the Establishment Subscriptions as a table it will illustrate the change:

	1914-5	1915-6	1916-7	1917-8	1918-9	1919-20
Individual	£2102	£2208	£3694	£4555	£5172	£5128
Sunday	£609	£661	£810	£967	£1109	
Saturday	£3051	£3664	£4454	£ 4362	£5277	
Establishment	£7905	£8492	£9647	£12267	£13889	£17319

Prices increased enormously during the war, and despite the increases in income the overdraft of the Infirmary would reach crisis levels of £21,000 in 1921.

When we look at the income levels attained by the Infirmary in those difficult years, we must single out the Saturday and Establishment Contributions. Both these would overwhelmingly represent 'Working class' contributions. This is especially significant when we recall that only a few years earlier, the whole edifice of such support was seriously in doubt. The newly formed committee with its widened membership was not only extremely successful, but clearly had caught the imagination of the district.

The Infirmary received a visit in 1917 from Gustav Nordstron on a fact finding mission from the Swedish Government. He was impressed with the 'democratic management' he saw at the Infirmary.

Hospital Carnival events in the Edwardian period, above at Biddulph Moor, below in Wolstanton..
From *Wolstanton in Words & Pictures*, Mervyn Edwards and
Biddulph Moor from Living Memory, Bill Ridgway

The Infirmary treated 2562 wounded soldiers, with 23 deaths, a very creditable result in that many patients were severely injured. The Infirmary still had a duty to the civilian population and these patients showed a steady increase in numbers over the war years, in 1910, 2193 inpatients were treated, in 1918, 2945.

Many of the medical staff were drawn into the war, and the Infirmary lost another of its housemen, killed at Suvla Bay in Gallipoli. The Resident Medical Staff, having been a solidly male preserve, now became entirely female. They must have worked extremely hard to cope with these levels of activity. By the last years of the War, it became hard to recruit 'even' female doctors, and final year medical students were recruited to assist the staff. The First World War is recognised as having presented a huge opportunity for young women to enter many areas previously closed to them. The minutes show a subtle change as the war years passed, from acceptance of these young female persons who had appeared on the wards, to seeing them as valued members of the staff. Indeed the ladies clearly had a rising perception of their worth, for as time went on they seem more assured in laying down the terms on which they would or would not be employed.

In addition to the heavy workload there were aspects of working conditions we associate more with the Second World War than the first. There were severe food shortages in the first war, due to the U-boat campaign. By 1917 there are references in the minutes to the fact that 'national difficulties with regard to food mean there will have to be a review of the Diets recommended for patients', while another note refers to 'Food Control Regulations'. Most people do not associate bombing of civilian targets in Britain with the First War, but there were raids by Zeppelins and people were killed. At this time all operating theatres had large plate glass windows and frequently large skylights to gather all available light. Brightly lit from within, at night they were thought to present an inviting target to a passing Zeppelin. These huge windows were thought to be difficult to black out, so night time operations were performed in the Anaesthetic Room, its smaller window covered with a blind. The emergency lights in theatre were darkened with brown paint, and the lights in the sterilising room were shaded to prevent glare.

Innovation was not dead in the war years. A major shortage affected the Infirmary in 1917. It is recorded that great difficulty was being experienced in obtaining supplies of champagne, brandy and port. Quarter bottles of champagne were unobtainable, so a special stand and stopper had been acquired, presumably to retain the fizz in a whole bottle. Whisky was substituted for brandy, and port was only available if a patient's friends brought some into hospital for his consumption. Stimulants had long been a part of of part of medical treatment. These were aimed at improving the patients appetite and feeling of well-being.

It may seem to us to be hilariously inappropriate to be worried about the lack of these imported luxuries in the midst of war, but they had long been a part of the treatment in the Infirmary. Notes from the 1890s show that champagne was prescribed for seriously ill patients, patients who were the ordinary people of the district, for there were no private patients here. We must remember that patients got better by

Part of a patient's notes with a prescription for milk, whisky and Champagne (1897).

overcoming their illnesses themselves. Food and rest was all that could be offered, and if a patient lost blood, transfusions were not available to top up his haemoglobin. He remained anaemic, listless and short of breath until his bone marrow had repaired the situation, a process that demanded a good diet. Infections had to be overcome without antibiotics, leaving the patient ill and weak for months afterwards.

Money for specific projects came to the Infirmary at the height of the War. In 1916, as a memorial to their leader, Mr Enoch Edwards MP, the miners gave £4250, enough money to endow four beds. Since the reforms of 1910, the miners had overcome an antipathy to the Infirmary, and encouraged by Mr Edwards had become most supportive. He said of his members, *'The miners of North Staffordshire are the best givers in the world, provided you stop it from their wages'*. In 1917, T. Griffiths, the representative of the Shelton Iron, Steel and Coal Company on the General Committee was elected Vice President, the first 'working man' to be so honoured, a very significant step in the now changed membership of the General Committee

The Infirmary housed the first experimental oxygen chambers which were to test whether the inhalation of oxygen would help the sufferers who had been exposed to poison gas. The Trench Warfare Committee of the Medical Research Council placed these chambers at the Infirmary, under the care of Dr Sowry. While oxygen cannot have had a long term curative benefit on such damaged lungs, the first reports were encouraging.

A real long term benefit which arose from the treatment of wounded soldiers was the recognition of orthopaedics as a specialty. A new department of the hospital was devoted to this specialty and treatment was extended to the civilian population.

War is a great catalyst for change. Even when it is over, nothing is quite the same again. The voluntary principle combined with Establishment Contributions were completely ingrained in the minds of the Governors and Medical Staff of the Infirmary. The patients were not charged, the consultants were not paid, it had been so for more than a hundred years. Towards the end of the War the status quo was interrupted by the necessity of deciding who should pay for the care of discharged servicemen. Many of them were in receipt of War Pensions, and many people thought that as such they were the responsibility of the Government through the agency of the Ministry of Pensions. Were they still the responsibility of the country for which they had fought or were they civilians again who were to be treated according to the time honoured traditions? The statement appeared in the press that *'Medical Staff might not be expected to give their services as charity to persons for whom the state is responsible'*. The British Medical Association recommended that if the state was paying for treatment, medical attention could not be gratuitous, and that the doctor should receive 10% of the amount paid to the hospital.

Another cross current rocked the medical boat as the War drew to a close. Venereal disease had always been present in the population, but after the dislocation caused by the War it rose to epidemic proportions (affecting perhaps 10% of the adult population). In order to cure and control the spread of these diseases a national scheme set up clinics across the country paid for by the Government in association with local authorities. On setting up the clinic its finances, management and staffing all had to be established. This was one of the first encounters between the fiercely independent voluntary hospital and the newly enlarged local authority.

The discussions were led for the Stoke-on-Trent Council by Dr Petgrave Johnson, the first Medical Officer of Health for the Federated Borough. He had been the Medical Officer of Health for the town of Stoke-upon-Trent prior to federation. We can see why he was selected over his fellows in the other Pottery towns, his replies to official requests for information in

1940 bomb damage to the newly opened extension to the Nurses' Home.

North Staffs Infirmary nurses in World War I.

Government papers were much the most detailed and considered. The post of Medical Officer of Health for a large borough was both important and influential. The discussions were held up for a while until another 'impasse' was resolved. The Medical Staff of the Infirmary refused to cooperate with the Stoke-on-Trent Council while it refused to have appointed representatives of the local medical profession at meetings of the Health Committee. This difficulty was overcome and negotiations were brought to a successful conclusion, the clinic being housed and staffed at the Infirmary.

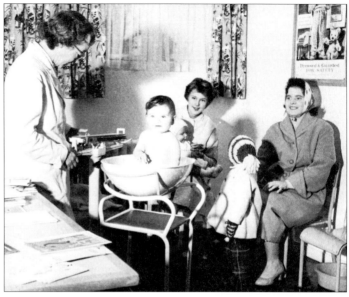

Child welfare and Antenatal clinics developed from the Mothers' Welcomes and the City Council's Public Health Department's initiatives dating from the early years of the 20th century.

Venereal disease co-existed with a desperately cherished wish for respectability. It led the Medical Staff to write to their defence organisations. The doctors wished to know whether or not they would be liable for an action for libel (libel be it noted, not negligence) if they referred patients to the clinic for diagnostic purposes in suspicious cases, and then the patients were shown to be clear of infection. We do not have the reply, but it must have been satisfactory as the clinic came into being. Venereal diseases were responsible for a substantial mortality and a great deal of chronic disease. Syphilis was the most important of these diseases as a cause of death. The clinic was responsible for the diagnosis and treatment of patients and for the follow-up of contacts and was therefore a step into the future. This meeting of two cultures, the voluntary principle and state medicine, took some time to get used to.

All too soon the Infirmary was again on a war footing. German bombing was much more of a threat to the population than had been the case in the First War. Major civilian injuries were more than a possibility, so hospitals were for the first time placed under government control. Although mercifully no casualties ensued, German bombs did strike the Infirmary. The eye ward and operating theatre were destroyed, the stairs outside the new Haughton Wards and the Nurses' Home were severely damaged. Fortunately the new home had only been opened a few days previously and had not yet been occupied.

At the start of the Second World War, hospitals across the country were placed under government control, the Emergency Medical Service (EMS). Due to the bombing campaign, city centre hospitals were damaged, and patients moved into the country. Country houses were converted, and EMS hospitals were built. These were typically standard single storey concrete buildings, wards and departments connected by long corridors. Many lasted into the National Health Service, and some were home to the distinguished departments of surgery that were developed across the country. The EMS, although originally an organisation born of the war, brought centralised control to a system that had largely gone its own sweet way before. The Second World War is discussed further in chapter 20.

CHAPTER 19
The Electrical Department

This chapter embodies the changes brought about by science applied to medicine. The story of the Electrical Department is an illustration of the development of many departments in a modern hospital, the change from simple and primitive apparatus to the very expensive computer controlled giants of today. The initial ambition to help sufferers from the effects of lead poisoning eventually spawned two new specialties, diagnostic and therapeutic radiology.

A letter from the Rev C.H. Simpkinson to the Board of the Infirmary, given in full in the Annual Report of 1900 details the essential facts surrounding the founding of the Electrical Department. The prime mover in this development was Millicent, Duchess of Sutherland, surely the most glamourous and unlikely champion of the working people in the late 19th century. A very rich society lady, she looks at us from the magnificent full length portrait by John Singer Sargent. She took the lead in the affairs of the Cripples Guild, which built and ran the Orthopaedic Hospital in Hartshill.

She became deeply concerned with the predicament of those suffering from lead poisoning. In 1901 she contributed a chapter on this subject to the book *The Staffordshire Potter* by Harold Owen, as part of a campaign to reduce the use of lead in the pottery industry. For one in her position it was a remarkable thing to do. Her activities did not commend themselves to the Pottery manufacturers. She was called Meddlesome Millie, and appears as the Countess of Chell in Arnold Bennett's novels of the Potteries.

Duchess Millicent Sutherland.
Beautiful philanthropist or 'Meddling Millie' of Bennett's *The Card*, she certainly had the courage to stand up to the manufacturers in a campaign to reduce the use of lead.

The Electrical Department was primarily directed to the use of electricity to restore function to paralysed limbs by stimulating the nerves that were damaged by the poisonous effect of lead, principally in the Pottery industry. A conference was held at Trentham in 1900 at which other uses for electricity were discussed, these naturally included X-rays which had been discovered in 1895, and whose potential medical value was becoming apparent. Millicent organised a collection of money from her friends, and £150 was donated to purchase equipment, a considerable sum at the time.

Unfortunately, the Infirmary at this time was lit entirely by gas, so the offer of a gratuitous supply of electricity from the tram network of the Potteries Electric Traction Company was most welcome. The cable came to the Infirmary from the tramway as it

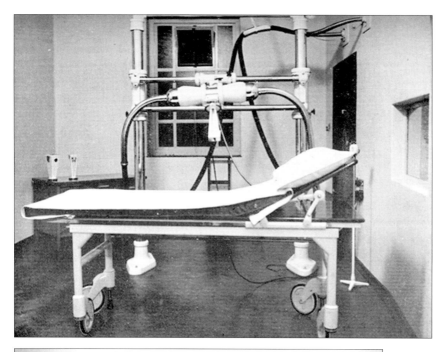

The Radiotherapy
Department 1938.

UPPER PICTURE
A Treatment Room, note the
window that allowed
observation of the patient.

LOWER
The Control Room.
Above the centre of the desk
is the microphone allowing
contact with the patient
receiving treatment.

HE POTTERIES CRIPPLES' GUILD was established some eight years ago for the relief and assistance of Crippled Children amongst the poorer classes in the Pottery towns. To-day this Guild has the names of nearly 400 children on its books, and is divided into three divisions, all of which merit the attention and interest of the public.

Firstly, there is the Convalescent Home at Woore, where sometimes for months spinal cases, hip cases and deformities of other kinds are treated, and the children, by good food and by healthy air and happy surroundings, are restored to a large measure of activity, and indeed, save in exceptional cases, to complete health.

The nine beds in this Home are filled by boys and girls sent from various districts in North Staffordshire, not always from the Pottery towns, although preference is given when possible to children from these towns. It is hoped, if more money is forthcoming, to increase the number of beds to eleven.

Secondly, there are Voluntary Committees in the towns of Hanley, Stoke, Longton, Fenton, Burslem and Tunstall. The ladies who belong divide amongst themselves the onerous duties of visiting the Cripples in their districts ; they become friends of the children, and report on their wants to the General Secretary or to the Honorary Medical Officer. Nourishing food is given at discretion, and a successful endeavour has been made to teach those crippled children who are fairly active the rudiments of needlework and other light forms of employment in Spare-Time Classes.

The ladies on these Committees are really carrying on a labour of love, and money is urgently needed by them to supply surgical instruments to the children under their charge, and to give them an oft-needed change at the seaside or in the country, for it may well be understood that the Woore Home with only nine beds cannot receive them all.

The introduction to the Bazaar for the Potteries Cripples' Guild and Duchess of Sutherland's School for Cripples, held at Trentham in 1908 to raise finance. The Cripples' Guild built and ran the Hartshill Orthopaedic Hospital. The fundraising of the Orthopaedic Hospital joined with the other three voluntary hospitals in 1936 in the North Staffs Contributory Association.

passed through Hartshill; a year later the supply was extended to the operating theatres, the Infirmary converting to electric lighting from the public supply in 1906. The original electrical installation was maintained without charge by the engineer of the Tramways Company; he rejoiced in the unusual title of *Consultant Electrician*.

The sum of £150 - which eventually grew to £300 - also paid for the electrical control apparatus that powered the various applications. Different voltages, both of direct and alternating current were required for the baths through which current was passed to an affected limb, and for the X-ray application. The initial installation was not lavish, there was no dark room in which to develop films, the doctor in charge of the electrical department took them to his house to do this. The films were very slow, exposure times were long, and so was the development process. Soon negotiations with Mr Dale, a chemist in the town relieved the radiologist of this time consuming task. Small films were developed for sixpence, large ones for nine pence. The oldest piece of X-ray apparatus known to survive in North Staffordshire is that held in the Newcastle-under-Lyme Borough Museum and which dates from 1899. It came from a photographer's shop, and is said to have been used occasionally at the Infirmary.

Because of an obvious relationship with the popular hobby of photography, and keen public interest in new scientific processes, many people were prepared to experiment. Photographers set up parlours where the latest toy could be demonstrated, in this way they beat hospitals in the race to show X-rays to the public. However, the lack of regulation of these activities and appreciation of the power for harm as well of good possessed by the new rays soon caused alarm as severe burns and intractable skin and bone cancers began to occur in those exposed to their indiscriminate use, most especially the operators of the machines themselves.

The early primitive X-ray equipment did not stand up to the moist atmosphere in the electrical department that arose from the proximity of the baths. This resulted in a falling-off in the power of the apparatus. Likewise a constant stream of developments in X-ray apparatus and techniques meant that major replacements of equipment and premises were needed at regular intervals from the earliest days.

The Annual Report of 1902 records that the department, which had been opened by the Duchess of Sutherland, was now in use, and that therapeutic as well as diagnostic work was being undertaken. The report speaks of the treatment of rodent ulcers, a most persistent form of skin cancer. It was not readily amenable to surgery and untreated it could literally eat away much of the face, whence its name likening it to the damage done by a rat. Superficial cancers were the obvious starting point for the use of the relatively weak apparatus of the early years.

The opening in 1902 in North Staffordshire of a department that was exploring the usefulness of X-rays in the treatment of cancers compares very well with the two great cancer hospitals in Manchester and London. The Christie began using X-rays for treatment of cancers in 1901, and the Marsden followed in 1903.

The site of the initial installation in the Infirmary is now obscure, probably in the outpatients, which became Ward 17 and is now the Department of Medical Illustration. When outpatients moved in 1911, proper facilities were provided, including a dark room. There was a gradual spread of X-ray facilities to the casualty department and to the wards in the form of portable apparatus.

In 1925 the apparatus and accommodation in the Electrical Department had become grossly inadequate. Given by Miss Twyford in memory of her father a completely new department was built and equipped as the Twyford Memorial, comprising the X-ray department and an orthopaedic department, above which were built the Henry Johnson and Matilda Burgess Wards. Prince Henry declared it open in 1927.

Ten years on, advances had rendered it necessary to totally modify and extend the X-ray and radiotherapy departments. An appeal was launched for £20,000, and a new department was built alongside the Twyford Memorial, particularly giving accommodation for more deep X-ray apparatus of varying strengths. Of the sum required £10,668, the cost of the building, was given by Mr G.H. Downing, who sadly died on the eve of the opening, in October 1937, by the Duke of Kent.

Radium had been discovered in 1898 by the Curies, and its usefulness as a treatment for cancer was soon appreciated. However, it is only present in small quantities in the ore from which it is extracted and therefore is enormously expensive to produce. The Governors wished to provide radium treatment in the Infirmary, but the cost was £12,000 for half a gram of the element. To put this in perspective, the cost of both the Haughton Wards at the Infirmary in the late 1930s was £25,000. Initially, the Infirmary hired radium for specific treatments, but the cost of this was £400 a year, a substantial slice of the drug budget.

In 1931 it was announced that a Radium Commission had been set up to supply radium to hospitals; a thank-offering for the recovery of George V from pneumonia. The radium was in effect free to the hospital, the only charge being an annual payment of notional interest set at 2%. Thus half a gram of radium, valued at £12,000, would cost the Infirmary £240 per annum. This was just over half the previous hire fee, and the radium would be constantly available for use. The amount supplied gradually rose through the 1930s to accommodate increasing usage.

The decision to supply radium meant that the Infirmary became a Regional Radium Centre in 1932. It was the first provincial hospital in the country, as opposed to a teaching hospital or university, to receive radium and be a centre designated by the Commission. The Commission made important stipulations as to the use of the radium they supplied. No radium was to leave the Infirmary, for example to be used at private clinics, a circumstance that gave a powerful impetus to the provision of private beds at the Infirmary. The Honorary Radiologist, Dr Bromley, who held a diploma in radiology from Edinburgh, was sent to attend postgraduate courses on radiotherapy in London, Paris and Stockholm. A special radium store was constructed and the detached Albert Ward was converted for the sole use of radium patients, having twelve male and twelve female beds.

Radium was used from the first in tubes and needles but by the 1930s larger centres were using 'bombs'. These were larger masses of radium, several grams in weight that had to be very heavily shielded to prevent scatter of radiation throughout the department. They cast a very powerful beam of radiation onto the patient, the dose of which could be precisely calculated. The department in North Staffordshire was asked to accommodate one of these bombs, but in those last years before the war there was no money to undertake such an expensive installation.

As World War II approached, the presence of radioactive materials that might be widely dispersed by a bomb blast caused great concern to the Commission. Initially, in1938 at the time of Munich, they withdrew radium to safe sites in the country, but they relented when it became apparent that patients were not getting the treatment they needed. Radium was returned on condition a bore hole was drilled in the grounds to store the radium in the event of an air raid. This was not an unreasonable attitude, as the Infirmary was in fact bombed, the bombs falling quite near to the X-ray department. The Royal Marsden Hospital in London took similar precautions. The bore hole was not required, as the radium work was transferred to an Emergency Medical Service (EMS) hospital at Cheddleton, in the depths of the country, while the deep X-ray work, which presented no danger of scattering radioactive material, continued at the Infirmary.

We know quite a lot about the Department in 1938, as a report of an inspection by the National Radium Commission has survived. It is very complimentary about the new department and about the enthusiasm of the staff. It describes the new department building as one of the best the visitors have seen. *It is spacious, well lighted, skillfully arranged....* There were two X-ray therapy tubes that cost of £2,500, together with a control room. There were noted to be two vacant rooms, in one of these it was hoped to place a 400Kv machine, and in the other a Radium Beam (Bomb). The Commission concluded by saying that this was *a centre that is so modern in its outlook and so up to date in its views... a suitable place for the Commission to encourage the formation of a Beam Unit.*

Under the Cancer Act (1939) the City Authorities became responsible for seeing that arrangements for cancer patients were adequate for the needs of the population. However, the War was to delay progress. The Department soldiered on with deep X-ray machines of various ages and powers. During the war, the supply of X-ray tubes, formerly from Holland, dried up, and replacements had to be sought from America.

In 1946 the Department was designated a Main Treatment Centre by the West Midlands Cancer Committee. In 1948 the responsibility to provide new apparatus fell to the Health Service. Since that date the department has been successively re-equipped with Cobalt Beam apparatus and Linear Accelerators.

The medical supervision was originally under the control of Dr List who began his career as Honorary Medical Officer in charge of the Electrical Department in 1903, a post he held until 1935. He continued with the non-radiotherapy work, for example, the baths and the artificial sunlight programme designed to reduce the incidence of rickets, most closely allied to the original purpose of the Electrical Department.

Dr D.J. Riordan's appointment in 1936 was more than usually significant. He became full time Radium Officer or Radiotherapist, having arrived from the Christie Hospital in Manchester. He was responsible for all radium cases. A Radium Curator was also appointed. Nearly all consultant posts at the Infirmary until the advent of the National Health Service in 1948 were honorary, i.e. unpaid; the Radium Officer was an exception. Being entirely occupied in the hospital he had no opportunity to have a private practice outside, he was therefore paid a salary. This appointment is the first evidence of a formal division between the diagnostic and therapeutic branches of radiology. Dr Binnie succeeded Dr Riordan in 1939, while Dr Bellamy became Honorary Radiologist in the diagnostic division of the specialty. He continued to be Honorary Medical Officer to the Electrotherapeutic Department until the National Health Service arrived in 1948.

Eric Young, House Surgeon and Surgeon at the Infirmary. He was President for a record 9 years until his death in 1945

E.R. Corn, Patron and President in the 1930s. He was a generous donor and transformed the financing and organisation of the rebuilding of the Infirmary at the time.

CHAPTER 20
The Infirmary and the Workhouse

It is often believed that the Voluntary Infirmary and the Poor Law Workhouse were absolutely separate institutions. While the relations between them were occasionally prickly, there were many points of contact and cooperation.

The history of British hospitals can best be understood as having two main strands. The voluntary hospitals, like the Infirmary, supported as a charity, and the Poor Law hospitals, supported by the Poor Rate. The Poor Law hospitals grew from the accommodation for the old and the ill in Parish poorhouses and later workhouses. Eventually of course the strands were united in the National Health Service. In practice both strands did interact and relate to each other, therefore it is not inappropriate to spend some time on the Poor Law side.

If we go back to the days of the monasteries, the impulses of doing good in the sense of caring for one's fellows, and the purchasing of a place in Paradise co-existed. After the donor's death, money was often left to endow good works, at the same time as paying for services to be said to secure the future of his or her soul.

After the suppression of the Monasteries by Henry VIII in 1538 there were only five major hospitals remaining, St Thomas's, St Bartholomew's and Bedlam (Bethlehem) among them. It is true that at that time, and for three centuries to come, these hospitals did not have much to offer any patient who could afford to pay for his or her medical attention, who had a family or servants to nurse him, and a home in which to stay. Hospitals were for the sick, the poor, the old and those who were away from home, typically pilgrims.

The monks also cared for outcasts of society, such as lepers, who had to live apart from the people at large. These leper hospitals were often on main travel routes but distant from centres of population, as in the case of St Loyes Hospital, the remains of which were recently discovered during building work on the City General Hospital site. St Loyes Hospital stood on the ancient North South main road (A34), but was carefully separated from the settlements at Penkhull and Newcastle. St Loyes was among those institutions suppressed by Henry VIII, by which time it was already in decline, because leprosy had become much less virulent in the preceding years.

By long tradition communities were expected to look after orphans, the very poor, the sick and the old. By 1601, at the end of the reign of Elizabeth I a major Act of Parliament codified these duties. A Poor Rate was raised as a form of local taxation to pay for these services. The Parish, which was the fundamental unit of administration, was confirmed as the body responsible for administering the service on the ground, through the agency of the elected Overseers of the Poor.

Many of the old and the sick were supported in their own homes with small weekly sums of money, a system known as out-relief. For reasons of economy it was often the practice to bring these people together and care for them in one building, a poorhouse. In later years job creation schemes were set up for the unemployed, who were provided with shelter - and work to earn their keep. Gradually the term 'the workhouse' came to describe all these parish-based institutions that cared for the poor. Throughout the 18th century the system underwent development. Parishes were allowed to combine to provide a centralised

The City General Hospital. Right in this modern photo (1980) is the 1842 Stoke-upon-Trent Parish Hospital. To the left is part of the 1830's building - formerly the school and sick bay.

workhouse, while some passed the management of the workhouse to a contractor.

In a reform of the Poor Law after the Restoration of the Monarchy, the Law of Settlement was passed in 1662. It stated that the Parish in which he or she was settled was responsible for a person's care, which was fine when few travelled far from home and strangers were a rarity: no Parish was keen on paying out for outsiders who had not contributed to the local rates. A person became settled in a Parish by being born there. This applied even if the child was illegitimate, thus unmarried girls who became pregnant were most unwelcome and even on occasion dumped outside the Parish before the baby was born to avoid the child gaining settlement in that Parish. For women settlement came with birth or on marriage, the wife took her settlement from her husband's Parish. Apprenticeship for a year had given settlement, but that changed in 1834. Equally, there were property qualifications to be satisfied if one sought settlement in a strange Parish. The real if unspoken question was not *how* shall we help this stranger should he fall ill, *but* has this man enough money or property to pay for his own care, or has he acquired the skills which will be advantageous to our Parish.

Complications could arise when a man moved from parish to parish in the course of his work, when the question arose as to which was the settlement parish. Some travellers carried a certificate when they moved from home saying that the home, the settlement parish, recognised his right of settlement and would reimburse the parish in which he found himself for any expenses, or for the traveller's repatriation. These complexities became increasingly inappropriate as the Industrial Revolution gathered momentum and more and more people travelled the country looking for work. However, the law was the law, and so questions of settlement were referred to the Quarter Sessions and took up endless hours in the Courts, spawning a huge and totally unproductive army of clerks.

This would be of purely academic importance but for the fact that it proved to be a remarkably sturdy system. With minor modifications the necessity of establishing the 'Chargeability' of a poor patient, that is, the question of which Parish was responsible for paying for his treatment, continued virtually to the coming of the National Health Service in 1948 and beyond, and much time was spent by hospitals shuttling paper back and forth to pay for treatment or to raise a bill on a distant parish. Post code funding is at least three hundred years old!

The Act of Settlement was already producing an extremely cumbersome system of charging and cross-charging between parishes, and this was destined to continue for the next hundred years and more. Why then did the Government, in the course of the major overhaul of the Poor Law of 1834, not introduce a simpler, uniform and centralised system of finance, after all they had by this time managed to introduce and collect income tax!

When one reads the Report that led up to the 1834 Amendment of the Poor Law Act it seems remarkably unconvincing on the question of Settlement. The Report acknowledged that it would have been a far simpler and cheaper system to have a National Charge, but it came down in favour of continuing with the existing system of Parish control and Settlement. It stated that the National Charge (Government taxing, financing and control) might be satisfactory for a while, but, without identifying exactly why, says control would gradually slacken and the cost would escalate as it had in the past. The drafting of the report seems deliberately obscure, almost as if it did not matter what was written because the decision had already been made, although the reasons were not spelled out. A fear was expressed in the Report that candidates for political power would bid for popularity, by promising to be good to the poor. Surely not!

We have to bear in mind that while voluntary hospitals were financed by gifts and subscriptions from wealthy donors or groups of workers, the Poor Law was financed by money paid as a rate, and was therefore raised by compulsion rather than goodwill. This was taxation, and it was resented; ratepayers could revenge themselves by opposing expenditure on the poor and by maintaining the rituals that made sure that the paupers never forgot their place at the bottom of the heap. Even when the former workhouses, the City General and Chell, later Westcliffe Hospital, became part of the National Health Service, their workhouse past was long remembered. Well into Health Service days admission into one of these hospitals was seen by many older patients as bearing the stigma of the workhouse. *'I'm not going in there, me Dad died in there'* was a cry that could be heard until the 1970s. It is worth noting that while admission to the workhouse carried a huge stigma, the fact of being treated at the Infirmary in a voluntary hospital as a Real Object of Charity did not seem to carry the same stain.

This subtle differentiation is worth exploring. We think of the class distinctions of 19th century Britain as being between the rich and the poor, but in practice the stratification went to every level of society. The man who has kept himself and his family and provided a home for them, even though it may have involved a Herculean effort and been a close run thing, will be properly proud of his efforts, a pride which will be his reward for avoiding the degradation of the Workhouse. Even if he acknowledges in his heart that 'there but for the grace of God go I', he may not wish to be reminded of or even associated with those who have fallen off the social ladder. If he has managed to pay a penny a week to the Infirmary as an Establishment subscriber, he would certainly feel himself substantially distanced from Pauperhood. (see the reproduced letter on page 45)

The person who entered the workhouse became a Pauper, this was his position in society, it was the description applied to him in the census returns. In the workhouse he gave up his freedom, the law could be invoked if he committed a serious offence against the rules. He could not leave without giving proper notice and when he left his dependent family went as well; he was almost a non-person. Nevertheless, the authorities had an ultimate responsibility for the Pauper. In case of extreme need, the parish or later the Guardians of the Poor had to give him out-relief, food or money or admit him to the workhouse and provide him with shelter, food and medical care, basic though it might be. It can be argued that there has been a national health service for centuries in Britain, at the utmost extremity of need there was a system on which to fall back. It may not have been attractive or efficient, but the intention was that it should be provided.

The patient who entered a voluntary hospital was specifically in need of medical care. He had to obey the rules and could be expelled for a serious breach of them. As opposed to the Poor Law institutions, the voluntary hospital, being an independent charity, could decline to admit him if they felt they could not help him. In practice, the voluntary hospital would admit the poor patient straight away in the case of accident or life-threatening emergency. Later, when it was found that no more could be done to help him, or if he had no home to receive him, he could be referred on social grounds to the workhouse.

The workhouse Infirmary provided a parallel and in some ways a complementary service to that of the voluntary hospital. By the 1940s, the voluntary hospitals provided about *one third* of the Nation's hospital beds, admittedly often the acute beds offering the most advanced treatment, while the former workhouses and municipal hospitals provided the less glamourous geriatric, chronic sick and psychiatric beds, but accounting for *two thirds* of the national total. The workhouses had to admit all those who came to them in need.

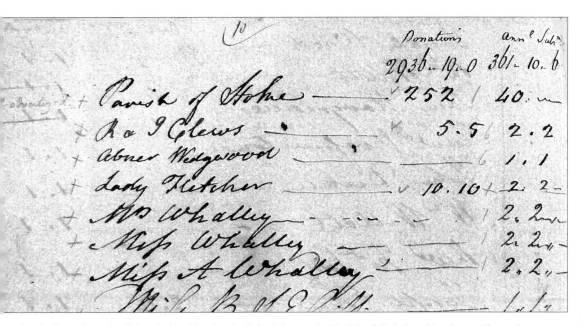

1814. Entry from the Subscription List. To the left of the words 'Parish of Stoke', written in pencil, are the words Not Advertised, referring to the donation of £252 and the annual subscription of £40. Entries elsewhere in this book show that the contributions from the parishes of Trentham and Norton in the Moors were also marked 'not advertised'. The subscriptions for Newcastle and Wolstanton were marked 'These have not been officially announced', an interesting distinction.

By 1870 Guardians were permitted to open infirmaries for the poor that were separate from the workhouse itself. The voluntary hospitals were generally much better staffed than the workhouse infirmaries. The voluntary sector had greater numbers of staff and there was much more competition for posts. Only in the later years of the 19th century and in the great metropolitan areas, especially in London, did the workhouse and municipal hospitals begin to compete with the voluntary hospitals in terms of staffing levels and quality of care.

In the 1790s, in the Napoleonic Wars, some parishes had set a level of Out-relief payments that were based on the price of bread. Bread was the staple food and the fluctuations in its price were the index by which relief was measured. By the 1820s the cost of the Poor Law payments had caused the rates to rocket, by a factor of ten in some parishes. Money was given to those who had no work, wages were subsidised. Opinion hardened among the ratepayers who became convinced that it had become more attractive to the poor to collect relief than to work, and that some employers were cutting wages, knowing that any shortfall would be made up by Parish funds. Worse, it was believed that in some families several generations had never known regular work; Out-relief was creating an underclass of *hereditary paupers* who never would work and were a moral danger to society.

Today there is the same concern at the development of a culture of dependency. Just as those who staff the benefit offices today seek protection from violent clients, dissatisfied claimants often attacked the Parish Officers. This was particularly disconcerting for a society that placed a high value on compliance with the law and appreciation of ones place in society. They saw these disruptive claimants as ungrateful recipients of that which they had omitted to earn, people who were a threat to society and to their own souls. There was a redemptive as well as a punitive motive for the harshness of the reformed Poor Law post 1834.

The reform of the Poor Law of 1834 was designed to make being in receipt of Poor Relief as unpleasant as possible. The generous Out-relief payments which had led to the escalation of the Rates were, as far as possible, ended. In order to receive relief the claimant had to enter the workhouse and submit to workhouse rule. Families were separated, male and female inmates segregated and parents separated from children. Work was expected in return for relief, and food and conditions were made as Spartan as they could be. The idea was to make the conditions worse than any other alternative, in the words of the Report, less eligible (desirable) in comparison to an independent labourer of the lowest class.

In practice the inhabitants of the workhouse were not drawn exclusively from an underclass, indeed such people were a minority. Extremes of age, illness or misfortune were the principal factors that brought the inmates to the workhouse. For the poor, there was little hope of accumulating sufficient savings to see out a dignified old age, although the Act of 1834 did allow magistrates to certify that aged persons were no longer capable of work and were therefore entitled to receive relief in their own homes. Illness might be mental or physical, acute or chronic. Whichever it was, illness could prevent the earning of a living, and if it befell the breadwinner, the whole family would be put into the workhouse. Lest we think that the middle classes were immune from this fate, few professional people had insurance or pensions, and illness could involve a rapid fall down the social ladder, a fear expressed in several of Dickens' novels, for example *Nicholas Nickleby*.

Examination of the 1881 census returns show that more than a third of the inhabitants of the Stoke-upon-Trent Workhouse were children, another third were aged, while the remainder were made up of the mentally ill, the chronic sick and a surprisingly small proportion of fit people of working age. Of those over 60 years of age, the vast majority were unmarried, widows or widowers. Thus most of the workhouse population were not present in family groups, most probably having been admitted when the usual family care links had broken down. Younger groups often consisted of a widow or widower with young children.

The main target of the Poor Law was always the able bodied Pauper, it being assumed that they were unwilling to work rather than unable to find work. Despite the strenuous efforts of the central authorities, Out-relief did continue. In reality it benefited society to keep families in their homes. It kept families together and allowed the workpeople to remain in an area during hard times, so that when trade improved, industry could expand again. In times of major catastrophe, such as the distress in Lancashire due to the shortage of cotton in the American Civil War, no expansion of the workhouses could have accommodated all the destitute in the country.

A perennial burden on the Parish was the care of unmarried girls who became pregnant. Despite all efforts to evade the responsibility and the cost, the workhouse infirmaries had to look after many of these girls and other cases needing hospital care and attention, and their offspring swelled the number of infant paupers. Of course, this meant that the workhouse doctor could attend more deliveries than most other doctors in the district, and it often happened that, as in North Staffordshire, the maternity services grew from expertise gained there, and they were eventually based at the workhouse hospital.

It is possible to believe that the Vestry of the Parish of Stoke-upon-Trent and the Governors of the North Staffordshire Infirmary were entirely separate and indeed opposed bodies; in fact we find the same names as members of both bodies. We know that in the

1830s when the new workhouse was being built, the finances of the Parish were rather shaky. Josiah Wedgwood II, so active in the affairs of the Infirmary, had been instrumental in the purchase of the land for the workhouse, and had advanced £1500 to buy the land, formerly the site of an old lead-works. The signatories on behalf of the Vestry of the agreement to purchase the land included John Heath>cote, Josiah Spode, William Bent, William Yates, Daniel Whalley and John Tomlinson, all names familiar to us as governors of the Infirmary. John Tomlinson, Wedgwood's solicitor, advised him that the Vestry's debt should be repaid over four years, up to 1836. In 1837, he advised that Wedgwood could sell the workhouse to recover his debt. He did not take this course of action. The Vestry had considerable problems financing the new workhouse and clearing the debt.

Both official bodies, Vestrymen and Governors, were therefore well known to each other and both groups were seeking to raise money for social and health care at the same time from the same people as subscribers and ratepayers.

We have seen how the prospect of keeping down the rates, and of economically providing skilled medical care for the poor were held out as attractions in the first appeals for the Dispensary in 1802, and when, in 1814, money was sought to move from the Dispensary to the new Infirmary in Etruria, the Vestry agreed to take out a subscription of £40 a year, on the basis of 25 patients being transferred for treatment from the Workhouse each year. They also gave a donation of £252 to the building fund of the Infirmary.

This was a very large donation and annual subscription. The original notebook in which donations were recorded has survived, and next to the entry of this donation, in pencil and in the hand of John Tomlinson, is the note *'not advertised'*. Donations to a charity were usually advertised widely, to encourage others. A letter from Tomlinson to Josiah Wedgwood explained: *'do not advertise the Parish subscription lest it damp down individual subscribers'*. He adds, *'it would be in order to mention it privately to other parishes in the area as a* (good) *example*. In other words, if ratepayers discovered they had already contributed to the Infirmary through the Vestry, they might not want to subscribe again in a personal capacity.

When in 1832 Cholera arrived in England and the Vestry looked for a building to use as a Cholera Hospital, being yet to build the new Workhouse, they arranged the hire of the old House of Recovery, the existing tenants were evicted. By 1833 the Stoke Vestry owed to the Governors of the Infirmary four years subscription (£160) plus the six months unpaid rent for the House of Recovery, £22. Mr Palmer and Mr Herbert Minton were deputed to wait upon the Vestry and request payment. This confirms the tightness of money both at the Workhouse and the Infirmary in 1833, and the extent to which their circumstances were interconnected. Later in that year a major fundraising concert at Stoke Parish Church raised £795 and rescued the Infirmary's finances. This was just as well as in February 1834 the Stoke Vestry *temporarily* cancelled their subscription to the Infirmary! The subscription was resumed in 1879 at the rate of £2 per annum. In the mean time it would seem that for Workhouse patients admitted to the Infirmary, payment was made on a case by case basis, giving ample opportunity for disputes. Newcastle, and Burslem and Wolstanton Guardians, continued their subscriptions at £10 and £15 per annum

Although there had always been accommodation for the sick in the Workhouse, in 1842 the Guardians built the Stoke-upon-Trent Parish Hospital which still stands in the City General Hospital grounds. At the time this building provided an unusually generous provision for a workhouse hospital. Could it be that this provision indicated a desire to bypass the Infirmary and to go it alone in providing medical care?

That different standards of medical care could be expected in a workhouse and in a voluntary hospital was appreciated by the Poor Law Commissioners, whose word was the ultimate arbiter in all workhouse matters. In 1843, they opined that *'if a patient could be safely removed... to an infirmary or hospital... paupers should enjoy the practised skill and combined judgment of the medical men usually connected with such establishments. While, therefore, the Commissioners would discourage the performance of important surgical operations in workhouses, they are ready to sanction any reasonable subscription to an hospital...'* This recognised a limit on the standard of work to be expected from the single-handed (and often grossly underpaid) workhouse doctor, and that difficult cases should be transferred to the Infirmary. Thus difficult (and interesting) cases were going to the Infirmary, while incurable and untreatable cases were going from the Infirmary to the Workhouse.

Should a workhouse patient die while in the Infirmary, who was going to pay for his coffin and funeral? Was this part of the deal struck with the Governors of the Infirmary or was it the duty of the Guardians at the Workhouse, and ultimately of the ratepayers? Of such small disputes are animosities built, each side believes it has been ill used, and, when money is tight, that the other party are taking advantage. The hospital accommodation at the Workhouse did gradually improve as the 19th century passed. Those like Mr Peake who wished to get at the Governors of the Infirmary could find patients who had experienced both institutions and were prepared to say that the Workhouse wards were the more comfortable.

While the system could work smoothly on the ground, with cooperation between the two institutions and their staffs, the two systems were still separated by an ideological and administrative wall. A report in the *Sentinel* in 1909 tells that after an explosion at a gasworks, when a considerable number of men were burned, no room could be found for two at the Infirmary, and they were therefore sent to the hospital wards at the Workhouse. The report states that they were well cared for and made good recoveries, but they were afraid that in future they would lose their old age pensions as a result of going to the Workhouse. The old age pension, introduced in 1908, was intended to keep elderly people from ending their days in the workhouse. However, when it was introduced the idea of deserving and undeserving poor was still alive. In addition to a sliding scale of income controlling the level of payment (the Means Test), there were several categories of people who were not eligible for the new pension. People who had received relief from the Poor Law in recent years were among these. Thus by being transferred to the Workhouse purely because of a bed shortage, and in spite of being Establishment Subscribers to the Infirmary, these men were in danger of losing their pensions. This clause was removed from the Pensions Act in 1911. The case illustrates the petty bureaucracy that bedevilled the old Poor Law system and made it so unpopular. Even the 1911 National Insurance Act left two thirds of the population uninsured, which led to many anomalies and considerable distress.

In 1902, more than 300 pauper children were relocated to the newly built St Christopher Homes in Penkhull. All the old buildings continued in use while more and more beds were provided; the Mental Illness Wards, Cheethams Block for children and much of the old Surgical Square.

In 1929 the Workhouse officially closed, the rule of the Board of Guardians ended and local authority control began. The City General site was administratively divided, half in a continuation of the old Workhouse type of social support, under the Public Assistance Committee of the City Council, the other half a municipal hospital under the Public Health Committee. This led to some new building, the Nurses' Home and the 'Nines' Block.

There was consternation at the Infirmary when it was discovered that the City Council planned a new 800-bedded hospital on the City General site. The plans suggested inter alia that more ward buildings like the Nines Block should be built, marching one behind the other to Hilton Road, and that two new sanatoria should be built. A Government enquiry was held and in the event only the Nines Block was built. The Governors of the Infirmary were particularly upset because the scheme seemed to have appeared without consultation, and to be a threat to the future of Infirmary.

In the 1920s and 1930s consultants from the Infirmary contracted with the Local Authorities to undertake operating lists at the City General site, particularly in general and ear, nose and throat surgery. Orthopaedic patients, particularly children who had tuberculosis affecting their joints, were referred to the Cripples Guild at Hartshill, while physicians from the Infirmary were consulted about cases in the wards of the City General Hospital. The Voluntary Hospitals Contributory Association, which took over from the Establishment Schemes in 1938, had joint arrangements with the City General Hospital whereby subscribers could be treated there. The Governors at the Infirmary had hoped to cement these friendly relations between the Voluntary and Municipal systems with the avoidance of duplication of expensive services, but it certainly appears that some members of the City Council were more concerned with competition than cooperation in the 1930s.

The approach of World War II brought about the setting up of the Emergency Medical Service which imposed cooperation on all the hospitals in the district. Having discovered the benefits of working together, hospitals were prepared for change when all were incorporated in the National Health Service in 1948. But that as they say is another story....

The 'Nines' Block at the City General Hospital.
This block of wards is the only surviving part of a proposed expansion in the years 1931-32.

The Pathology Laboratory which replaced the Smith Child Ward in 1940. Right, the Plaque recording these events over the Laboratory doorway.

BELOW

The Boardman Ward was built in the 1960s with money donated by the Boardman family. The original donation was made in 1917, but being entailed was not immediately available. It was thus the last of the major benefactions received by the Infirmary.

CHAPTER 21
Between the Wars, World War II and the end of an era

The last years of the Infirmary as a voluntary hospital. The self-governing institution drew on the benefits which accrued from the reforms of 1909, with greatly increased public support. Led by a series of active and influential presidents the accommodation and services were increased despite the extremely difficult economic circumstances in the Potteries and the Country at large. Gradually we see the growth of central funding and control, leading up to the coming of the National Health Service in 1948. Despite all the changes and difficulties, the Infirmary joined the Health Service in good order, and continued to develop the services it offers to North Staffordshire. As it faces absorption into the University Hospital, it carries the tradition of service into its third century.

In January of 1918, the military patients left the Infirmary for Stoke Military Hospital, as the City General Hospital was then called. A total of 2562 soldiers had been treated, with 23 deaths. When the extra beds that had been provided for the soldiers became available for the use of the civilian population as temporary extra wards, the number of beds in the Infirmary had risen to 280.

One result of the war was that the waiting list for treatment had grown again. Whether it was due to the privations of wartime, a greater awareness of the benefits that treatment could offer, or whether the Infirmary had acquired a better and more accessible image in the mind of the public, the fact was that many more patients were presenting for admission. Despite all the reforms, the number of beds available to the people of North Staffordshire was barely a third of those generally agreed on a national basis to be necessary for the population. A thousand cases on a waiting list are a statistic, an individual case is a person, and it is easier to feel for a person than a statistic. The Annual Report for the year 1918-19 quoted this letter from a Parent:

I received your post card all right, saying we can bring our child as an in-patient. I am very sorry to say that he does not need a bed at all now, as he is dead. I thank you for your kindness. I think that if only you could have had our little sonny at first he would have been here today.

This dignified letter must have concentrated minds wonderfully.

The reforms of 1909-10 would have been completed in spirit as well as in practice if Mr T. Griffiths, representative of the miners, had been elected to the Presidency. Mr Griffiths, who would have been the first working man to hold that office declined on account of ill health. However he *was* the first working man to be elected Vice President of the Infirmary.

In the event, new ground was broken when Mrs Harrison of Maer Hall was elected Vice President in 1919, and President in 1920 and 1921, the first and only woman to hold these positions. She followed in the footsteps of her husband as President. Mrs Harrison was clearly a popular and very effective holder of this position. She was faced with a deficit on the past two years work of £21,000. This was partly due to the high price of commodities that the Infirmary had to buy in the immediate post war years, coinciding with major strikes that reduced the income from Hospital Saturday and Establishment Contributions. Nonetheless, as in the pre-war period the slippery slope into bankruptcy beckoned unless rapid action was taken. She immediately made an appeal to the leisured classes, who, as she forcefully observed, did much less for the Infirmary than did the working people. She appealed to employers to add a personal contribution to their workers subscriptions. The Infirmary faced problems on two fronts. In order to stand still it needed an increase in its regular income to £15,000 a year. In order to tackle the waiting list a huge sum of money would be required to expand the hospital, together with a consequent increase in income to sustain the new facilities.

At the end of the war in 1918, the *Sentinel* reveals an extraordinary level of medical fund-raising in North Staffordshire. In addition to appeals for the Infirmary, there were appeals for the Orthopaedic Hospital in Hartshill, a huge Red Cross campaign and an appeal for £10,000 for soldiers of the North Staffs Regiment who were in POW camps.

The next year the overdraft grew to £23,822. There were 20,000 people unemployed reported in North Staffordshire; a bad time for raising money. There was discussion of a plan for the voluntary hospitals to cooperate in pooling their purchasing to obtain better rates. The Annual Report darkly muttered that *'one Hospital'*, perhaps the Haywood or Longton, was unduly favoured by the pottery manufacturers, and paying much less for crockery than the Infirmary! It is wonderful to see, when an organisation is hugely adrift in its finances, indeed facing ruin, the amount of effort that can be wasted on small and futile worries!

Much more to the point, having given a large recreation hut for the soldiers at the Infirmary, Mrs Harrison gave a *'temporary'* 24 bedded ward, together with hutted accommodation for the additional nurses associated with it, and she raised the £5000 revenue required to run it. Organised by Miss Twyford, the people of the village of Whitmore raised the money required to equip the ward. The 'temporary' ward lasted for many years, serving many different uses.

The need expressed by Sir Henry Burdett in 1909 to keep up the level of staff in order to provide a proper service had clearly been remembered after the War. In 1920 nine honorary Medical and Surgical Registrars were appointed, to help in outpatients and to encourage younger practitioners to study for higher degrees, and so fit themselves to apply for consultant posts. The Infirmary Staff had always hoped that a *'Teaching Institution'* could be added to the Infirmary. In the 19th century they had frequently referred to the need for a medical school, the Infirmary being larger and busier than many London teaching hospitals. They expressed their ambitions now as a need to *'keep up to London standards'*, they travelled to London as often as possible to attend educational meetings at the Royal Society of Medicine and wanted to see a postgraduate teaching institution in North Staffordshire.

The total deficit stood at nearly £27,000. Fortunately, a grant of £5000 came from the Voluntary Hospital Commission together with another of £4875, that was promised providing there was match funding of £5000 raised by next January. £3000 came in from War Memorial funds in Burslem and Hanley. In this the second year of her Presidency, Mrs Harrison saw the sum of £32,000 raised and for the first time in many years the institution was free of debt.

In 1922-23, the Infirmary lost both those benefactors of the Infirmary, Mrs Harrison and Miss Twyford It was therefore especially encouraging when others came forward to repair the loss. For the first time Establishment Contributions passed £20,000; their spectacular and sustained rise owed much to the efforts of the new President. The first working man to be President, Sam Clowes was elected for the first of a then record four terms. He had been an Establishment Governor and Committee member and was the leader of the Pottery workers. A Member of Parliament, and a charismatic figure, he was devoted to the Infirmary and had encouraged and organised the collection of Establishment payments. His election was formally proposed by Col Heath, who pressed the Governors to be bold in the launch of their appeal for the Infirmary, to ask for at least £150,000. Major building works were needed, including 100 new beds, a new X-ray department, a new operating theatre and a Nurses' Home with 60 rooms.

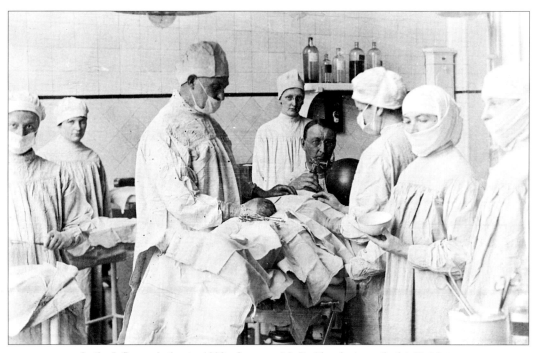

In the Infirmary's theatre 1930s. Surgeon, Mr R. Alcock, Anaesthetist, Dr Mott.

The Infirmary operating theatres in the 1920s with the Theatre Nursing Staff and the Anaesthetists. On the trolley is the anaesthetic apparatus, Shipway's Warm Ether Apparatus. There is no 'Anaesthetic (Boyle's) Machine', these were expensive and needed costly gas cylinders while Shipway's apparatus used air to carry the ether or chloroform vapour to the patient.
Until the 1930s many hospitals saw Boyle's machines as an avoidable expense.

The King and Queen, George V and Mary, with Matron Miss MacMaster in 1925,
when Stoke-on-Trent became a city and the Infirmary became the Royal Infirmary.

Dr Sowry reported that the outpatients department was again a bone of contention. It was back to standing room only: he reiterated the view that it should be providing a consulting service for difficult problems, and patients who were referred for a second opinion, not trivial cases who should have consulted their own doctor. As for inpatients, Ward 1 frequently had patients lying on couches or mattresses on the floor. The X-ray apparatus had become so antiquated that half the films failed to come out, while the number of beds available for the population was a third of the nationally recommended number. He thought that they should ask for £300,000.

The implementation of National Insurance in 1912 had been rather dreaded by the Governors of the Infirmary. They feared that people would no longer subscribe to the Infirmary now that the Government had stepped in. In fact the provision of the new Act was not nearly as generous as had been expected. Only one third of the population were insured, basically all those who were employed in manual work, regardless of their earnings, but those not employed in manual work were only covered if their income was below the level that was below the threshold for income tax, then £160 per annum, rising to £420 by 1942. Even for the insured, the medical cover only paid for such treatment as would be provided by a general practitioner in his surgery. Hospital treatment was only paid for in cases of tuberculosis requiring treatment in a sanatorium. Thus there was every reason for workers to continue to subscribe to the Infirmary. Women were worse off than men - wives (unless insured as employed persons) and children were not covered at all.

Insulin had just been isolated and made available for the treatment of diabetes - the future cast its shadow; it would bring many new treatments, often needing long term, even

Mr. Enoch Haughton cutting the first turf for the Haughton Wards, February 1939.

The 1937 extension to the Xray department, building costs paid for by Mr Downing life-long provision. As with all new treatments, insulin was very expensive and the problem was compounded in that the patient's life expectancy had been enormously prolonged. Working people could not afford to pay for such treatment. Let us consider a married couple, one of whom developed diabetes. If the husband was the patient and was insured, he was a Panel patient and the National Insurance Committee supplied his medicine, i.e. insulin. If it were the wife who became a diabetic, she would have to apply for admission to the Workhouse system to obtain her insulin. Perhaps the great achievement of the National Health Service was the removal of these anomalies and indignities. Dr Myott urged that insulin should be placed within the reach of the public regardless of any entitlements.

In its first year, the ward provided by Mrs Harrison had treated 401 patients. At some large firms like the Shelton Steel, Iron and Coal Company, and Johnson Brothers, the workers agreed to double their subscriptions. Despite this the increasing demand for services meant that more and more money was needed to satisfy that demand. Miss Twyford bequeathed £12,000 for new buildings to house the X-ray department and the Orthopaedic Department, with £1000 towards the revenue consequences. This was the Twyford Memorial, above it two large wards were built, one dedicated to Henry Johnson, the other to Matilda Burgess, a ward known to generations of staff as Mattie B.

When the President, Sam Clowes, greeted George V and Queen Mary in 1925, the King was told that the building fund had passed £100,000. A remarkable achievement, remembering that the necessity of raising the annual running costs still continued every year. The King laid the foundation stone of the new buildings. He announced the creation of the City of Stoke-on-Trent, and that the Infirmary would become the Royal Infirmary. In honour of the occasion an additional donation to the Building Fund came from a special Empire Day Collection, which brought forth £4666. It was proposed to make it an annual event.

The following year was the year of the General Strike, indeed strikes had afflicted the area for seven of the past twelve months. It was deemed inappropriate to hold the Empire Day collection, and the income of the Infirmary fell by £7593. Philosophically the Annual Report said things could have been worse. The deficit rose again. Remarkably, despite the economic difficulties the Building Fund continued to climb to £124,000, though the total outlay on the planned work had also risen to £180,000.

Many and various means were explored to raise money, and as many to reduce expenditure. The motor car was a fruitful cause of accidents, averaging five a week. These patients were brought in as emergencies, therefore they were admitted and treated without charge. They often required long and complicated treatment, and contributed little or nothing to the revenue of the Infirmary. Frequently they were not subscribers. Worse, only the relatively well off could be motorists at this time, thus the thought of these people getting free treatment added insult to injury, particularly if they then pocketed a payment from an insurance company. The Governors were aware how much value they should place on the honorary (unpaid) services of their senior staff. Had they to pay the senior doctors at a private patient rate, it would have been the straw that broke the camel's back. They were concerned about the age old question of hospital abuse, patients who could well afford to pay for treatment getting it for nothing.

It was not yet time for the idea of private wards, where the better off could be charged, raising money for the Infirmary and paying their doctors fees, but among those who could and should have paid a fee, and who were seen as free-loading on the goodwill of the medical staff, were patients covered by insurance companies and local authorities. Insurance companies benefited when the treatment was shortened by hospital care. Education authorities referred large numbers of children for the removal of tonsils and adenoids or the provision of spectacles, and should pay for these services. The Infirmary affirmed that it was happy to see those patients who needed the advice and attention over and above that they could get from Panel or Private doctors.

A Lady Almoner had been appointed in 1927. Her work was to ensure that discharged patients received proper after care, that they were provided with necessary appliances and nourishment, and to check abuses (patients who obtained free treatment for which they should have paid). Her annual report showed that she had discovered 29 cases of abuse, a minuscule proportion of those attending, so while this was in one way gratifying in that there was little abuse, there was little scope for saving money!

The Almoner's report is a snapshot of social conditions of the time. Convalescence was provided for sick children, as were fares to outpatients, and many other small payments, indeed the payments were often so small that the very need for them gives a measure of the reality of poverty. They are evidence of the lives of quiet desperation which were the lot of so many in living memory. One case can be our illustration, a mother was to be discharged after major surgery, but could not rest as she would have to be up and about to care for her children immediately on returning home. The Almoner was able to find the money to make up the wages of the eldest daughter so she could remain at home and care for the family. The era of social work had begun.

Mr E.J. Johnson served as President in the years 1927 to 1931. As Sir Ernest Johnson he would also serve as the last President, 1945 to 1948, when he oversaw the handover to the National Health Service. His first period of office was one of consolidation, bringing the supporting services up to standard and overseeing changes such as the refurbishment of theatres and wards. Another Royal visit saw Prince Henry open the new Nurses' Home, the Twyford Memorial and the two new wards above it. The building fund grew, but slowly, reaching £146,616. The gap to be bridged between the Infirmary's income and expenditure is graphically demonstrated by the following example. The cost of treating an inpatient was £9-7-11 a week. If we take 2 old pennies a week as an average subscription, the Establishment subscriber had to contribute for 20 years to pay in the cost of one week's admission. The deficit on the day to day running of the Infirmary was climbing again, reaching £16,000. The building programme was curtailed, some firms increased their subscriptions, while some owners of businesses added a proportional sum to the employees' subscriptions.

The Infirmary lost a good friend in Sam Clowes who died in 1928. Fortunately another good friend, Edmund R. Corn of the firm Richard's Tiles was taking a close interest in the affairs of the Infirmary. Serving as Chairman of the Building Committee he worked closely with E.J. Johnson, who he succeeded as President, serving for the years 1931 to 1936. He took over a current account accumulated deficit of £16,370, and a Building Fund deficit of £41,532, nearly £58,000 in total, the gap between planned expenditure and money received. The Establishment Contributions were reviewed and settled at threepence for a man, twopence for a woman and one penny a week for a child. I t was decided to be content with the planned new X-ray department, wards and nurses' home extension, laundry and new boiler room chimney. New kitchens, mortuary and workshops would have to wait. Mr Corn's greatest contribution was to institute a tightly controlled programme of direct works, saving large sums of money on contractors' prices. Personal generosity had provided a new operating theatre, the cost entirely covered by £2000 from Mrs Montford and £1000 from the late Mr H.J. Johnson.

Another huge donation of £50,000, a residual legacy from the estate of Miss Twyford enabled the money owed by the building fund to be paid off. The fund was closed in a happier state than anyone could have dreamt of. Mr Corn was not about to jump back into the frying pan by incurring new debts. Wards were converted, an operating theatre and steam and hot water mains all renewed, a new staircase rose from the front hall and a new boardroom was provided, all of this by direct labour. The operating theatre was reopened by Sir Harold Gillies.

In the year ended 1930, Miss McMaster who had been Matron for 26 years retired, and received a leaving present of more than £500. She was succeeded by Miss Eva Blakemore who came from the Norfolk and Norwich Hospital.

As a matter of relief for the reader from unrelenting finance, a selection of occupations of patients listed among those attending the Infirmary reminds us of the range of employment still to be found in North Staffordshire in the late 1920s. The list included 1 butler, 3 footmen, 2 bottlewashers, 1 governess, 18 messenger boys and girls, 148 domestic servants, 5 hawkers, 1 saggar maker and 1 well sinker, a reminder of how employment patterns have changed since that year.

1930 and 1931 were periods of considerable distress. The income of the Infirmary fell with the depression of trade. Two large collieries were closed, nevertheless many people struggled to keep up their contributions even though they were on half time working. Even the weather was poor, reducing the takings from outdoor fundraising activities. Renovations continued, the experimental oxygen chambers had fallen out of use and were converted to maids' bedrooms. The accident wards were modernised with their own X-ray equipment. The Casualty that had been housed on a Ward 17 was moved to a new purpose built department erected as a memorial to Alfred Chew at a cost of £10,000. Ward 17 became the Dorothy Twyford Ward. As part of a thanksgiving for the recovery of George V, radium to the value of £12,000 was given, making the Infirmary the first centre to be accommodated outside a teaching hospital.

It was now recognised that there was a need for a ward for private patients. It was felt that there was a group of patients who were not eligible to be patients of the Infirmary because of their income, were neither Establishment Subscribers or Real objects of Charity, and who would be willing and able to pay for their care. These people were not abusing the Infirmary, they knew they were not eligible for free care, they were willing to pay, but under the current rules this was not possible. The Infirmary would benefit once it was able to charge the private patients for their accommodation and nursing care, thereby receiving an additional source of income. At the same time the consultants would be able to charge these private patients for their medical or surgical care, they would be entitled to this income which would go some way to recompensing them for the fact that most of the Infirmary's patients were still treated free of charge. It was felt that the working class were eligible for any treatment gratis, but the middle class, who were often generous supporters of the Infirmary were barred. It was intended that those earning £400-500 a year would thus become independent of charity.

A further powerful argument for the provision of private wards came in 1930, when the Infirmary became a Radium Centre. It was a condition of the supply of radium that all treatments should be undertaken in the Infirmary; no radium could be taken outside to private establishments. A private patient, should they need radium, could not be accommodated in the Infirmary. As treatment grew more and more complex, treatment at home or in small nursing homes became less and less desirable due to lack of facilities and resident medical staff, giving a further impetus to the movement for private beds.

The President of the Royal College of Surgeons opened the ward and the operating theatre for private patients in 1933. It was paid for by specific loans and not from the general funds, Mr Corn had guaranteed the financial stability of the Private Patients Fund. He later donated £6,200 to provide a new Ophthalmic suite, new wards and a new operating theatre for the Infirmary. The gift was a thank offering for the recovery of Mrs Corn from illness.

The Annual Report for 1932-3 reported the appointment of Sir Harold Gillies as Honorary Plastic Surgeon. He held a monthly clinic at the Infirmary, and equally importantly he trained the staff in new techniques. By this means, Infirmary patients had access to the most famous plastic surgeon in the world. The following year plastic surgery was among three new specialist departments being developed, along with dermatology and neurology. An accident ward was created from the fabric of Wards 1 and 3, extended in length by 30 feet, and with a plaster room, dayroom and lift. It was paid for by a gift of £5000 in memory of Robert Lewis and Sarah Johnson. In 1934 another member of the Johnson family, Mr A.E. (later Lord) Webb Johnson, Senior Surgeon of the Middlesex Hospital, declared the ward open.

The Infirmary still had a deficit of £7,500, even though Establishment Contributions had risen to £32,196 for 1934. There had been some difficulty when the Miners' Welfare Fund was asked to contribute £1,000 towards the £6000 needed for the refurbishment of Ward 1 and had declined to help. Their reply was that Pithead baths were more important, even though many of the Infirmary's patients were miners, and because of the severity of their injuries they were expensive patients to treat. It was requested that miners at least pay the full 3d a week.

In the next few years arrangements for the care of miners improved, as did the relations between the miners and the Infirmary. Regular fracture clinics and a centralised fracture service developed, with income from the North Staffordshire Collieries Mutual Indemnity Company Limited. This service became a part of the Orthopaedic Department and was extended to the general public.

Discussions with the other voluntary hospitals and with municipal hospitals continued with a view to cooperation, but did not make any satisfactory progress.

In 1935 Edmund Corn was re-elected President. Less than ten years after the Twyford Memorial was built, the X-ray equipment it housed was declared obsolete. Additionally the pathology department needed to be renewed; together they would cost at least £35,000, and an appeal was mounted for this sum. Mr G.H. Downing, High Sheriff of Staffordshire, offered to pay the building costs of a new wing which faced onto Princes Road, amounting to £10,668. The total cost of the new Downing wing, was £21,500. The appeal was extended to cover £22,500 for the rebuilding of the pathology department. The original Smith Child building dated back to 1876, it had been a nurses' home, children's ward, pathology department and coroner's court. The new pathology department was built on that site. In addition, a further extension of the nurses' home was required, containing 100 bedrooms.

The last major development was the provision of two new medical wards to augment the existing meagre total of 60 beds. These wards, named after Enoch and Cicely Haughton, were paid for by them with a donation of £25,000.

Sadly, Mr Downing died on the eve of the opening of the new department that bore his name, and Mrs Haughton did not survive to see her ward completed.

In 1936, Mr Eric Young, Surgeon to the Infirmary was elected President in succession to Mr Corn, while Mr Corn was elected Patron, an honour vacant since the death of the Duke of Sutherland in 1913. Mr Young would serve the record number of nine years as

President, remaining in office though the war years until his death. He made consistent efforts to bring about cooperation with the other voluntary hospitals and with the municipal hospitals, mainly the City General, controlled by the City Council. The latter proved most difficult, as the then Mayor and councillors would not even meet with the Infirmary Governors to discuss the matter. The 1930s were years of high unemployment, money was hard to come by, and duplication of services was a waste of resources.

> The outstanding progress made by the Contributory Association during the two years of its working will be a source of great satisfaction to all who have assisted in any way to achieve the splendid results outlined in this report. All concerned in bringing the Contributory Scheme to its present high level are deserving of the highest praise for their loyal support.
>
> Over 150,000 wage earners and others are now contributing regularly and thereby assisting in no small way to furnish the participating hospitals with incomes more stable than in the past. The results are most gratifying to the Executive Council and the Committees of the hospitals concerned, showing as they do the great esteem in which the Voluntary Hospitals of Stoke-on-Trent are held, not only by those who contribute, but by many others who render active service in various voluntary capacities.
>
> To all who have contributed in any way, however small, to the success of the Scheme the Executive Council tenders its most grateful thanks.
>
> ERIC E. YOUNG,
> Chairman of Executive Council.

From the minutes of the Contributory Association which brought together the fund raising activities of all the Voluntary Hospitals in North Staffordshire.
The large number of subscribers made it one of the largest such schemes in the country.

At the same time as the appeals for the radiological and pathology departments were in hand, the accumulated deficit had reached £16,301 by 1937. It was recognised that the Establishment Scheme was not as efficient a revenue provider as it might have been, there were many employed in small businesses who were not under its umbrella, and separate overlapping appeals for individual voluntary hospitals in the area were counter-productive.

There had always been a dichotomy in attitudes to the Establishment Scheme, were the patients subscribers or objects of charity? Cooperation with the other voluntary hospitals in North Staffordshire at last came to pass, so the opportunity was taken to reform the whole system of collecting money. The level of contributions was standardised, and the proportions of the fund to be divided between the four hospitals was agreed. Crucially, an upper income limit, above which it was no longer possible to subscribe was set for the first time. Equally, those who could have subscribed and had chosen not to do so were excluded from the new schemes. Only the elderly and those truly destitute could in future expect gratuitous attention. The upper income limit for subscribers was set at £4 a week, which created another poverty trap. For years there had been concern about the provision of care for those who were not poor, but often at the cost of considerable sacrifice just avoided the acceptance of charity. The upper middle class could be treated as private patients and well afford to pay, but those on lower incomes that just exceeded the £4 weekly limit were excluded from becoming patients in the voluntary hospitals. They could be accommodated in the municipal City General Hospital, but remember, this had only recently been part of the workhouse. In 1940 it was hoped to address this problem with a graduated insurance scheme, but the pressures of war delayed its introduction until the National Health Service made it superfluous.

When the North Staffordshire Contributory Association came into being, 1224 firms agreed to cooperate in collecting subscriptions from workers, and the total membership was 113,00. The estimated income was £59,198, an increase of £12,000 over the previous figure of £46,875. The following year 145,000 subscribers were on the books and by 1939 the figure was 150,000.

I have said that the efforts to raise money were legion. Between the wars whist was very popular, and competitions brought in a regular income of £1500 to £2000 a year. The Carnival of Queens, with which Mrs Cicely Haughton was particularly involved, regularly raised in excess of £1000. There were special efforts associated with particular companies, groups and districts. For an example we may take the staff of the Burslem and District Co-operative Society, who in 1936 sent a cheque for £500 being an act of thanksgiving for the benefit of good health.

In 1938, there was increased activity in the Infirmary at the time of the Munich crisis, while we have seen that the radium was withdrawn. New appointments had been made to improve the range and quality of care available to Infirmary patients. These included the neurosurgeon Harvey Jackson from the National Hospital for Nervous Diseases in London, and in 1942 (Sir) Clement Price Thomas from Westminster and the Brompton Hospitals, the Thoracic Surgeon who later operated on George VI. Sir Harold Gillies, who had been joined by his cousin (Sir) Archibald McIndoe on the Honorary staff of the Infirmary, was now Director of Facio-Maxillary Surgery for the Emergency Medical Service and set up a major plastic surgery unit at the Infirmary. This was under the care of Mr J. Grocott who had been trained by Messrs Gillies and McIndoe.

The War obviously brought a need for flexibility. In 1939 it was agreed that the dependents of the British Expeditionary Force were to be treated without charge. In 1940, dependents who were not earning were treated gratis - serving members of the forces were invited to contribute to their dependent's care. Those who were engaged in Civilian Defence (Home Guard, A.R.P. etc) were told to pay up! The war badly affected the peacetime fund raising activities. The regular subscriptions were augmented by money from Government, received through the Emergency Medical Service. In 1942 the standard contribution for adults was raised by one penny a week. Nonetheless, the overdraft was £33,822.

The Architect's drawing of the Infirmary as it was planned to be after the War. It was produced by the well known firm of architects Adams, Holden and Pearson, who were leading architects in the field of Hospital design.

THE FUTURE!
Birds eye view of the existing buildings and proposed future developments— planned by Messrs. Adams, Holden and Pearson, F.F.R.I.B.A., The University, London

KEY TO THE PLAN

1. Proposed Out-Patient Building.
2. Administration Department.
3 & 4. New Surgical Units.
5. Existing Surgical Block.
6. New Operating Theatre Unit.
6a. Regional Radium Centre.
7. Edmund Corn Eye Dept. extended.
8. Extension to Haughton Wards.
9. New Kitchens, Dining Rooms and Stores.
10. Central Admission Dept. with new Radiological Department.
11. Laundry and Power Station.
12. Department of Pathology.
13. Original (1869) Buildings remodelled and extra storey added.
14. Nurses' Home, original, 1902.
15. Nurses' Home, 1926.
16. Nurses' Home, 1940.
17. Nurses' Home, proposed extension.
18. Proposed Domestics' Hostel.
19. Matron's House (new).
20. Resident Medical Officers' Hostel.
21. Hostel for trained Nurses.
22. Main Entrance Drives from Princes Road.

THE BEGINNING OF THE END

There were extensive series of discussions about the direction the provision of hospital care would take. Would it be purely a state service, would it be mixed, state and municipal? Would the voluntary system survive, would consultants still be willing to give their services free, relying on private patients for their income? Just like the mines and the railways, the hospitals had struggled on with ever increasing dilapidation of their buildings, the need was for renewal of equipment and to accommodate new advances and increasingly costly treatment. If the consultant staff were to be paid, could this be afforded?

With hindsight, the Second Wold War was a watershed in the history of voluntary hospitals. The War and the future of health provision are inextricably entwined, so I propose to deal with the end of the old ways in this chapter.

War became very real in 1940 when a stray German bomber dropped a stick of bombs on the Infirmary. The Eye Department was hit, so was the corridor and staircase leading to the new Haughton Wards, cutting them off from the rest of the Infirmary. The final bomb fell on the just opened new extension to the Nurses' Home, fortunately it had not yet been occupied and there was no loss of life. Nonetheless, it took time and the then large sum of £10,000 to repair the damage. Blackout precautions, blast walls and air raid shelters, all the impedimenta of aerial warfare surrounded the buildings. In addition to sporadic attacks from the air, there were the restrictions of wartime, uncertain supplies, shortages, rationing, as well as the extra burden of providing services for injured service personnel and civilians. As it happened, rather more war wounded were treated at the Infirmary in the Second World War than in the First. Work was dictated by the war, developments concentrated on new departments such as plastic surgery and the treatment of maxillofacial injuries and burns. Urgent work was carried out to renew and maintain the essential services of the Infirmary, water, heating and electricity. Convoys of injured soldiers arrived after the invasion of Normandy in 1944..

At the beginning of the War all hospitals were brought under the control of the Emergency Medical Service, effectively the Government. This involved the grouping of the hospitals in an area, be they municipal, voluntary or charitable. For the first time the Infirmary was no longer under the control of its supporters, the Governors. One result of this centralisation was an increase in costs, not only from increased administrative costs themselves but also because of the imposition of nationally agreed wage and salary settlements. These included all employees, particularly the nursing staff.

At the end of the war changes in medical staffing presaged the end of the honorary system with the creation of paid full-time posts, and the change of the conditions of service for new consultant appointees so that they could no longer also be general practitioners - this would serve to drive a wedge between hospital doctors and general practitioners in the years to come. All these changes would have profound for the future of the Health Service.

The Honorary (consultant) staff members had always been unpaid and nurses across the country, especially those in training, were paid so little that they had fallen far behind other comparable occupations. It was clear that the existing system was one of exploitation of staff hidden by the name of dedication. A Government grant was given to cover the rise in pay for nurses, and approximately £50,000 a year was received via the Emergency Hospital and Medical Service.

These Government payments were reduced or ended after the war, however the pay rises they had instigated continued. The Infirmary in its last months had an Annual Expenditure of £187,000 and it was effectively losing money at the rate of £4,000 a month. Bankruptcy beckoned again, and some assets were sold to fund pressing expenditure. With the end in sight, it was agreed to ask all subscribers to raise all subscriptions by two pennies a week so that the hospitals could be handed over to the new National Health Service in a solvent condition. Contributions had not been increased since 1942, the cost of maintenance had risen by 55%, and national pay agreements had led to an increase in salaries and wages of 77%.

The mood of the people as the War ended was shown in the election of the Labour Government, inviting the change from a voluntary or charitable system to Nationalisation. The 60 years of the National Health Service since have seen an escalation of services, expectations and costs that have even stretched the national finances. Certainly the former methods of local money raising could not have coped: Britain chose nationalisation, other countries have followed the insurance route; whichever route was taken, there had to be change.

But it must not be thought the Infirmary and its Governors were morally or intellectually bankrupt. They were looking forward to the post war years with renewed vigour and certainly had not given up on the Infirmary. In1943-4 they commissioned a review of the buildings and a set of plans for future developments. They chose Mr Pearson of the firm of architects, Adams, Holden and Pearson, who had built the last teaching hospital to be completed before the war, Westminster Hospital in 1939. There is a nice symmetry in the Governors consulting the architects of a new building for the first voluntary hospital as they planned the next stage in the life of their own voluntary hospital.

The plan that survives shows an extra floor added to the existing ward blocks of 1869, a remarkable testimony to the strength and quality of Charles Lynam's buildings. Along Princes Road were to be, in order: a new Outpatients Department, two ward blocks for surgical patients parallel with Henry Johnson and Matilda Burgess wards; between the new surgical wards a new Regional Radium Centre, and further back from the road, a block of operating theatres. Further up Princes Road were to be extensions to the eye department and to the Haughton Wards. In the centre of the site was to be a new admissions block.

Yet more extensions were planned for the Nurses' Home, a hostel for trained nurses and another for the resident medical staff. These would have given the Infirmary 780 beds, a 50% increase, and produced one of the largest integrated hospitals in the country. Plans were on hand to increase the range of services in children's illnesses, thoracic surgery and neurosurgery, each department to have new permanent consultant staff appointments,ending the need for visiting consultants from London to travel to look after these groups of patients. The Governors certainly had not run out of steam.

As we look at the years after 1948, we see that there was not to be the great rash of new building many had hoped for. There was such a pent up demand for medical services, including the famous rush for spectacles, false teeth and even surgical corsets, and such was the financial state of the country in the post war years that there were few major building programmes until the 1960s in North Staffordshire, or indeed most other towns. The only local exception was the replacement of the Infirmary's operating theatres after an outbreak of infection in the 1950s. The demand for beds was mostly supplied by the continued use of elderly buildings in other hospitals in North Staffordshire. Not until

2008 will the aim of a modern integrated hospital be achieved on the site of the City General Hospital.

For many the passing of the voluntary hospitals was a sad occasion. The voluntary hospitals were a source of intense local pride. In 1948, the die was cast, and on July the 5th the voluntary system would pass away. We should not mourn the passing of the old buildings. This has been the story of the people inside and outside the Infirmary who created and maintained the institution, saw it through many crises and trials. It was a remarkable triumph of self help and cooperation right across the community, from the rich and famous to the mould runner paying a farthing a week. It always endeavoured to make the best medical attention available to those who otherwise had no hope of receiving it.

From the early days the Infirmary, its staff and supporters cherished the hope of a Medical School in North Staffordshire. Now that is reality, let us look forward, remembering the achievements of the past as an inspiration for the future.

Valete.

The Committee cannot conclude this final report on the termination of One Hundred and Forty-Seven years of successful voluntary administration without sincere expression of thanks to all staffs of the hospital for their loyalty and co-operation throughout the years.

From July next the staffs will become employees of the Regional Hospital Board under the new National Health Service ; their immediate controllers will be the Hospital Management Committee to be set up to direct all the hospital services in North Staffordshire ; that their initiative, keenness and ability will find expression in the new service is the sincere wish of the Committee.

It should never be forgotten that a hospital exists primarily and essentially for the reception and treatment of patients.

In planning the future hospital service, therefore, let the needs of the patient be the prime consideration, let all branches of the health services work together for the betterment of the health of the civil population, utilising to the full the fine resources available in our midst.

The Committee knows full well that the Royal Infirmary has the esteem and affection of countless numbers of benefactors and patients alike, and that it is assured of a full measure of sympathy and support in the days to come.

On behalf of the Committee,

ERNEST JOHNSON,   **THORNBURROW GIBSON,**
President.   Secretary and House Governor.

VALETE - FAREWELL, a gracious message from Sir Ernest Johnson as President, and Thornburrow Gibson, Secretary and House Governor, as they say farewell to the old Voluntary Hospital system and look forward to the Infirmary's continued usefulness in the National Health Service.

APPENDIX 1

5 pages extracted from *The North Staffordshire Royal Infirmary* by Ralph Hordley 1902

Honorary Medical Officers of the Institution since its Foundation in 1802, to 1902.

NAME	Consulting Physician	Physician	Medical Officer	Assistant Physician	Consulting Surgeon	Surgeon	Assistant Surgeon	Ophthalmic Surgeon	Assistant Ophthalmic Surgeon	Dental Surgeon
Francis H. Northen	1834—1861	1802—1834								
John Robinson		1802—1804				1802—1804				
James Bent		1804—1812				1802—1826				
Bernard Coombe						1802—1825				
W. H. Smallwood					1839—1845	1802—1839				
George Wood						1805—1821				
Robert Bentley										
Henry Stephens Belcombe		1814—1823								
T. G. Coombe					1851—1871	1822—1834				
James Spark		1812—1814				1827—1850				
Richard Bent		1831—1848								
Thomas Mackenzie		1835—1836								
Thomas Davidson					1858—1894	1835—1858				
Daniel Ball		1836—1858								
Edward Wilson						1839—1845				
Joshua Seddon					1858—1863	1845—1858				
Samuel Mayer Turner		1848—1852								
George J. Wood					1864—1890	1851—1864				
Robert Garner						1855—1890				
Wilson Fox		1858—1861								
Joseph Walker			1866—1889		1869—1875	1858—1869				
William Henry Folker	1891—1898	1861—1890	1866—1867							
John T. Arlidge		1861—1866	1867—1869							
Augustus F. Gooday			1869—1870			1865—1898				
John Alcock			1870—1890		1901 to date	1869—1901				
Charles Orton	1889 to date									
George Barnes			1881—1890							
William Dunnett Spanton			1889—1890		1892 to date			1890—1892		
William Walsh		1890—1891								
Michael H. Ashwell	1891									
A. Watts Whittingham				1891 to date						
J. G. Uvedale West							1890—1898			1881—1886
William Bartlett							1890—1901			1887—1889
Arthur Baines								1892—1894	1890—1892	1889 to date
Alex. Morrison McAldowie		1890 to date		1890—1891						
James Charlesworth		1891—1897		1890—1897						
S. King Alcock		1897 to date								
G. Stokes Hatton						1898 to date				
Wheelton Hind						1901 to date				
Hubert Nicholls								1894 to date	1892—1894	
Herbert H. Folker									1894 to date	
John Fred Arlidge				1897—1899						
T. Treffry Cockill				1899 to date						
Reginald Alcock							1898 to date			
John Russell							1902			
William C. Allardice										

Honorary Officers of the Institution, since its Foundation in 1802, to 1902.

NAME	Patron	President	Vice-President	Treasurer	Trustee	Auditor
Walter Sneyd	...	1802	1814, 1816 & 1824	...	1802	...
Sir John Edensor Heathcote	...	1805	1802, 1812 & 1817	...	1802	...
Rev. William Robinson	...	1807	1802	...	1802	...
Rev. Edward Powys	...	...	1802 & 1810,	...	1802	...
Josiah Wedgwood	...	1811	1802 & 1821	1802—1820	1823	...
James Bent	...	...	1802 & 1811	...	1802	...
Thomas Byerley	...	...	...	1802	...	...
F. H. Northen	...	...	...	...	1823	...
Rev. R. E. Aitkens	...	...	1809 & 1812	...	1802	...
John Davenport	...	...	1807	...	1802	...
The Marquis of Stafford, K.G.	1804—1833	...	...	...	...	...
Hugh Henshall	...	...	1805	...	...	...
John Gilbert	...	1808	1805	...	...	...
John Wedgwood	...	...	1805	...	...	...
Walter Hill Coyney	...	...	1805, 1810 & 1812	...	...	...
Rev. Clement Leigh	...	...	1805	...	...	...
Daniel Whalley	...	1809	1807 & 1813	...	...	...
John Smith	...	...	1807 & 1822	...	...	...
Daniel Whalley, junr.	...	...	1807 & 1811	...	...	...
John Hales	...	...	1807 & 1813	...	...	...
John Sneyd	...	...	1808	...	...	...
Thomas Kinnersly	...	...	1808, 1814 & 1826	1823—1855	...	1823—1825
George Steedman	...	...	1808	...	...	...
William Bent	...	...	1808	...	...	1816
Randle Wilbraham	...	...	1809	...	...	...
E. J. Birch	...	...	1809	...	...	...
Rev. Thomas Butt	...	...	1809 & 1814	...	...	...
John Tomlinson	...	...	1809 & 1826	...	1823	...
Thomas Allen	...	...	1809	...	...	...
James Caldwell	...	...	1810 & 1813	...	...	...
Hugh Booth	...	...	1810	...	...	...
Josiah Spode	...	...	1810, 1813, 1817, 1824 & 1827	...	1823	...
Thomas Swinnerton	...	1810	...	...	...	...
Charles Hassells	...	...	1811	...	...	...
William Kenwright	...	...	1811	...	...	...
William Yates	...	...	1811	...	1823	1817—1824
Lord Granville Leveson Gower	...	1812	...	...	...	...
Rev. William Corser	...	...	1812	...	...	...
Ralph Bourne	...	...	1812	...	...	...
William Pownall	...	...	1813	...	...	...
Edward John Littleton, M.P.	...	1814	1816	...	1827	...
John Mare	...	...	1814	...	...	...
John Rogers	...	...	1814	...	...	...
Earl St. Vincent, G.C.B.	...	1816—1818, 1820—1822	...	...	...	...
W. S. Kinnersly, M.P.	...	...	1820	1820—1822	...	1816—1818
Viscount Granville	...	1824—1846	1818	...	...	...
Edward Mainwaring	...	1813	1818	...	...	...
Thos. H. Parker	...	...	1820	...	...	...
Mr. Snape	...	...	...	...	...	1820
Sir J. Fenton Boughey, Bart.	...	...	1821	...	...	...
Thomas Mills	...	...	1821	...	...	...
The Dean of Lichfield, The Very Rev. W. Chappell Woodhouse	...	...	1821 & 1830	...	...	...
Herbert Minton	...	...	1843	...	...	1821—1833
Richard E. Heathcote	...	...	1822 & 1838	...	1828	...
John Bateman	...	...	1825, 1839 & 1852	...	...	...
Spencer Rogers	...	...	1825	...	...	...
Francis Wedgwood	...	1886—1887	1855-56, 1863-67	...	1861	1825—1863
Charles Mainwaring	...	...	1827	...	...	...
Viscount Anson	...	...	1828	...	...	...
John Wood	...	...	1828 & 1838	...	...	...
Earl of Macclesfield	...	...	1829, 1839 & 1854	...	...	...
Thomas Fitzherbert	...	...	1829	...	...	...
Josiah Wedgwood, junr.	...	...	1830 & 1837	...	...	...
Sir Thos. F. Boughey, Bart.	...	...	1831 & 1840	...	...	...
Ralph Sneyd	...	...	1831 & 1856	...	...	...
Rev. John W. Tomlinson	...	...	1832	...	...	...
William Hammersley	...	...	1832	...	...	...
Sir Oswald Mosley, Bart.	...	...	1833	...	...	...
The Duke of Sutherland, K.G.	1833—1860	...	...	...	...	...
Jesse Watts Russell	...	...	1833	...	...	...
Edward Buller, M.P.	...	...	1834 & 1863	...	...	...
James Beech	...	...	1834	...	...	...
Edmund Peel, M.P.	...	...	1835	...	...	...
Lord Hatherton	...	...	1840	...	...	...
Arthur Minton	...	...	...	...	...	1834 & 1835
William Taylor Copeland, M.P.	...	...	1836	...	1861	...
Sir Smith Child. Bart.	1892—1895	1871 & 1881—1884	1836, 1848, 1862, 1867	...	1839	...
William Parker	...	...	...	...	...	1836—1842
Marquis of Anglesey	...	...	1837 & 1851	...	...	...
Frederick Wright Tomlinson	...	...	...	...	1839	...
Sir C. B. Adderley, Bart., M.P.	...	...	1841	...	...	...
Charles Bourne Lawton	...	1846—1859	1841	...	...	...

Name						
Edmund Buckley, M.P.			1842			
J. Ayshford Wise			1842, 1860 & 1864		1850	
Josiah Spode			1845			
H. H. Williamson			1843			
Nicholas Price Wood						1843—1858
The Earl of Shrewsbury			1844			
James Stamford Caldwell			1844 & 1850			
Edward Kinnersly			1845			
John Lewis Ricardo, M.P.			1846			
Joseph Mayer			1846			
Earl Granville, K.G.		1863—1870	1847, 1848 & 1853			
Robert Philips			1847			
William Keary			1848, 1873 & 1881			
Thomas Godwin			1848			
David Watts Russell			1850			
John Bill (Farley)			1851			
Frederic Bishop			1852 & 1857			1870—1873
Thomas Hackwood			1853			
The Duke of Sutherland, K.G.	1862—1891					
John Edensor Heathcote		1860, 1861 & 1862	1854 & 1857		1861	
Francis Stanier			1855			
W. C. Gemmell				1855—1877		
Michael Daintry Hollins		1879	1855,1862,1869,1876		1861	
Rev. Sir Lovelace T. Stamer, Bart. Bishop of Shrewsbury		1888 & 1889	1858 & 1860		1861	
Robert Brown			1858			
James Bateman			1859		1863	
Joseph Bull			1859			
Christopher Dickinson			1861			
Colin Minton Campbell		1880	1868		1869	1859
William Davenport			1861		1861	
William Bates			1865			
Enoch Wedgwood			1866			
Godfrey Wedgwood		1890, 1891 & 1892	1870			1864—1870
Frederick Wragge			1875 & 1884			1864—1887
Thos. F. Twemlow					1863	
John William Philips		1894	1868, 1890 & 1891		1869	
Rev. E. J. J. G. Edwards			1869			
Harry T. Davenport			1871		1870	
F. Stanier Broade			1872		1870	
Robert Heath		1885	1870			
James Meakin			1871 & 1883			
The Earl of Shrewsbury		1872				
Joseph Knight		1893	1872			
Capt. J.H.Edwards-Heathcote MP			1873 & 1888			
Herbert Minton-Senhouse						1873—1891
Rev. Walter Sneyd		1873—1878				
Harry Coghill			1874 & 1883			
W. F. Gordon			1874			
John Robinson			1875			
Taylor Ashworth			1875			
George P. Wragge					1876	
Atkinson Habbishaw				1877—1888		
Lovat Ayshford Wise			1877			
J. F. Wileman			1877			
Clement F. Wedgwood			1878			
William Woodall, M.P.			1878			
Thomas Udall			1879			
Robert Heath, junr.		1895	1879			
W. S. Allen, M.P.			1880			
George Meakin			1880			
W. Y. Craig, M.P.			1881			
Charles Bill, M.P.			1882			
Charles Challinor			1882			
William Meakin			1884			
Charles M. Beech			1885			
Josiah Hardman			1885			
John Robinson			1886			
Thomas Bertram Udall		1896,1897,1898 1899	1886,1887,1888			
George F. Paddock						1888 to date
Alfred Meakin			1887			
John T. Harris			1889, 1890 & 1902			
Ralph Sneyd			1889			
John George Todd				1889 & 1890		
Henry Thring				1890 & 1891		
Thomas Henry Nicholls				1891		
Francis Elliott Kitchener			1891 & 1892			
Basil Fitzherbert			1892			
Robert Clement Clive						1892 to date
John F. Campbell			1893			
W. W. Dobson			1893 & 1894			
John George Child			1894			
Archibald F. Coghill		1900, 1901 & 1902	1895 & 1896			
James H. Meakin			1895			
Thomas Bullock			1896 & 1897			
The Duke of Sutherland	1896 to date					
Thomas W. Twyford			1897 & 1898			
William E. Bowers			1898 & 1899			
Arthur H. Heath			1899 & 1900			
James Maddock			1900 & 1901			
John B. Ashwell			1901 & 1902			

(left margin, rotated and partly cut off) ... OF THE INSTITUTION SINCE ITS FOUNDATION in 1802, to 1902.

NAME	Chaplain	Dispenser	Architect	Secretary and Collector	Secretary and House Steward	Assistant Secretary and Collector	Lady Superintendent	Superintendent of Nurses	Matron	Housekeeper
Joseph Snape				1818 (Secretary)						
Thomas Mellor		1840 –1847				1822—1841 (Collector)				
William Scarlett		1847—1850		1841—1855						
Isaac Bragge		1850—1853								
Frederick Ruffe		1853—1856								
Isaac Cartwright										
Joseph Bache										
George H. Morewood		1856 & 1857		1855 & 1856						
Ralph Hordley				1856—1874	1874—1899					
James Peacock		1857—1860								
Rev. C. J. Stirling	1858—1863									
Thomas G. Forshaw	1860									
W. Coker		1860								
C. J. Brookes		1860 & 1861								
Robert Wm. Jones		1861—1864								
Rev. Robert Topham	1864—1868	1864 & 1865								
J. S. Jackson		1865—1873								
Edward Henry Croydon		1873—1880								
Charles Lynam			1870 to date							
Rev. J. G. Gifford	1869									
Rev. H. H. Horton	1869—1873									
Arthur J. Tansley										
Rev. P. M. Benson	1874—1875									
Rev. Charles Cotterill	1875—1881									
F. B. Hordley	1881—1886	1899 to date								
Rev. G. H. Tovey	1886 to date									
Rev. Alex. T. Whitehead						1881 to date				
J. H. Bates					Secretary and House Governor, 1899 to date					
Mary Birch									1804—1807	
Mary Berks									1807—1815	
Mary Campbell									1815—1825	
Ann Massey									1825—1827	
Sarah Brown									1827—1837	
Elizabeth Cotton									1837—1853	
Eliza Ledward									1853—1854	
Anne Derry									1854—1869	1870
Catherine Tolson Duck (Honorary)							1869			
Sarah Ann Cartwright							1870 & 1871	1871 & 1872		1870—1895
Sarah Ann Oakden								1872—1874		
Agnes Crawford								1874—1891		
C. H. Simmonds								1891—1897		
Catherine Burnet Annan										1895—1897
Elizabeth A. Wilkinson										1897—1899
Mary Keeling										1899 to date
Gertrude M. Creagh								1897—1899		
Sarah J. Warburton								1899—1901		
K. Cameron								1901 to date		
E. J. Jessop										
H. E. Pearse										
Albert E. Boyce										
F. W. Downar		Assistant Dispenser 1902								

Resident Medical Officers of the Institution since its Foundation in 1802, to 1902.

NAME	Apothecary and Secretary	House Surgeon and Secretary	House Surgeon and Apothecary	House Surgeon	Assistant House Surgeon	House Physician
Isaac Wild	1804 & 1805	...	...	...	...	...
Edward F. Cleavin	1805—1809	...	...	...	...	...
Richard Heath	1810—1814	...	...	...	...	...
Thomas Woolrich	...	1814—1818	...	...	...	...
William Lamb	...	1818 & 1819	...	...	...	...
Joshua Seddon	...	1820—1836	...	...	...	...
Hugh Davies	...	1836—1841	...	...	...	...
Samuel Mayer Turner	...	...	1841—1844	...	...	...
Stephen S. Alford	...	...	1844—1846	...	...	...
J. W. H. Mackenzie	...	...	1846 & 1847	...	...	...
Richard Allen	...	...	1848 & 1849	...	...	...
William G. Dalgairns	...	...	1849—1853	...	...	...
William Henry Folker	...	...	1853—1856	...	...	...
Henry Gibbons	...	...	1856 & 1857	...	...	...
John Alcock	...	...	1857—1859	...	...	...
Charles Parsons	...	...	1859—1862	...	...	...
Charles Orton	...	...	1862—1864	...	...	...
William Dunnett Spanton	...	...	1864—1866	...	...	...
James Mare Taylor	...	...	1866—1869	1869—1870	...	...
J. Alexander Ross	...	...	...	...	...	1869—1870
Alfred Cotterill	...	...	...	1870—1873	...	...
J. T. Leigh	...	...	...	...	...	1871
J. G. Uvedale West	...	...	...	...	...	1871—1874
W. Ashley Cox	...	...	...	1873—1875	...	...
William J. Faulkner	...	...	...	...	...	1874 & 1875
William Walter	...	...	...	1875 & 1876	...	...
Benjamin Jumeaux	...	...	...	...	...	1875 & 1876
William Adams Frost	...	...	...	1876—1878	...	...
Alexander Morison McAldowie	...	...	...	...	...	1876—1880
George Russell	...	...	...	1878—1881	...	...
William Shaw	...	...	...	...	...	1880
Horace Elliott	...	...	...	...	...	1880 & 1881
Walter T. Clegg	...	...	...	1881 & 1882	...	...
G. Stokes Hatton	...	...	...	1882—1884	...	1881 & 1882
William R. Buckell	...	...	...	1884 & 1885	...	1882—1884
Robert Garner Lynam	...	...	...	1885—1889	...	1884 & 1885
S. King Alcock	...	...	...	...	1885	1885—1888
R. Cann	...	...	...	...	1885	...
Alex. H. Whicher	...	...	...	...	1886	...
Herbert H. Folker	...	...	...	...	1886	...
A. Knight Holt	...	...	...	...	1887	1888—1890
Alfred E. Nuttall	...	...	...	...	1888	...
Alfred S. Barling	...	...	...	1889—1892	...	...
Sidney L. Hinde	...	...	...	...	1890	...
Robert W. Cameron	...	...	...	...	...	1890 & 1891
C. S. Wood	...	...	...	...	1890	...
J. F. Gillett	...	...	...	...	1891	...
W. H. Coupland	...	...	...	...	1891	...
J. Frank Crombie	...	...	...	...	1891	...
T. Treffry Cockill	...	...	...	...	...	1891—1894
Reginald Alcock	...	...	...	...	1892	...
Douglas Drew	...	...	...	1893 & 1894	...	...
Courtenay S. Parsons	...	...	...	...	1893	...
E. A. S. Swainson	...	...	...	...	1894	...
John L. Sawers	...	...	...	1894—1897	...	...
William C. Allardice	...	...	...	1897 & 1898	...	1894—1897
T. H. Price Morris	...	...	...	...	1894	...
W. E. L. Horner	...	...	...	...	1895	1897—1900
Reginald Tuxford	...	...	...	...	1896	...
G. Stanley Foulds	...	...	...	...	1897	...
Francis Carter	...	...	...	...	1897	...
A. N. Brushfield	...	...	...	...	1898	...
H. H. Sanguinetti	...	...	...	1898 & 1899	...	...
Arthur P. Square	...	...	...	...	1898	...
Herbert Davies	...	...	...	1899 & 1900	...	...
Harold Hartley	...	...	...	1900 & 1901	...	1902
Thomas O'Neill	...	...	...	...	...	1900 & 1901
G. H. H. Mansfield	...	...	...	...	1902	...
C. A. S. Ridout	...	...	...	1902 & 1903	...	...
A. Hilton John	...	...	...	...	1902	...
Trevor Howell	...	...	...	...	1902	...

APPENDIX 2
MEDICAL STAFF 1911-12

Honorary Consultant Physician	Alex Macaldowie MD, FRS (Edinburgh)
Honorary Consultant Surgeon	W.D. Spanton FRCS
Honorary Physicians	S. King Alcock MD Hubert Nicholls, MD John Russell
Honorary Surgeons	G. Stokes Hatton FRCS Ed Wheelton Hind MD FRCS Reginald Alcock FRCS
Honorary Ophthalmic Surgeon	Herbert H. Folker
Honorary Assistant Physicians	W.E.L. Horner MD G.H. Sowry MD E.C. Myott MD
Honorary Assistant Surgeons	W.C. Allardice MD FRCS H. Hartley MD FRCS E. Young MS
Honorary Assistant Ophthalmic Surgeon	R.H. Dickson FRCS
Honorary surgeon in charge of Ear, Nose and Throat Department	G.A. Carter FRCS
Honorary Medical Officers in charge of the Electrical Department	G.H. List MD A.H. John
Honorary Dental Surgeon	Richard J.Hall
House Physician	W.D. Dunlop
House Surgeons	T.G. Gilmour G. Blair FRCS R.B.M. Yates
Matron	Miss MacMaster
Secretary	T. Basil Rhodes MB BS

APPENDIX 3
MEDICAL STAFF 1918

Honorary Consultant Physician	Alex MacAldowie
Honorary Consultant Surgeon	W.D. Spanton
Honorary Consultant Ophthalmic Surgeon	H.H. Folker
Honorary Physicians	S. King Alcock MD Hubert Nicholls MD John Russell MD
Honorary Surgeons	Lt Cpl Wheelton Hind FRCS (war duty) Reginald Alcock FRCS W. C. Allardice FRCS
Honorary Ophthalmic Surgeon	R.H. Dickson FRCS
Honorary Assistant Physicians	W.E.L. Horner MD G.H. Sowry MD FRCS Capt E. Myott (war duty)
Honorary Assistant Surgeons	H. Hartley FRCS E. Young MS W. Webster FRCS
Honorary Assistant Ophthalmic Surgeon	S. McMurray FRCS

Honorary Surgeon in charge of the Ear, Nose and Throat Department G.A. Carter FRCS

Honorary Medical Officers in charge of Electrical Department	G.A. List A.H. John
Honorary Anaesthetists	G. Blair FRCS C.H. Mott
Honorary Dental Surgeon	John W. Skae LDS
House Physician	Miss K. Hanby
House Surgeons	Miss M.A. Gallacher (R.M.O.) Miss P.E. Inglis
Matron	Miss MacMaster
House Governor	William Stevenson

APPENDIX 4
MEDICAL STAFF 1929

Honorary Consultant Physician	S. King Alcock MD
Honorary Consultant Ophthalmic Surgeon	R.H. Dickson FRCS
Honorary Consultant Surgeon	Reginald Alcock FRCS
Honorary Consultant Anaesthetist	C.H. Mott
Honorary Consultant Dental Surgeon	J.W. Skae
Honorary Physicians	W.E.L. Horner MD G.H. Sowry MD FRCS E.C. Myott MD
Honorary Surgeons	W.C. Allardice FRCS H. Hartley FRCS E. Young MS FRCS
Honorary Ophthalmic Surgeon	S. McMurray FRCS
Honorary Assistant Physicians	A.W. Gill MD C.I. Milne MD B. Maclean MD MRCP
Honorary Assistant Surgeons	G. Blair FRCS T.H. Richmond FRCS
Honorary Assistant Ophthalmic Surgeon	J. Magill, MD
Honorary Surgeon in charge of Ear, Nose Throat Department	G.A. Carter FRCS
Honorary Assistant Aural Surgeon	E.H. Richards FRCS
Honorary Medical Officer in charge of Electrical Department	G.A. List MD
Honorary Radiologist	I.F. Bromley D.M.R.E. Cambridge
Honorary physician in charge of Electrocardiographic Department	A.W. Gill MD
Honorary Pathologist	E.C. Myott MD
Honorary Orthopaedic Surgeon	W.C. Allardice
Honorary Assistant Orthopaedic Sufgeon	L.M. Zinck MD FRCS
Honorary Anaesthetists	G.H. Williams Miss E.M.P. Law R.R. Gamble
Honorary Dental Surgeons	R.J.Skae A. Courtney Campbell
Resident Surgical Officer	F.W. Duthie FRCS
House Surgeons	A.W. Bayley A. G. Minn Miss E.M. Carless
House Physician	T. Craig
Assistant House Physician	Miss A.P. Montgomery
Matron	Miss MacMaster
House Governor	William Stevenson

APPENDIX 5
MEDICAL STAFF 1941

Honorary Consulting Physicians—
S. KING ALCOCK, M.D., Lond.; M.R.C.S., Eng.
W. E. L. HORNER, M.D., B,S,, Lond.

Honorary Consulting Surgeons—
REGINALD ALCOCK, C.B.E., J.P., M.B., Vict., F.R.C.S.E.
W. C. ALLARDICE, J.P., M.D., C.M., Glas.; F.R.C.S.E.
HAROLD HARTLEY, M.D., Lond.; F.R.C.S.

Honorary Consulting Plastic Surgeons—
Sir HAROLD D. GILLIES, C.B.E., K.af D., F.R.C.S.
A. H. McINDOE, F.R.C.S.

Honorary Consulting Electro-Therapist—
G. H. LIST, M.D., Ed.

Honorary Consulting Anaesthetist—
C. H. MOTT M.R.C.S., Eng.

Honorary Consulting Neurological Surgeon—
HARVEY JACKSON, F.R.C.S.

Honorary Consulting Dental Surgeon—
J. W. SKAE, L.D.S.

*Honorary Physicians—
E. C. MYOTT, M.D., Lond.
A. WILSON GILL, M.D., Ed., M.R.C.P., Lond.
C. I. MILNE, M.D., Ch.B., Ed.

*Honorary Surgeons—
ERIC E. YOUNG, M.S., Lond., F.R.C.S.
T. H. RICHMOND, M.B., Glas.; F.R.C.S.E.
R. A. KEANE, M.B., F.R.C.S.I.

*Honorary Ophthalmic Surgeon—
S. McMURRAY, F.R.C.S.E.

Honorary Assistant Physicians—
B. MACLEAN, M.D., M.R.C.P., Lond.
J. LINDSAY BOYD, M.D., F.R.C.P., Ed.
A. D. BLAKELY, M.D., Glas., F.R.F.P.S., Glas.

Honorary Assistant Surgeons—
J. S. RAMAGE, M.B., Glas., F.R.C.S.E.
F. W. DUTHIE, F.R.C.S.E., L.R.C.P.
L. M. ZINCK, M.D., C.M. (Dal.), F.R.C.S.E.

Honorary Assistant Ophthalmic Surgeon—
T. AUBREY JONES, M.R.C.S., L.R.C.P., Lond., D.O., Oxon.

*Honorary Surgeon in charge of the Ear, Nose and Throat Department—
G. A. CARTER, F.R.C.S.E.

Honorary Assistant Aural Surgeon—
E. H. RICHARDS, F.R.C.S.E.

*Honorary Radiologist and Honorary Medical Officer in charge of the Electro-Therapy Department—
R. A. KEMP HARPER, M.B., Ch.B., Edin., D.R., Edin.

Honorary Physician in charge of the Electro-cardiograph Department—
A. WILSON GILL, M.D., Ed., M.R.C.P., Lond.

Honorary Assistant Cardiologist—
B. MACLEAN, M.D., M.R.C.P., Lond.

Honorary Pathologist—
E. C. MYOTT, M.D., B.S., Lond.

Honorary Psychiatrist—
W. D. WILKINS, M.R.C.S., L.R.C.P., Lond., D.P.M., Camb.

Honorary Assistant Psychiatrist—
J. H. MALLOY, M.D., D.P.M., Lond.

Honorary Neurologist—
A. WILSON GILL, M.D., Ed. M.R.C.P., Lond.

Honorary Assistant Neurologist—
B. MACLEAN, M.D., M.R.C.P., Lond.

Honorary Dermatologist—
J. LINDSAY BOYD, M.D., F.R.C.P., Ed.

*Honorary Orthopaedic Surgeon—
PAUL BERNARD ROTH, M.B., Ch.B., Aberd., F.R.C.S.
Honorary Anaesthetists—
*Miss E. M. P. LAW, M.A., M.B., Ch.B., Aberd.
R. R. GAMBLE, M.B., B.Ch., B.A.O., R.U.I.
M. S. SUTHERLAND, M.B., Ch.B., Aberd.
Honorary Surgical Registrar :
J. GROCOTT, M.B., F.R.C.S.
Honorary Medical Registrar :
J. P. P. STOCK, M.D., Ch.B.
Honorary Dental Surgeons—
R. J. SKAE, L.D.S.
A. COURTNEY CAMPBELL, B.D.S.
*These Officers are Ex-Officio Members of the General Committee.
Regional Radium Centre—Radium Officer :
D. J. RIORDAN, F.R.C.S.I.
Consulting Physicist :
H. M. PARKER, M.Sc.
House Surgeons—
A. W. MACKENZIE, M.B., Ch.B. (Glas.).
J. J. MURRAY, M.B., Ch.B.. (Glas.).
J. A. MALLOCH, M.B., Ch.B., (Edin.).
J. A. ELLIOTT, M.D., (Toronto)
C. H. THOMSON, M.B., Ch.B. (Edin.)
J. BURKE, M.B., Ch.B. (Man.)
House Physicians—
A. CUMMING, M.B., Ch.B. (Aberd.).
H. T. LEVI, M.B. Ch.B. (Leeds)
Dispenser—
R. C. PLANT, M.P.S.
Assistant Dispenser—
Miss A. C. E. WILLIAMS, M.P.S.

Honorary Chaplain—
The Ven. Archdeacon PERCY HARTHILL.
Almoner—Miss C. K. HEPPER.

Matron—	Sister-Housekeeper—
Miss E. BLAKEMORE.	Miss L. ARMSTRONG.
Assistant Matron—	Assistant Secretary—
Miss J. BURTON.	GEO. MOTTERSHEAD.

Secretary and House Governor—WILLIAM STEVENSON.

Out-Patients Admission Days are as follows :—
MONDAYS :—Dr. BLAKELY and Mr. ZINCK (9-0 to 11 a.m.)
TUESDAYS :—DR. LINDSAY BOYD and Mr. DUTHIE (9-0 to 11 a.m.)
TUESDAYS :—(Ear, Throat and Nose Cases)—Mr. RICHARDS (9-0 to 11 a.m.)
TUESDAYS :—(Orthopaedic Cases)—Mr. ROTH (9-0 a.m.)
TUESDAYS :—(Skin Cases)—DR. LINDSAY BOYD (2-0 p.m.)
TUESDAYS :—(Neurological Cases)—DR. WILKINS, DR. MALLOY, DR. A. WILSON GILL, DR. B. MACLEAN (3-0 p.m.)
WEDNESDAYS : (Eye Cases)—Mr. McMURRAY (9 to 11 a.m.)
WEDNESDAYS :—(Dental Cases)—Mr. SKAE (1-0 p.m.)
THURSDAYS :—(Ear, Throat and Nose Cases)—Mr. CARTER (9-0 to 11 a.m.)
THURSDAYS :—(Orthopaedic Cases)—Mr. ROTH (9-0 a.m.)
FRIDAYS :—DR. MACLEAN and Mr. RAMAGE (9-0 to 11 a.m.)
SATURDAYS :—(Eye Cases)—Mr. JONES (9 to 11 a.m.)
SATURDAYS :—(Dental Cases)—Mr. A. COURTNEY CAMPBELL (9-0 a.m.)
Patients who attend the Out-Patients Department for the first time and who are insured under the National Health Insurance Act must bring a note from their Panel Doctor.
IN-PATIENTS are admitted every Week-day at noon by arrangement with the House Surgeon or House Physician.
The Hospital is at all times open for the reception of cases of emergency and accident.
Members of the Medical Profession are admitted to witness operations on presenting their Cards.

APPENDIX 6
MEDICAL STAFF 1947

HONORARY CONSULTING STAFF.

Physicians	W. E. HORNER, M.D., B.S., Lond. E. C. MYOTT, M.D., B.S., Lond. J. LINDSAY BOYD, M.D., F.R.C.P., Ed. A. WILSON GILL, M.D., Ed., F.R.C.P., Lond.
Surgeons	W. C. ALLARDICE, J.P., M.D., C.M., Glas., F.R.C.S.E. HAROLD HARTLEY, M.D., Lond., F.R.C.S. T. H. RICHMOND, M.B., Glas., F.R.C.S.E.
Aural Surgeon	G. A. CARTER, F.R.C.S.E.
Ophthalmic Surgeons ...	S. McMURRAY, F.R.C.S.E. T. AUBREY JONES, B.A., M.R.C.S., Eng., D.O. Oxon.
Orthopaedic Surgeon	PAUL BERNARD ROTH, M.B., Ch.B., Aberd., F.R.C.S.
Electro-Therapist ...	G. H. LIST, M.D., Ed.
Pathologist	E. C. MYOTT, M.D., B.S., Lond.
Anaesthetist	C. H. MOTT, M.R.C.S., Eng.
Dermatologist	J. LINDSAY BOYD, M.D., F.R.C.P., Ed.
Plastic Surgeons	Sir HAROLD D. GILLIES, C.B.E., K.af.D., F.R.C.S., F.A.C.S. Sir A. H. McINDOE, C.B.E., F.R.C.S., F.A.C.S.
Thoracic Surgeon	C. PRICE THOMAS, F.R.C.S.
Neurological Surgeon ...	HARVEY JACKSON, F.R.C.S.

VISITING STAFF.

Physicians	BRUCE MACLEAN, M.D., F.R.C.P., Lond. A. D. BLAKELY, M.D., Glas., F.R.F.P.S., Glas. C. W. HEALEY, M.C., T.D., M.D., Ch.B. C. H. CATLIN, M.D., Birm., M.R.C.P., Lond.
Surgeons	R. A. KEANE, M.B., F.R.C.S.I. J. S. RAMAGE, M.B., Glas., F.R.C.S.E. L. M. ZINCK, M.D., C.M.(Dal.), F.R.C.S.E. J. GROCOTT, M.B., F.R.C.S.
Gynaecologists and Obstetricians	F. W. DUTHIE, F.R.C.S.E. L. M. EDWARDS, M.D., B.Ch.(Wales), M.R.C.O.G.
Aural Surgeons	E. H. RICHARDS, F.R.C.S.E. B. S. CARTER, F.R.C.S.E.
Ophthalmic Surgeons ...	W. N. MURRAY, M.A., M.B., Ch.B., D.O.M.S. P. J. M. KENT, M.R.C.S., Eng., L.R.C.P., Lond., D.O.M.S., Eng.

VISITING STAFF—continued.

Orthopaedic Surgeons ...	C. S. WALKER, M.B., Man., F.R.C.S.E.
	A. K. MITTING, M.B., Ch.B., F.R.C.S.E.
Plastic Surgeon	J. GROCOTT, M.B., F.R.C.S.
Radiologist	C. BELLAMY, L.R.C.P. & S., L.R.F.P. & S., Glas., D.M.R.E., Edin.
Cardiologists and Neurologists	BRUCE MACLEAN, M.D., F.R.C.P., Lond.
	C. H. CATLIN, M.D., M.R.C.P.
Psychiatrists	W. D. WILKINS, M.R.C.S., Eng., D.P.M., Camb.
	J. H. MALLOY, M.D., D.P.M., Lond.
Paediatrician	D. C. THURSBY-PELHAM, M.R.C.P., D.C.H.
Dermatologist ...	F. M. DONALDSON, M.D., M.R.C.P.E.
Surgeon in charge of Electro-therapy Dept. ...	A. K. MITTING, M.B., Ch.B., F.R.C.S.E.
Anaesthetists	ELEANOR M. P. LAW, M.A., M.B., Ch.B., Aberd.
	MARY S. SUTHERLAND, M.B., Ch.B., Aberd.
	J. T. TURNER, M.A., M.B., B.Ch., Cantab., D.A.
Dental Surgeons	R. J. SKAE, L.D.S.
	A. COURTNEY CAMPBELL, B.D.S.
Registrars to the Anaesthetic Dept. ...	MARY M. RAMAGE, M.B., B.S., Lond.
	ANNE TELLWRIGHT, M.B., Ch.B., Aberd.

OFFICERS.

Radiotherapist	G. G. BINNIE, M.B., Ch.B., D.M.R., Eng.
Physicist	A. E. CHESTER, M.Sc., Ph.D. (Man.).
Pathologists	A. J. McCALL, M.D. (Liv.), M.R.C.P., Lond.
	B. GODWIN, M.R.C.S., L.R.C.P., D.C.P.
Biochemist	E. C. BUTTERWORTH, M.Sc., Ph.D., A.R.I.C.
Assistant Radiologist	C. G. EDWARDS, M.B., Ch.B., D.M.R.(D.).
Resident Surgical Officer ...	K. G. F. MACKENZIE, M.B., F.R.C.S.

Four Resident Registrars.
Eight Resident Medical Officers.

MEDICAL BOARD.

Chairman	L. M. ZINCK, M.D., C.M. (Dal.), F.R.C.S.E.
Hon. Secretary	THORNBURROW GIBSON, M.A. (Cantab.).

BIBLIOGRAPHY

Percival, Thomas Medical Ethics; a code of institutes and precepts, adapted to the professional conduct of physicians and surgeons. 1803. Classics of Medicine Library, Birmingham Alabama. 1985

The Wedgwood Circle, Wedgwood Barbara & Hensleigh Wedgwood , Westfield, New Jersey, 1980

Diseases of the Ovaries, their diagnosis and treatment, Spencer Wells, Sir Thomas, London 1872

A Manual of Surgery for Students and Practitioners, Rose and Carless, 4th edition, London 1901

Staffordshire Advertiser, from 1795 Keele Library, also at Stoke on Trent Archives

The Sentinel from 1854 Stoke on Trent Archives

North Staffordshire (Royal) Infirmary 1802 to 1948 Minutes, Annual Reports, correspondence Stoke and Staffordshire Archive Service at Stafford County Record Office and at Stoke on Trent Archives, Hanley

On the Sanitary State of the Staffordshire Potteries, Arlidge, J.T. British and Foreign Medical and Chirugical Journal July 1864

Report to the General Board of Health on the parish of Stoke upon Trent, 1850, Rawlinson R

The Nightingale Nurses: The Myth and the Reality, Baly Monica E. In *Nursing History, The State of the Art*, Maggs C. ed

Early nursing reform in 19th century London: a doctor driven phenomenon, Helmstadter, Carol. In *Medical History* 2002 July pp325-350

Reports on the Hospitals of the United Kingdom, (No 1 North Staffordshire Infirmary). *The Hospital* October 2nd 1909 to June 25th, 1910, Burdett, Sir Henry

The Medical History of England, The Staffordshire Potteries and The North Staffordshire Infirmary Medical Times and Gazette. 7th, 14th & 21st May 1864 Richardson, Sir Benjamin Ward

Dr John Thomas Arlidge and Victorian Occupational Medicine. Medical History, Holdsworth, Clare 1998 pp 458-75

Lichfield Diocesan Registry Lichfield Diocesan Calendars 1865-72 The Nursing Association for the Diocese of Lichfield.

The Obstetric Forceps and its Use, Crawford, Mabel Dobbin. Lancet June 11th 1932. Failed Forceps delivery in General Practice in Liverpool.

Caesarean Section: the History and Development of the Operation from the Earliest Times, Young, J.H London, 1944

Combined Textbook of Obstetrics and Gynaecology for Students and Medical Practitioners, Munro Kerr et al. 3rd 1939 Edinburgh. Lead as an agent for producing abortion.

Stoke on Trent Medical Officers of Health Reports 1910-1974 Stoke on Trent Archives, Hanley.

Correspondence about the Infirmary with members of the Wedgwood family in respect of their close involvement with its management. Wedgwood Archives, Keele Library.

INDEX

Abdominal surgery 124, 159, 170, 204

Act of Settlement 219

Address to the Working Classes 42

Aitken, Robert E 77, 79

Almoner's report 233

Anaesthesia 70-71, 169-170, 184

Annan, Miss 129, 148-149, 154-155

Apothecary 34, 36, 67, 127, 132-133

Appendicitis 164-165

Arlidge, Dr J.T. 48, 75, 97, 116, 130,
143, 189, 254

Aseptic surgery 166, 184

Bache, Mr, dispenser 138

Ball, Daniel 87, 104

Bent, Dr 31

Birch, Mrs Mary 133

Bishop 112-114, 125, 131

Blakemore, Miss Eva 155, 234

Board of Health 26-28, 36, 254

Brown, Sarah 134

Buckle, Fleetwood 68

Burdett, Sir Henry 71, 76, 89, 175, 180,
192, 194, 196, 199, 201, 228

Burslem 30, 112-113, 120, 126, 134,
167-170, 196, 223, 228, 237

Butt, Thomas 77, 86-87

Byerley, Thomas 14, 20, 23, 46, 56-57

Caesarean Section 167-168, 170,
182, 254

Campbell, Colin Minton 109, 125

Campbell, Mary 134

Cartwright, Miss 145-146

Cheethams Block 224

Chew, Alfred 234

Childhood diseases 175

Children's Wards 122, 175, 183,
195, 235

Cholera, 1832 223

City General Hospital 90, 217, 223,
225, 227, 237

Cleavin 29, 36, 127

Clowes, President, Sam 228, 232-233

Contributory Association 55, 236

Corn, Edmund R. 233, 235

Coxon, Mr 23

Crawford, Miss 148

Cripples Guild, Hartshill 225

Davy, Sir Humphrey 61

Derbyshire General Infirmary 22, 83, 86

Derry, Miss 139, 143

Diarrhoea 182, 185, 187

Dispensary, House of Recovery 21-27,
37, 57, 79, 101, 127, 203

Downing wing 235

Downing, Mr G.H. 235

Duchess of Sutherland, Millicent
174, 211, 214

Duchy of Lancaster 103, 108, 118, 125

Duck, Miss 144

Duke of Sutherland 235

Earl Granville 35, 102-103, 105-106,
121, 126, 198

Earl St Vincent, of Meaford 203

Edwards, Mr Enoch MP, 208

Electrical Department 174, 190, 201,
211, 216, 247

Electricity 211, 239

Emergency Medical Service (EMS)
210, 225, 237

Establishment Contributions/Scheme
42, 45-46, 52, 66, 87, 111,
126, 147, 193-194, 205, 208,
227-228, 233, 235, 236

Etruria 9, 11, 23-24, 26, 30, 32, 37, 45-
46, 51, 57-58, 76, 79, 82-83,
86, 90-91, 99, 101, 107, 109,
112, 117, 120-121, 125, 132-
133, 142-143, 148, 154, 203-
205, 223

Explosion, coal mine in Talke 64

Eye injuries 174

Florence Nightingale 6, 68-70, 79, 88,
106, 113, 116,
141-144, 147,
151, 164

Folker, Dr 138, 144, 150, 198

Fox, Dr Wilson 75 91-93, 97-99

Garner, R.C. 68-69, 72, 171, 178

Garner, Robert 72, 89, 92, 95, 113

General Strike 232

Gillies, Sir Harold 235

Gooday, Dr 93, 97-98, 127

Governors 22-28, 34, 37, 42, 45, 48,
52, 60-61, 65-69, 71, 76,
79, 86-87, 91-92, 95-99,
102-108, 111-113, 117,
122, 125-128, 130-133,
138, 141, 145-146, 149,
160, 164, 175, 180, 182,
193-195, 198-201, 208,
214, 222-225, 228,
236, 239-240

Griffiths, T. 208

Grocott, Mr J. 237

Guardians 221

Harding, Miss 148

Harrison, F.J. Maer Hall, 179, 202,
227-228, 232

Harrop, Mary 134

Hartshill 72, 82, 88, 101, 106, 110-113,
118-122, 128, 142, 154, 159,
164, 168, 177, 193, 202, 213

Haughton, Cicely 235

Haughton, Enoch 235

Haycock, Mr 81, 126

Heath, Col. A.H. 200, 201, 228

Heath, Mr Richard 36

Heathcote, Mr 41, 78, 111, 113, 125, 131

Heathcote, Sir John 77

Hollins, Michael Daintry 113

Hordley, Ralph 5, 7, 242

Hospital Abuse 48, 232

House Surgeon 67-68, 89, 93, 99, 106,
117, 121, 127, 133-138, 144,
148-149, 170, 204, 247

House-fly 186

IMR 182, 186

Infectious diseases 149, 171, 173, 175,
177, 184

Infirmary pigs 52-53

Insulin 179, 230

Insurance 46, 55, 57, 205, 222, 232,
237, 240

Jackson, Harvey 237

Jedediah Strutt 79

Jenner 16

Johnson, Dr Petgrave, MOH 184

Johnson, Mr A.E. (Lord) Webb 235

Johnson, Mr E.J. 233

Johnson, Sarah 235

Jones, Sister Mary 154

Kinnersley, Charles 87

Lady Almoner 233

Lady Superintendent 142-147, 164, 201

Lady Visitors 140

Lamb, Mr 37, 95

Lead 173-174

Ledward, Mrs Eliza 138

Lewis, Robert 235

Lynam, Charles 89, 114, 195

MacMaster, Miss 4, 155-156, 201,
230, 247

Malnutrition 191

Marquis of Anglesey 203

Marquis of Stafford 20, 77-78

Massey, Mrs 134

Matron 4, 21, 49, 104, 106, 127,
132-144, 150, 155, 201, 230,
234, 247, 249

McIndoe, Archibald 237
Medical Library 61
Medical Officer of Health
            188-191, 208
Medical Research Council 208
Medical School 65-67, 90, 99, 108,
            116, 150, 180, 228, 241
Mental Illness Wards 224
Miners' Welfare Fund 235
Mitchell, Mr 138
Money raising
      Bazaars 49, 87, 213
      Concert 49, 52, 54, 223
      Saturday and Sunday funds
            194, 124, 205, 227
National Insurance 224 230
Newcastle-under Lyme 9, 11, 40,
      49, 52, 67, 79, 87, 91, 93,
      101, 103, 106, 115, 117-119,
      171, 213, 217, 221, 223
Nicholls, Mr, of West Bromwich
            89, 248
North Staffordshire Collieries Mutual
      Indemnity Company Limited 235
North Staffordshire Contributory
            Association 237
Northen, Dr F.H. 18, 31
Nursing Association,
      Diocese of Lichfield 142
Objects of Charity 234, 237
Obstetrics 182
Orton, Charles 160
Out-relief 217, 222
Outpatients 123, 192, 195, 198-199,
            214, 228, 240
Oxygen chambers 208
Peake, Mr 108, 111-113, 121, 224
Percival, Mr 18
Poor Law 224, 219
Porter 82, 137, 140, 195
Potter, Mr of Litchfield, 80-81, 126
Potteries Electric Tramway Company
            174
Potters' Rot or Potters' Asthma 172
Powell, Robert Hutchinson 97
Prince of Wales 6

Prince Regent 87
Private patients 234, 232
Probationers 149
Radiotherapy 214
Radium 214
Radium Centre 234
Radium Commission 214
Recommendations 39, 42, 45, 198
Reforms 52, 68, 155, 164,
            201, 208, 227
Return 67, 165, 184, 222
Rheumatism 178
Richardson, Benjamin Ward, Sir 71-76,
            117-118, 133, 151,
            164, 171, 254
Roberton, Dr 116
Roscoe, Dr 198
Royal Humane Society 60
Scarlet fever 177
Seddon, Joshua 37, 66, 91, 94
Silicosis 173
Simmonds, Miss 148
Sister 132, 154
Smith Child 122, 162, 183, 226, 235
Sneyd, Reverend Walter, Keele Hall
            130-131
Sowry, Dr 179, 208, 230
Spanton, W.D. 93, 127-128, 160,
            200-204, 247-248
Spencer Wells, Thomas Sir 160-161,
            254
Spode II, Josiah 14, 77, 81
St Christopher Homes, Penkhull. 224
Staffordshire Advertiser 13, 91-94, 254
Stamer, Rev. Sir L.T. 88, 112-117, 146
Steele, Captain 97
Strutt, William 79-80, 86
Subscribers, Establishment 193-194,
            224, 234
Subscribers, Individual 42, 193, 223
Superintendent of Nurses
            128, 146-148,
            154-155, 164, 201
Surgical Square 224
Sylvester, Charles 86
Syphilis 178

The Hospital 196, 198
Thomas, Clement Price 237
Thyroid extract 179
Tomlinson, John 13, 36, 41, 77, 87-88,
            146, 223
Tovey, Mr 128-129
Trained nurses 142, 148, 240
Trainees 148, 149
Trench Warfare Committee 208
Tuberculosis 185, 189, 196, 225 173
Twemlow 113
Twyford Memorial 235
Twyford, Dorothy 228, 234
Vaccination 16, 25, 29, 31, 45, 101,
            175, 179
Venereal disease 178, 210
Vestry, Parish of Stoke-upon-Trent 222
Vestrymen 223
Victoria Wards 51, 124, 163
Virchow, Professor 97
Voluntary hospital 39-40, 45, 55, 60,
            77, 91, 95, 127, 181, 194,
            198, 208, 213, 217, 220,
            224-225, 228, 235-241
Wedgwood 23, 46, 57, 60-61, 77, 81,
            86-87, 93, 99, 101, 114-115,
            118, 121, 127, 143, 151, 190,
            199, 205, 223, 254
Wedgwood, Francis (Frank) 56, 65, 93,
            104, 110, 114-115, 118,
            125, 135, 199 120
Wedgwood, Godfrey 56, 109, 115, 128
Wedgwood, Josiah 67, 77, 79, 134, 181
Wedgwood, Josiah II, 14, 29, 34-36,
            41-42, 45-46, 78-
            79, 81, 86-88
Wedgwood, Lucie 190, 205
Westminster Hospital 60, 95, 240
Wilkinson, Miss 149-150
Wood, Edward 97
Workhouses: City General and Chell
            (Westcliffe) Hospital 22•
X-rays 172, 178, 211, 214
Yates 108
Yates, William 106
Young, Mr Eric 235

ERECTED AND SUPPORTED BY VOLUNTARY CONTRIBUTION